CREATING THE SHORT STORY

CREATING THE
SHORT STORY

A SYMPOSIUM-ANTHOLOGY
WITH AN INTRODUCTION

by

HENRY GOODMAN

INSTRUCTOR IN ENGLISH
(EXTENSION TEACHING AND SUMMER SESSION)
HUNTER COLLEGE OF THE CITY OF NEW YORK

HARCOURT, BRACE AND COMPANY
NEW YORK

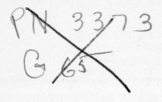

*When the creator turns critic, we are
certain of a feast.*

WALDO FRANK

ACKNOWLEDGMENT

THIS collection does not pretend to be a collection of the best American short stories, nor one affording a full representation of the numerous types of stories now being written. It is, however, offered as representing, on the whole, an extensive view of creative writing along the various levels which obtain in the contemporary short story.

The stories selected, many of them by the authors themselves, others by the editor, are characteristic of the writers who are included.

It is a pleasure to be able to acknowledge publicly my gratitude to the writers for their generous sharing with my pupils and myself, their experiences in the field of the short story.

CONTENTS

WRITING—GAME OR ART?

THE WRITING GAME

THERE'S a far cry from the short story of the formula to the short story as it is practiced by the writers who are making contemporary literary history. The amazing thing, in view of this difference, is the persistence of faith in the formula. To that faith, cherished ardently by the thousands who attend courses in the short story, in person or by mail, must be attributed the prevalence of the jerry-built story. And, of course, one must not overlook the effectiveness of the teachers who encourage this tenacious belief in these thousands of young students.

Although teachers of the short story are agreed on the rules of the art they teach, writers of short stories do not seem to enjoy the same sort of agreement about the principles of the art they practice. And while teachers have no difficulty in analyzing the technical requirements of the short story, nor in pointing to the best illustrations of these essentials in the work of successful writers, the writers themselves confess they do not understand just what the teachers have in mind. They admit, furthermore, that they are not always as fully aware of the principles as the teachers would like them to be. As Thomas H. Uzzell, himself a teacher, says of a general rule he has set down: "The greatest story writers, poets, playwrights, never heard of it."

Meanwhile some critics, amazed by the prosperity of literary America as evidenced by the inexhaustible stores of magazine fiction, have sought to explain this abundance by reference to the economic law of supply and demand. Others, who would go to the very source of this fecundity, seek the explanation in a closer study of what William

McFee has pointed to as "one very remarkable characteristic of modern American life . . . the practice of
training large bodies of students in schools, colleges, and
by mail, in the profession of novel and story writing."

Bewilderment of the Young Writer

The phenomenon is bewildering. The beginning writer,
if he is also critical-minded, wonders about himself. He
reads the words of one of the successful students-by-mail:
"It is surely significant that, with only about nineteen
months of actual experience in writing, the first three stories written after beginning the S.T.C. have reached mar-
kets." Significant! It took Joseph Hergesheimer fourteen
years of concentrated effort to prepare himself for a literary career.

The young writer is bemused. If he fails to avail himself of what short-story teachers can give him, is he missing that vital something which, as a beginner, he should
experience? Is he behind the times in supposing that literary power waits on his own grappling with his problems
and on his own development? Is it merely a romantic delusion, after all, that attainment in writing, like genius, is
an infinite capacity for taking pains? What of that other
cherished notion that college cannot make, but only spoils,
the writer? Are there secrets of fiction writing which
would make him a sturdier practitioner of his art? May it
not well be that his very absorption in the toil and revision, in the planning and rewriting of his own stories has
brought him so close to his materials that he has lost the
perspective and the scientific precision of which Poe
boasted, and which these teachers have developed and fixed
in a code of laws?

Editors Object to Sameness

The answers to these questions are various. Some reassert the validity of the old contention that you cannot teach writing. "Fiction can't be taught," says Sir Gilbert Parker. McFee, as forthright as he is angry, makes the zestful announcement that "literature comes out of our lives. It is not embedded in textbooks." And he is equally emphatic about teaching "the rules about 'structure.'" Drawing on his own experience, he admonishes the young writer to "break every rule in every textbook ever published," as "the best way to sell a story." To give weight to this view, McFee names Conrad, Sherwood Anderson, Katherine Mansfield, and A. E. Coppard as writers who have broken with all the rules.

Reënforcement of this point of view comes from an unexpected quarter. Even editors of popular magazines have begun to object publicly to the type of writing which, they charge, has become prevalent because of schools of fiction, countless courses, and textbooks of the short story. These editors admit that manuscripts all exhibit a high degree of technical skill. But, they add, the manuscripts all exhibit a sameness and uniformity which point to a definite method of manufacture.

In an article, "After the Fiction School—What?" Ralph E. Perry, one time Associate Editor of *Frontier Stories*, describes in detail the cycle of training undertaken by members of fiction schools as they pursue their ideal: mastery of technique. Take, as a picture of a fiction-student's paradise, these few words:

"Structure Easy; Art Impossible"

"The ambitious writer of today takes a course in short-story writing. He gets a thorough grounding in the mechanical elements of plot structure, which is logical, scientific, and comparatively easy to teach, and a few hints on the art of writing, which is almost impossible to teach because it depends so largely on the personality and equipment of the writer. After graduation, the student has trouble placing his work, so he takes another course— to learn more plot structure."

Mr. Perry, very clearly, does not approve of this dashing after plot-courses. In his article he goes thoroughly over the field of short-story writing from the view of those who place their reliance in the schools of fiction. He offers them this stone of a conclusion: "However, now that formal construction in fiction has become general, the importance of technique can be overemphasized. It gives the student a false perspective . . . at the best, technique is a means which many students mistake for an end."

On this same theme of technical perfection, Professor James F. Royster of the University of North Carolina has this to say: "The high mechanical perfection of the compact, concise form of the short story has, indeed, produced a hard and rigid mold. A conventional technique has been established."

One editor, somewhat braver than the rest, goes so far as to challenge the great industry of teaching fiction writing, in language that is decidedly plain:

"Having been a magazine editor for twenty years," Arthur Sullivant Hoffman of *McClure's* declares, "I had become more and more rebellious against present methods of teaching fiction writing, for year by year their fruits poured across my desk by the thousands—stories technically correct but machine-like, artificial, lacking in real individuality. American fiction as a whole is characterized by this result of the curse of formula and, until that curse is removed, American fiction can never attain the place to which native ability entitles it."

But for each of these objections to the work of the fiction smithies, there is an alluring pronouncement issued by correspondence schools and writing teachers. Dr. Esenwein announces: "One pupil won a $2,000 prize. Another pupil earned over $5,000 in spare time." Dr. Burton proclaims that "Short story writing is really the short cut to recognition in Photoplay writing. Increase your income. Learn Short Story Writing." George B. Potter says: "Don't Twiddle Your Thumbs. Rather sit down at your typewriter and turn out salable manuscripts. My service will show you." And, reporting on the dearth of "literary magazines," the *S.T.C. News*, maintained by *The Author & Journalist*, announces: "Perhaps the purely experimental (story) has given way to the overwhelming demand for the strictly approved-of types."

What wonder that the formula prevails?

The Formula Prevails

What cannot be longer denied, in addition, is the fact that the existence of a formula in the field of writing bespeaks a two-fold condition: first, a state of mind among writers which makes them think of writing in terms of a game with well-defined rules for them to master; secondly, a writer or group of writers regarded as holding the position of dictator and therefore the right to set the rules of the game.

That two-fold condition exists.

In consequence the woods are full of young men and young women who are getting into the "writing game." They write plots, and character sketches; devise complications; invent struggles, and plan surprises and counter-surprises in the belief that happiness and wealth will be theirs through the mastery of those few tricks about the success of which, they are assured, there can be no question. These tricks include the surprise ending; the beginning in which the ending is invisibly tucked away, and the casual introduction, early in the story, of some important element on which the outcome depends. They include, in addition, the memorizing and practicing of such feats as the following: "*First Practical Rule:* To secure the maximum intensity of emotional conflict look for the desire or desires present in the given material, give them maximum intensity and set against them maximum opposition. *Second Practical Rule:* To secure maximum dramatic intensity arrange the action so that the actors face enough alternatives in the emotional conflict to give an unequivocal picture of their characters. *General Formula for Dramatic Intensity:* The intensity of a dramatic situation varies as the intensity of the conflicting desires, and as the pattern of the conflict is made to reveal character."

Or, from still another work on story writing, consider the instructions set before the pupils by the teacher, this time a professor at a university. First, examine the quotation from Henry James, offered in Lesson 2, to the earnest students: "The deepest quality of a work of art will always be *the quality of the mind of the producer.*" (*Italics mine.*) Obviously enough here is a recognition of the uniqueness of any work of art. What, then, shall we make of the request that follows in Lesson 5: "Plan a story that demands Jamesesque treatment: that must make something apparent without direct statement; that has significance or import."

Poor students, casually invited to take on "the quality of the mind" of Henry James!

In all earnestness these students imitate the writers they study; simulate feelings that are not their own; borrow observations they have never made.

Seeing the devout efforts of these young people "industriously fagging through courses in fiction and play-writing and short-story writing," McFee reflects mournfully that "they might have had true happiness in making engines, or clocks, or tables and cabinets," and concludes with gloomy reflections on the tragic disillusionment that awaits them.

To the writer who plays this game, characters are puppets and the material he uses is standardized as are the parts of a machine. That writer, if told that his story lacks the power to carry the reader because his characterization is shallow and his narration thin, falls back upon his comforting faith that the story will prove satisfactory for "commercial" purposes.

"The Poison Plot"

When Sherwood Anderson, condemning this whole practice of over-plotting, levels his strictures at "The Poison Plot," his words have the sting of outraged bitterness. "The plots," he says, "were frameworks about which the stories were to be constructed and editors were inordinately fond of them. One got 'an idea for a story.' What was meant was that a new trick had been thought out. Nearly all the adventure stories and the well-known American western stories were so constructed. A man went into the redwood forests or into the deserts and took up land. He has been a rather mean, second-rate chap in civilization but in the new place a great change comes over him. . . . The writer could make a regular angel of him, have him rescue downtrodden women, catch horse thieves, exhibit any kind of bravery required to keep the reader excited and happy.

"In the construction of these stories," Anderson observes, "there was endless variety but in all of them human beings, the lives of human beings, were altogether disregarded. An Alabama Negro was given the shrewdness of a Connecticut Yankee, a trick that made some writer temporarily famous and brought him wealth . . . there was nothing to stop the writer producing a thousand tales with the hybrid Negro as the hero of them all."

What Anderson says about the large-scale production of Negro stories is thoroughly borne out in the observation recorded by a much more conservative critic. Professor Royster found, for example, that the enthusiasm aroused in this country by Thomas Burke's stories of Chinese life in London, led American writers to make "much use of the Chinaman in our country as story material."

Such an awakening to the attractiveness of new material is not, in itself, to be condemned. But what is to be said of the kind of evaluation of that material implied in the further comment of Professor Royster:

"Through his unusualness *the Chinaman does not require a great deal of individuality in character portrayal* to mark himself off from the rest of us. By his very name he is a man apart. The conflict, also, is obvious. The Chinaman brings from his home a civilization which is in direct contrast with what he finds among us."

Recipe for Plot-making

With such sanction of the superficial (and this is approval from a source held more authoritative than is the ordinary magazine-reader), one needs only to substitute for the word "Chinaman" the words "Jew," "Italian," "aviator," "prize-fighter," to come at once into those enchanted provinces where the short-story writers who play the game have struck pay-dirt. With no need to regard characters as human beings, the author is called on merely to devise new plots or to vary old plots in order to maintain capacity production.

Exaggerated as these words seem, they are merely that truth which is stranger than fiction, as may be seen from the experience of Mr. James W. Earp, set forth in his article "A Recipe for Plot-Making," in *The Author & Journalist* for October, 1927.

Just what rank Mr. Earp holds among American short-story writers is not immediately discoverable. Judged by the most superficial of writers' tests, publication, Mr. Earp seems to have standing of a sort. He has appeared in *Munsey's, True Story, Top Notch, War Stories, Breezy Stories, Smart Set,* and *Tales of Temptation.*

"In twelve years," says Mr. Earp, "I've landed in thirty-two magazines for a total of three hundred sales, which ought to speak a language all its own for my methods. I've written stories of the railroads, of love, of the oil-fields, of mining, of the prize-ring, of the various sports—even sex. I've dealt in humor, in psychology, and sociology, *and never varied the old formula one iota.*"

One applauds this devotion to "the old formula" even while deploring the martyrdom of such restraint on Mr. Earp's part. Sympathetically, one is saddened by his self-reproaching (?) confession: "My simple formula may be subversive to art."

The Literary Engine at Last

Mr. Earp need reproach himself no longer. An extension of possibilities comes as a fitting climax to the whole system of formularies for the writing of fiction. The year that witnessed the practical demonstration of television has seen also the perfection of Plotto, the super-literary device. So helpful is this exact system to the seeker of the sure-fire success in fiction that, by means of its "1,800 formulas of dramatic incident, beginning with the Bible and Herodotus and working down through the ages to the Jewish-Irish drama and the underworld and stolen oil-well folklore of the present day," the writer may group and recombine these 1,800 units, and by following the laws of chance, may "develop several million original works."

The quotations are from an article in the *New York Herald Tribune*, September 2, 1928, by Alva Johnston, who was having his fun with this labor-saving contraption. In this article, Mr. Johnston setting forth the hopes of the inventor, describes the "invention which reduces literature to an exact science" as "an engine for the scientific production of fiction without lost motion or false starts."

Due credit must be given, of course, to the inventor of this literature-making device. Of him Mr. Johnston further says that he "has been a tremendous producer of fiction for forty years. He was Burt L. Standish for two years, and has been many other famous short-story writers and novelists." A veritable Ouija board,—a Cabinet of Ouijas, in fact.

As a measure of the practical value of the device, consider this commendable feature: "The plots are practically interchangeable. If any one incident doesn't fit in a short story or scenario, 1,799 spare parts are available." What more could the most meticulous story-smith want by way of assistance in the exacting task of assembling parts, than the knowledge that "some of the sub-plots have detachable angles and these are designated by 'minus' signs"? Or that "The symbol *, for instance, calls for the amputation of one of the members of the sub-plots"? Or, finally, that "some of the sub-plots are particularly esteemed for their handiness and versatility and are practically universal joints which can fit anywhere into the action and work in any direction"?

There is a point in infinity where the ridiculous puts a familiar hand upon the shoulder of the sublime. In Plotto, the super-invention hoped for and only dimly foreshadowed by all the makers of formulas, that point has been reached.

MASTERS OF THE GAME

The incongruity of introducing the name of Edgar Allan Poe at this point is lessened only by the greater propriety of doing so in view of the assertion, too frequently made to be disregarded, that Poe is the one man who has done most for the American short story. There are many reasons for questioning that assertion, other than the vagueness of the evaluation. But the truth, stated more baldly perhaps, is that no one man, with the possible exception of O. Henry, has done more for the prosperity of the seekers of the magic formula. This has been not of Poe's doing at all, but out of the inevitable mischance that teachers of fiction have elected to honor Poe as the father of the short story when O. Henry has so much better enacted the rôle of exploiter of the facile formula. The need, if the writing game was to be elevated to a place in the curriculum of correspondence schools, colleges, and universities, was for some sanction in classic lore. Unfortunately, O. Henry had given no thought to philosophies of composition. But Poe had. He had, furthermore, committed his philosophy to writing. Today there is hardly a treatise on the short story, or a text-book of that art, which fails to name Poe as the father or at least as the master of short-story writers, from whom all others have learned their art.

Speaking of fiction in America shortly before Poe, Schweikert says, "The time was ripe for some story-telling genius to develop the new type by stories of his own, or to define that type accurately. It happened that an American did both, first by stories of his own, and then by an essay which remains a criterion."

Of the central thought of this essay on Hawthorne's *Twice Told Tales*, Professor Royster says, "Poe's pronouncement has remained the bedrock of the established technique of the short story." He observes, furthermore, that the principle set forth by Poe "has been so generally accepted that it has dominated the large output of the short story which began to appear shortly after Poe's day."

"Poe," says Uzzell, with a desire to be moderate in his estimation, "was the first formulator of the theory of the single effect, not its father." And, as if still somewhat fearful that this formulation is not an unmixed blessing, Uzzell adds, qualifyingly: "He does not say, you observe, that every one who writes brief narrative should strive for this ideal; he merely says he will do it if he is 'wise.'" It is understood, however, that failure to be wise will result in stories which are not acceptable according to the laws.

Genius and Fudge

In many ways it was eminently fitting that these laws should have originated in Poe,—in that part of him that was "sheer fudge," according to Lowell. It had been Poe's delight to solve cryptograms; to perpetrate hoaxes, pseudo-scientific and literary, and to decode word-puzzles; to investigate mechanical chess-players, and to present his findings with the solemnity of a scientist before a congress. It was in keeping with his singular genius to assert that he conceived of writing in the terms of mathematical problems which he set himself. Was it anything more than the feeling that he had to bolster up this assertion which led to that fabrication, the "Philosophy of Composition"?

And although, as John Macy points out significantly, the theory and essays do not "obviously, account for Poe's magic," the theory receives far more attention today than does the magic of Poe's work.

In view of that magic in his verse and prose, Poe's questionable assertions set forth in his *Philosophy of Composition* can be explained only through a realization that artistic genius can make itself thoroughly absurd when it seeks to flatter the world of efficient affairs by assuming its habits. Poe, for reasons not altogether clear, wanted to prove that he was practical-minded. To a generation that was beginning to venerate efficiency, he wanted to show himself, in his own domain, a miracle of efficiency. Plotto, we have seen, does away with lost motion and waste of effort. Poe, as we shall see, made much of his economy of effort and of the directness with which he could compose.

He laughed at poetic frenzy—shades of William Blake! He derided as "authorial vanity" the reluctance of authors to discuss the processes by which their work came to completion. He charged predecessors and contemporaries with fear of "letting the public take a peep behind the scenes *at the elaborate and vacillating crudities of thought, at the true purposes seized only at the last moment, at the innumerable glimpses of idea that arrived not at the maturity of full view, at the fully matured fancies discarded in despair as unmanageable, at the cautious selections and rejections, at the painful erasures and interpolations,*" which marked their literary activity.

Those last words reveal Poe, the artist; Poe who has recaptured in his work the tragic rhythms of his imagination, and who has wrested a tragic beauty even from the commonplace externals of an uneventful life. This is the artist who has labored and lain in wait for the song of Israfel, and not the mental prodigy who has challenged the audience to set him a puzzle he could not unravel.

Poe Knew the Truth

How well he knew the reachings out of creative intuition, its hesitancies, uncertainties, and its unexpected triumphs! Was it the actor in him that helped him carry off the self-imposed rôle when he said, "For my own part, I have neither sympathy with the repugnance alluded to, nor at any time the least difficulty in recalling to mind the progressive steps of any of my compositions. . . . It is my design to render it manifest that no one point in its composition ('The Raven') is referable either to accident or intuition; that the work proceeded, step by step, to its completion with the precision and rigid consequence of a mathematical problem"?

Of an entirely different complexion, as the late Professor Newcomer pointed out, were Poe's own words appearing in the 1845 edition of his poems: "With me poetry has been not a purpose, but a passion, and the passions should be held in reverence." Nor, in considering the explanations of Poe's writing of the *Philosophy of Composition*, should we overlook the comment of Professor Newcomer, who said: "The present editor is inclined to regard it merely as part of a defense which Poe had been moved to make against an insinuation that in *The Raven* he had imitated the repetitions of phrases in Coleridge's *Ancient Mariner*."

It is well to remember also that sympathetically as Professor Vernon Louis Parrington speaks of Poe, whom he regards as "an aesthete and a craftsman, the first American writer to be concerned with beauty alone," he yet is constrained to record Poe's "deliberate fabrications about his life and methods of work," and to question "the value of his theory of the tyrannizing unity of mood in the poem and short story."

Unfortunately for the short story, the writers of texts have taken literally a statement of Poe's which is valid only for its suggestions. With exaggerated insistence they have given an emphasis out of all proportion to that side of Poe's analysis which is least tenable in view of his own artistic merits. They have disregarded the "three-fifths of him genius" for the "two-fifths sheer fudge."

Because in a moment of self-glorification Poe overstressed the conscious dependence on means, commentators, critics, technicians, and teachers have followed him blindly and have overlooked what he knew to be the deeper truth of psychological impulse manifested in every expression of the creative spirit. The schools, because they must give their pupils something so tangible that even the most inept of the students may be persuaded that they are being taught, have magnified the significance to the writer of conscious planning. By planning, it is worthy of note, they mean the laying out of scenarios of action, ground-plans of plot and diagrams of complications and of scenes. To attain the complete externalization they applaud, the schools have developed for the writer systems of indexing ideas and of filing newspaper clippings. They have built up, in addition and in full keeping with their ideals of efficiency, classifications which must delight those who see in the field of short-story writing room for their particular and specialized talents. These categories now include the mystery story, the action story, the ghost story, the detective story, the sports story. Allowing for their interest in specialization and their initiative, it is surely no false optimism which predicts courses in the humorous story, the sea story, the railroad story, the marriage story, the divorce story, the western story, the war story, the peace story, the business story, the business-girl story, the animal story, the boy-and-girl-scout story, the airplane story—all in keeping with the demand of the specialized magazines. Furthermore, the correspondence schools have reduced to mathematical formulae the exact proportions of emotion which, if properly combined, should result in the single effect desired. They have overlooked only the fact that the writer who is honestly concerned with his materials is as genuinely concerned only with making a *good story*.

Because Poe had said that the wise literary artist conceives a "certain unique or single effect to be wrought out" the schools of story writing have elaborated the dictum into a law with ramifying sub-divisions. They have overlooked, what Poe never overlooked, that in his case the single effect was in itself an expression of those inner forces, unconscious or subconscious, which he experienced as an artist. They have disregarded, almost altogether, the influence in the writer's work of those emotional drives and stirrings which lead him to express one mood as against another; which dictate his choice of subject matter; which color both his experience and his artistic expression. And because Poe had set down the idea with the conclusive air of a scientific truth discovered by him, the principle acted on by fiction schools is that what was true for Poe must be true for every writer.

De Gourmont and Spingarn Explain

De Gourmont knew better, and Spingarn has urged a broader truth. The French writer has taken into account the fact that every artist is a law unto himself and that every artist's theory explains and justifies only *his* practice. "The whole effort of a sincere man," De Gourmont said, "is to erect his personal impressions into laws."

"No rule," says Spingarn, "no theory, no 'law' coined by critics or scholars has any validity for the poet in the creative act, and when that act is completed and the poem achieved, the critic must make his theory of tragedy chime with the new poet's poem, not the poem with the theory."

In these views of De Gourmont and Spingarn, there is reflection of the doctrine of Spinoza that all things are determined by the laws of their own being. For the artist this principle of an organic determinism must be singularly illuminating. It must direct him always to a study of his materials for those implicit indications and half-hints as to form, rhythm, and construction which he must organize to achieve the completed work he has undertaken.

This is the discipline he must set himself, if, from the chaos of hints and whispers, fragmentary observations, corners of events glimpsed by him, he is to shape into harmonious completion the story he is writing.

It is to Poe's great fame that he submitted to this discipline. And that he did so with the detachment he boasted proves only that the vaunted singularity of his temperament did not lessen in him the respect which the artist owes the creative forces within him. In itself, however, that detachment was not altogether a virtue. It may have indicated, on the other hand, a lack of something very vital, even from the point of view of esthetic achievement.

It was his boast (as we have seen) "that the work proceeded, step by step, to its completion with the precision and rigid consequence of a mathematical problem." The words raise a nice question as to the relationship of the writer to his material. Ardently as the artist may direct his imagination, and shape and refine it, if he look upon the motions and expressions of life as upon symbols performing their function in a mathematical firmament, it is little wonder that that alienation will rise up to accuse him. It is not without justification that Lewis Mumford says of Poe: "In him the springs of human desire had not so much frozen up as turned to metal: his world was, in one of his favorite words, plutonian, like that of Watt and Fulton and Gradgrind: the tears that he dropped were steel beads, and his mind worked like a mechanical hopper, even when there were no appropriate materials to throw into it."

Mumford's criticism is of a personal limitation which, at the same time, emphasizes the peculiarity of Poe's unconscious genius. More striking, however, is the denial by Poe of the rich emotional soil from which, in the work of such dissimilar poets as Shelley, Keats, Browning, and Whitman, the poems spring pungent and humanly significant. "Let us dismiss," says Poe, "as irrelevant to the poem per se, the circumstance—or, say, the necessity—which in the first place gave rise to the intention of composing a poem. . . ."

Let us cut the flower from the stem, says Poe. The stem is irrelevant to the flower per se. This may be true enough of the florist arranging his display, but it is a dangerous analogy in literature, as we can see if we but examine it. The flower cut from the stem lasts a day. The poem, however, endures. Why? It endures because, although it is the flower of the creative process, it yet contains within itself the root, stem, and even the seed of the force which created it. This is the essential difference between natural and artistic beauty. The one reveals neither author nor cause; the other always implies and, indeed, reveals the author. "Who touches this book touches a man," said Whitman. It is that sane truth which explains the perpetual loveliness of the *Song of Songs*, the enduring power of *Prometheus Bound*, and the lasting delight of a Beethoven sonata.

Writing Divorced from Life

In these words of Poe's that would cut the poem from its roots we have the sanction for that divorce from life which has encouraged writers down to our own day to make and plan, to map out according to scale, tales and stories, which have no relevance to human experience. On the face of it it seemed the kind of divorce which Poe's genius was powerful enough to survive in the microcosm of his own making. But even the people and the poems of Poe's devising have their roots in his life. However, the disaster caused by that critical pronouncement is not yet over. Too many writers acting on the naïve thought that life can be one thing and art another, are still engaged in the manufacture of pretty contrivances which, like the boxes within the boxes of the Japanese game, can be assembled and taken apart to the apparent delight of the grown children who buy them.

The whole temper of Poe's day, and of many days succeeding his, was opposed to acknowledging, let alone accepting, life, as, on his own terms and as an exceptional instance, Walt Whitman was doing. Other writers, their eyes turned from the stirring life that was to fill with resonance and compelling power the best lines of Walt Whitman, led to the exotic haunts laid out by them in the stories of atmosphere. Presently they took the readers to the rosy-tinted and therefore attractive regions made accessible in the stories of local color. With the vogue initiated by Bret Harte, they brought to the reader, thirsting for novelty in a work-a-day world, eccentricities exploited in stories of character (?). Finally, to overcome the ennui of a too-regulated life, there was the story of plot with its thrills and excitements for the reader made passive by duties in counting-house and shop.

Describing this same period as it was reflected in the poetry of the time, Louis Untermeyer says, "From 1866 to 1880 the United States was in a chaotic and frankly materialistic condition; it was full of political scandals, panics, frauds. The moral fiber was flabby; the country was apathetic, corrupt and contented. As in all such periods of national unconcern, *the artists turned from life altogether,* preoccupying themselves with the by-products of art: with method and technique, with elaborate and artificial conceits, with facile ideas rather than fundamental ideals. . . . All of these authors, in an effort to escape a reality they could not express and did not even wish to understand, fled to a more congenial realm of fantasy."

It was a period characterized largely by isolation and literary provincialism. It was marked by the literary provincialism of the kind which brings John Macy to the paradoxical conclusion that it "is not provincial enough," because as he says, "American books too seldom come to grips with the problems of life, especially the books cast in artistic forms." In the failure of the writers of this time to seize on the intensities and the significance of life, Macy finds, also, an explanation of the amazing fact that the Civil War did not bring a piece of fiction of artistic distinction.

The sectionalism which had preceded and which followed the Civil War intensified in writers their interest in particular localities so that, looking back on the literary history of the fifty or sixty years after Poe, one is able to identify sections by writers or vice-versa. Thus, the region around New Orleans is known in the stories of George Washington Cable; Tennessee is falsely pictured in the sentimental stories of Mary N. Murfree ("Charles Egbert Craddock") ; Virginia in the pages of Thomas Nelson Page; Kentucky in the sweet flutings of James Lane Allen, and in the sentimental romances of John Fox; the Far West in the turbulent tales of Bret Harte; the Middle West in the work of Edward Eggleston and John Hay; New England, subdivided in turn into its own localities, in the novels, tales, and stories of Rose Terry Cooke, Sarah Orne Jewett, Mary E. Wilkins Freeman, and Alice Brown; New York in the writings of Henry Cuyler Bunner, Brander Matthews, and in later times in the work of Richard Harding Davis and, finally, in that of O. Henry.

Exceptions All Too Few

It goes without saying that a literary activity marked by so much diligent exploitation of particular spots resulted in a good deal that was, and still is, meritorious. However, there is always the reservation that these writers were acquiescent to the mode of their time—a mode which, for most part, made them willing to dissemble and made them partner to that separation of life and art which resulted of necessity in a fleshless, insubstantial literary output. There were exceptions, of course, chief among them Edith Wharton, who, in *Ethan Frome*, has achieved a dignified and tragic story of a texture that seems destined to endure. But her story of New England life was written when the fashion in writing had taken a new turn.

The criticism of the local color story as it was practiced by most of the writers mentioned and by many more whose achievement was even less substantial, is leveled at a quality of mind of which these stories was a direct expression. In that criticism no words show more awareness of the sorry provincialism of this type of writing than those of James Lane Allen, himself a noted local colorist, who died without completing the introduction to his last book, *The Landmark*.

"The development of the American short story," he says in that introduction, "has been directed along the paths of locality: we have asked for and received only the story that is true, the story that exists at all, only as true, only as it exists, somewhere in the United States— the neighborhood.

Failure of Local Colorists

"Now, while our American literature insists upon being one-sided, we Americans insist upon not being ever one-sided. We insist upon not being of a neighborhood; we insist that no single local background will do for us, will measure us, bound us. We assert that we overflow neighborhood, and in thus insisting we merely insist upon the truth.

"How much of our actual lives depends upon the fact that we come from Indiana? that we were born in Kentucky? From day to day how often do we heed the fact, or make use of it, that Georgia bore us, or Massachusetts is solely responsible for our birth?"

And again, in protest that "critics try to push our lives back into a corner," he demands, "Is being an American in its fullest, truest sense, aught but being most fully and most truly human?" Finally, in exasperation, he asks of those critics: "Well, how many New Jersey passions have they? How many Rhode Island emotions?"

Eloquent as they were, the questions came too late as far as he was himself concerned. His own words pillory the whole school of local colorists who did not write as though they believed that being "most fully and most truly human" meant also that they were most fully and most truly American. It was their failure that they did not accept and write of life in terms of that fullness which he urged too late.

It was their failure that they did not accept what Defoe, Fielding, George Eliot, and Hardy had accepted as the writer's sacred duty. The writer is a perpetual witness on a witness-stand which he never leaves. His is the duty of telling "the truth, the whole truth, and nothing but the truth," however much the truth may offend or embarrass.

Within the limits of his craft, and to the fullest limits of that craft, the writer is to shape that truth so that the form in which he finally presents it is truth *illuminated by his insight*. Willful refusal to look at what is before him or within him—that is perjury. Trimming of the facts because the writer thinks the jury wants ready-to-wear facts —that is perjury.

That kind of perjury these writers committed without a thought of the betrayal.

As Carl Van Doren points out, "they thought first of color and then of form, first of the piquant surfaces and then—if at all—of the stubborn deeps of human life. . . . Moreover, they accepted almost without challenge the current inhibitions of gentility, reticence, cheerfulness. They confined themselves to the emotions and the ideas and the language, for the most part, of the respectable; they disregarded the stormier or stealthier behavior of mankind or veiled it with discreet periphrasis; they sweetened their narratives wherever possible with a brimming optimism nicely tinctured with amiable sentiments. Poetic justice prospered and happy endings were orthodox."

O. Henry, Apostle of Local Color

The culmination came in the work of O. Henry—local colorist par excellence, whose stamping ground was Bagdad on the Subway. In him are summed up in exemplary fashion all those refractions of vision which mark the work of most other local colorists. In him abound sentimentality with a smiling awareness that he is being sentimental, exaggeration and the triumph of the good except where the exigencies of the surprise twist demand an ending that, like a sudden wind which seizes the drooping kite, sends the story careering out of the grasp of the astonished and pleased reader.

The truth was that the compelling life of the latter nineteenth and the first decade of the twentieth century, broke in a wave even upon the readers bent on fleeing the actualities. Invention succeeded on invention, new social adjustments had to be made, new social types were evolving. Pleasant simplifications of life were in demand.

For such readers O. Henry performed the miracle of transfiguring New York City overnight. He slipped a turban upon its head and a roomy cloak of many colors over its shoulders. From those romantic folds the new Haroun-al-Raschid drew surprise package after surprise package. He had transformed the city into a cloudy wonderland where the highest hopes of a present-day reader of the *Graphic* might come true. That was his contribution, that he cast a false color and glamour upon facts and people, which, seen honestly, would have revealed their own authentic glamour, if of a different kind.

In O. Henry's shop as in almost no other literary confectioner's of so recent a date, or so exalted a position, one obtained prize packages—little pellets of sweetness, and bitter chocolates with just the right degree of bitterness to show what a precarious business buying chocolates can be. Thus the repentant hobo goes to jail just when he has decided to reform; the little girl goes wrong in the right hands when the very forces of guile and evil had rejected her.

Admiringly as he speaks of the "intensely human" characters in O. Henry's stories, Elias Lieberman in his book *The American Short Story* admits that "the incidents and situations are frequently bizarre, unusual and very often strained."

This reservation, however, does not really touch an even more fundamental fault in the work of O. Henry.

Do his stories touch you, move you, give you even remotely a sense of "the most fully and most truly human"? In the more than two hundred stories he wrote, O. Henry has perhaps less than a score of which one may say with assurance, "Here is work which in power, insight, organization of matter and form, fulfills the high demands of literary art."

Skimming the Surfaces

What the widely-read person thinks of O. Henry may be gathered from these brief views expressed by several teachers of English in a New York City high school:

"I used to like him when I was fifteen."

"Give a boy a book of O. Henry's and he will read it through without stopping."

"I just loved his stories when I was sixteen. Today I can find no subtlety in him."

"Although his writings show at every turn that he knew life—that of New York City and of the small town —he does not ever come to grips with it. He skims the surfaces."

"If I read two of his stories together I feel that I have had enough."

"My interest in the craftsman makes me aware of O. Henry's sense of life, keenness of observation, the swift certainty of his word. But when I go back to him I feel that his work is meretricious."

It may be objected that these are the judgments of men and women who are a little over-zealous in their quest of literary merit. On the other hand it is clear that their experience as readers has made them impatient of

O. Henry's "insubstantial symbols of humanity," as Professor F. M. Perry describes the men and women in the stories of O. Henry.

Professor Perry has high praise for the work of this writer. Yet she says of him, "However perverse O. Henry may be in other matters, he can be relied upon not to make his reader think; when he is in danger of thinking O. Henry makes him laugh."

And again, "Our author understands perfectly the easily mastered art of giving only a newspaper reality to characters and situations that might tempt a more experimental writer, one less sure of his range and purpose, to use them for a more profound appeal."

As if the "more profound appeal" were something to be abjured by the writer. But Professor Perry explains what, in the last analysis, must be accounted the defect which kept O. Henry from attaining to greatness. In her book, *Story Writing*, she discusses Poe and O. Henry and says: "Their stories are not life; they are not lifelike; *they discreetly remind the reader of life but avoid all entangling alliances with it.* The steadily focused goals of the two writers, for the one the shudder, for the other the laugh, were to be gained in exchange for less precious metal than reality. Where papier-mâché will serve the purpose, frugal craftsmanship will have no commerce with recalcitrant nature."

Life and writing in America, however, have left behind these writers who avoided "all entangling alliances" with life, as we shall see.

BACK TO LIFE

Discussing Whistler and Henry James, Waldo Frank shows to how little extent these artists were American.

Their alienation from American life "was achieved," he says, "by a rigorous avoidance of native stuff and native issues. Literally, they escaped America." This was true, of course, also of many American artists who, unlike Whistler and Henry James, stayed at home. These were the writers and painters who took to their ivory towers to avoid being swept away by the whirling currents of American life. Others, more venturesome, were carried along the streams and came to shore with their flotsam of facts: facts, as we have seen, about places close by but so rouged by the colors of a false optimism as to make them seem the distant habitat of romance; facts about blustering and violent ruffians in whose hard hearts were hidden, in a dusk of secrecy, unexpected cores of tenderness.

Special Reporting Not Enough

At its very best, this writing had merely a journalistic validity. The writers were reporters who had come upon feature story material which they dressed up in the garments of fiction. It is hardly in censure of that quality as a shortcoming that Professor Fred Lewis Pattee characterizes F. Hopkinson Smith's collection of stories—*At Close Range*—in the following way: "His brilliant narratives are the work of one who would have made a most efficient special reporter for a city daily." What praise for a literary master! But Smith was not alone among these glorified "special" reporters. These writers, carried away by the external novelties of their materials, did what the journalist does. They seized on the isolated *story*—on the happening, event, accident or occasion, as of importance in itself. They overlooked what the artist never does,—that the event is of no significance in itself; that it gains significance only by way of its implications of the eternal forces, of the lasting emotions and desires of mankind. Their failure to bring out the relations of the event to those organic processes in life of which the event is a natural outgrowth, explains why the work of so many of these diligent writers falls on deaf ears today. Bayard Taylor, H. C. Bunner, Frank R. Stockton, Rose Terry Cooke, Thomas Bailey Aldrich, F. Hopkinson Smith, Alfred Henry Lewis, Richard Harding Davis,—turn open their pages and read. How shall one explain the sensation as of fingering earth too long defrauded of rain? The grains crumble in the hand; the narratives know the blight of dry rot. For a sense of living reality, by way of contrast, one might turn to *Richard Cory* or to *Flammonde* by Robinson. Because in the view of these writers the story could be an isolated experience without relationship to the life from which experience flows, it was in no way strange that trivial things remained trivial in their hands.

But general as had been the divorce from the realities of American life, there were those writers who, at the very height of this fashion in writing, had probed realities which they recognized as authentic, and which they were attempting to record with candor.

Romantic Dreams and Reality

The turn in literary expression came in an expression of dissent from the flagrant optimism that had attended the extension and conquests of the frontiers. It was, in a measure, an act of social protest characterized by the propagandist's appeal to an awakening social consciousness. It was, too, a tacit admission that the life of industrial expansion and commercial solidification was not, in its results, consonant with the roseate dreams and the romantic wish-realizations nourished by the popular literature of the times. It was a confession, voiced more stridently than is the way of confession, that this was not the best of all possible worlds.

This was the burden of *Main Traveled Roads*, by Hamlin Garland, which appeared in 1891. Oppressed by the distress and disaster attending life on the frontier, Garland undertook to present veraciously the truth of existence as it was known to the frontier farmers and their wives. Nor was he contented with the mild-mannered realism of his friend, William Dean Howells. He wrote with an intense interest in the fate of the people who had engaged his pen. His stories, written with a passionate honesty, are full of those details which give life to his characters. They have an immediacy of appeal which the three decades that have passed over them have not lessened. May it not be that this power is due, in no small measure, to the fact noted by Dr. Blanche Colton Williams, that Garland, as a realist, "does not use the artifices of structure employed by the romanticist who feels the need of forecast, clews, suspense, and coincidence to heighten and intensify his plot"?

To what effect Mr. Garland used the realist's method of directness and veracity in his early work is to be gathered from these judgments voiced by Mr. Van Doren and Professor Pattee:

"There is a clear, high splendor," Mr. Van Doren finds, "about his landscapes; youth and love on his desolate plains, as well as anywhere, can find glory in the most difficult existence; he might strip particular lives relentlessly bare but he no less relentlessly clung to the conviction that human life has an inalienable dignity which is deeper than any glamour goes and can survive the loss of all its trappings."

And although Professor Pattee denies that these stories have a "golden light upon them," he yet agrees that "they tell the truth with brutal directness and they tell it with an art that convinces." He adds, furthermore: "They are not mere stories; they are living documents in the history of the West."

Mr. Garland Sees Man, the Pioneer

To find that these stories by Mr. Garland are documents is by no means to their discredit even from the point of view of a stricter artistic standard. Documentation of the kind represented by *Main Traveled Roads* and by the realistic novels of the latter nineteenth century was needed if only for the reason that it helped bring home a truth more enduring than the ephemeral truth of "local color." It is even true that these realists, Edward Eggleston in *The Hoosier School-Master* and E. W. Howe in his grim novel, *The Story of a Country Town*, struck, ingenuously, the note of discovery as if they were not a little amazed at finding human nature what they reported it to be. But that type of testimony as to the reality of the feelings and passions of America was necessary, for out of it was to come that fecund awareness of American life, its aspirations and defeats, its secret desires and intensities, which was to be given artistic significance in the work of later writers. These passionate facts of life, of suffering and frustration, of brutality and high hopes, voiced with a tone of incredulity by the "documentarians," were to be evolved later into art forms of distinction by such dissimilar writers as Theodore Dreiser, Willa Cather, Sherwood Anderson, Glenway Wescott, and Waldo Frank.

If only Mr. Garland, who had "clung to the conviction that human life has an inalienable dignity," had recognized as surely the inalienable dignity of the artist, he might have gone beyond the elementary function of the artist as secretary to society, past the stage of writing documents, to the full realization of the creative powers he had evinced in his earliest work.

Returns to Original Sources

That Mr. Garland later deserted the method of rigorous artistic candor in novels which were so many concessions to the school of "local color" is to be taken as an indication of a state of affairs in American letters which, fortunately, is growing less common in our own day. Instead of intrenching himself more and more profoundly in the matters he had found originally so congenial to his powers, Mr. Garland turned to slight romantic themes which, at best, had only a superficial interest. In his later autobiographic works, *A Son of the Middle Border* and *A Daughter of the Middle Border*, Mr. Garland returned to the straightforward veracity which had served so well to communicate the sense of actuality found in his earliest stories. It is hardly necessary to point the moral of Mr. Garland's defection. It is so fully instructive of the danger to the artist who fails to respect his personal vision and his own experience. Fortunately artistic integrity and self-confidence are becoming more widely characteristic of American writers. Thus, the examples of Theodore Dreiser and James Branch Cabell, differing as these writers do in artistic aim, cannot but hearten the young writer who must admire them for the unswerving devotion to their own esthetic beliefs.

"Not Responsible for Vision"

A similar faith in his own integrity also distinguished the brilliant but short-lived Stephen Crane, whose stories and sketches have been overlooked in the more general favor accorded his novel, *The Red Badge of Courage.*

In words that reveal eloquently the respect of the artist for his own outlook as well as for his materials, Mr. Crane wrote:

"The one thing that pleases me is the fact that men of sense invariably believe me to be sincere. . . . When I was the mark for every humorist in the country, I went ahead; and now when I am the mark for only fifty per cent of the humorists of the country, I go ahead; for I understand that a man is born into the world with his own pair of eyes, and he is not at all responsible for his vision— he is merely responsible for his quality of personal honesty. To keep close to this personal honesty is my supreme ambition."

It is no wonder that holding such views, Mr. Crane should have sought to impart to his readers some of that intensity of vision and response which made life always meaningful to him. Nor is it any wonder that, with the eager delight of one who can see beyond the facts of experience through "loving the beauty of the fact," as Mr. Untermeyer puts it, Crane should have sought his material in the realities of city life, of child life, of life at the battlefront.

Mr. Mumford has only a pitying disdain for the writers who, after the Civil War, sought to escape the post-war conditions by "idealizing the real." To think that Stephen Crane should have been the mark of "every humorist in the country" for the efforts he made in the direction of realizing the real!

It is surely no idle speculation to suppose that Mr. Crane might have achieved his aims if he had lived longer. In the brief Sullivan County sketches which he left he proved himself a master of atmospheric effects. "The Mesmeric Mountain," "The Snake," brief as they are and without any building up to a climax in narrative, have nevertheless a living sense of the dynamic quality of things in nature. It was his keenness of vision which enabled Mr. Crane to see through placid, immobile surfaces to the moving life underneath. In the few war stories in the recently compiled volume, *Men, Women and Boats*, he had shown a power to make unforgettable those realities of feeling never mentioned by returning soldiers. In the story "The Open Boat" in that same volume, he concentrated, by way of an integration which he had mastered in *The Red Badge of Courage*, all the emotions of terror, expectancy, hope, and escape from death. There is in this story an inevitability of selected detail and phrasing which, together with its tone of restraint, gives it a texture of subtle and fine weaving.

In the stories by Hamlin Garland, Ambrose Bierce, Stephen Crane, and in the artistic purposes of Frank Norris, announced by him in his program—*The Responsibilities of the Novelist*—we get the beginning flow of a new tide in American writing. It is a tide that, as it mounts, is to carry into the cities and towns, into the streets and houses of America, a new impulse for self-searching and self-realization. On the mounting waves of this new literary impulse the old preoccupation with picturesque externalisms is to be left behind. The superficial facts of existence, the signs of material success, the glorying in a childish optimism, are presently to give way before a grappling with the deeper realities of man's inner longings and needs.

Something of those inner realities is intimated in these words of Frank Norris:

"Turn your eyes inward upon yourself down, down to the heart of you; . . . it is life, and it is that of which you have to make your book—your novel—life, not other people's novels."

Finding Beauty in Life

For the experimental and venturesome writers of the decades following those in which Crane and Norris had done their work, this was the direction and the goal. Back to life in the spirit of acceptance, rather than of denial. Back to the complexities of existence with the desire to wrest from them a meaning to be turned into new beauty, of a kind more human and more humane than that chiseled by Poe. From this exploration have already come clews that have led to "new vistas into the land of the soul," which, as Ludwig Lewisohn points out, are the best signs of a vital literature.

Of the contemporary writers who have dared this adventure there are some names that suggest themselves immediately. Dreiser is of the group; so are Sherwood Anderson, Waldo Frank, Ruth Suckow, Willa Cather, Joseph Hergesheimer, Ring Lardner, Zona Gale, and Manuel Komroff. Each of them has confronted life with the artist's faith in his own power to transmute the experiences of life into forms that have meaning and beauty. Having accepted life they are free to work out their personal modes as artists. They need not document; they may create by transmuting their experiences—by reworking the stuff of life into stories that give proportion and meaning to life.

The new attitude of the contemporary writer comes, as we have seen, in the nature of a rebellion. Is it forcing the point to say that that rebellion, barring the differences of time and mental attitude, is not unlike the one officially fathered by Wordsworth in the famous preface to the Lyrical Ballads? It was Wordsworth who deplored the blunting of "the discriminating powers of the mind," caused, as he said, by "the great national events which are daily taking place, and (by) the increasing accumulation of men in cities, where the uniformity of their occupations produces a craving for extraordinary incident, which the rapid communication of intelligence hourly gratifies." And it was Wordsworth who announced the return, in literature, to the ways of life, in the words: "My purpose was to imitate, and as far as possible to adopt, the very language of men. . . . I have wished to keep the Reader in the company of flesh and blood, persuaded that by so doing I shall interest him."

Nor can it be said that this new impulse in American short-story writers has been unrecognized. Professor Royster explains that "when a literary form becomes fixed or rigid, a revolt toward freedom almost always sets in." He sees especially in the writings of Sherwood Anderson and Waldo Frank "signs of an attempt to break away from the established form." He concedes, too, that their works are "interesting experiments," and that the unconventionality of their form is related directly to the unconventionality of their views of life.

That unconventionality is further explained by Professor Perry, who says of Anderson, "Careless of the acquired refinements of life that loom so large with such an author as James, his concentration has been on the cramped and hidden self in his neighbor and his neighbor in himself. . . . He has not given the sordid accidents of their lives for their objective value, but for their bearing on the natures of those subject to them."

One may be tempted to think the short story of today is still concerned with local color. The generalization is true. It *is* a story of local color; it is even provincial. But there is a difference. That difference is in the direction of intensified, more candid, and, at times, clarifying insight into the lives of human beings. The difference in emphasis is vastly significant as a measure of the distance which the American short story has traversed since the vogue of the local colorists.

Those writers, as we have seen, did in the field of literature what the pioneers and the industrialists were doing in the field of material aggrandizement. They sought, seized and exploited new territories. The pioneers had sent back word of the sensational bounties of the new lands; the writers had sent back word of the rhetorical, sensational, melodramatic gestures of the adventuring pioneers.

The stories of our day, however, dig through these surfaces. They are windows opening upon the inner forces and the dynamic energies of human beings. In the work of the significant short-story writers of our own day, the short story has touched in a sure way the deep springs which nourish an authentic, growing art.

These writers are concerned not with the geography of their respective states, but with the topography of the souls of their characters. And to the extent that the writers permit their explorations and discoveries to shape the form of their expression, rather than imposing formulated and conventionalized modes on their materials, they are artists who are true to the best impulses of their creative powers. It has been asserted of some of these writers that they have a way of dealing with materials commonly held to be distressing, if not distinctly unpleasant. But from the point of view of a growing literature it is of special significance that these writers are bringing America to intellectual and cultural adulthood.

In a real sense it may be said of these writers that, like Father Mapple whose sermon Melville gave us in *Moby Dick*, they say: "Woe to him who seeks to pour oil upon the waters when God has brewed them into a gale! Woe to him who seeks to please rather than to appal! Woe to him whose good name is more to him than goodness! Woe to him who, in this world courts not dishonor! Woe to him who would not be true, even though to be false were salvation! Yea, woe to him who, as the great Pilot Paul has it, while preaching to others is himself a castaway!"

RING LARDNER

HOW TO WRITE SHORT STORIES [1]

A glimpse at the advertising columns of our leading magazines shows that whatever else this country may be shy of, there is certainly no lack of correspondence schools that learns you the art of short-story writing. The most notorious of these schools makes the boast that one of their pupils cleaned up $5000.00 and no hundreds dollars writing short stories according to the system learnt in their course, though it don't say if that amount was cleaned up in one year or fifty.

However, for some reason another when you skin through the pages of high class periodicals, you don't very often find them cluttered up with stories that was written by boys or gals who had win their phi beta skeleton keys at this or that story-writing college. In fact, the most of the successful authors of the short fiction of today never went to no kind of a college, or if they did, they studied piano tuning or the barber trade. They could of got just as far in what I call the literary game if they had of stayed home those four years and helped mother carry out the empty bottles.

The answer is that you can't find no school in operation up to date, whether it be a general institution of learning or a school that specializes in story writing, which can make a great author out of a born druggist.

But a little group of our deeper drinkers has suggested that maybe boys and gals who wants to take up writing as their life work would be benefited if some person like I was to give them a few hints in regards to the technic of the short story, how to go about planning it and writing it, when and where to plant the love interest and climax, and finally how to market the finished product without leaving no bad taste in the mouth.

Well, then, it seems to me like the best method to use in giving out these hints is to try and describe my own personal procedure from the time I get inspired till the time the manuscript is loaded on to the trucks.

[1] From *How to Write Short Stories,* by Ring Lardner, copyright, 1924, by Charles Scribner's Sons. Reprinted by permission of the author and of the publishers.

39

The first thing I generally always do is try and get hold of a catchy title, like for instance, "Basil Hargrave's Vermifuge," or "Fun at the Incinerating Plant." Then I set down to a desk or flat table of any kind and lay out 3 or 4 sheets of paper with as many different colored pencils and look at them cockeyed a few moments before making a selection.

How to begin—or, as we professionals would say, "how to commence"—is the next question. It must be admitted that the method of approach ("L'approchement") differs even among first class fictionists. For example, Blasco Ibañez usually starts his stories with a Spanish word, Jack Dempsey with an "I" and Charley Peterson with a couple of simple declarative sentences about his leading character, such as "Hazel Gooftree had just gone mah jong. She felt faint."

Personally it has been my observation that the reading public prefers short dialogue to any other kind of writing and I always aim to open my tale with two or three lines of conversation between characters—or, as I call them, my puppets—who are to play important rôles. I have often found that something one of these characters says, words I have perhaps unconsciously put into his or her mouth, directs my plot into channels deeper than I had planned and changes, for the better, the entire sense of my story.

To illustrate this, let us pretend that I have laid a plot as follows: Two girls, Dorothy Abbott and Edith Quaver, are spending the heated term at a famous resort. The Prince of Wales visits the resort, but leaves on the next train. A day or two later, a Mexican reaches the place and looks for accommodations, but is unable to find a room without a bath. The two girls meet him at the public filling station and ask him for a contribution to their autograph album. To their amazement, he utters a terrible oath, spits in their general direction and hurries out of town. It is not until years later that the two girls learn he is a notorious forger and realize how lucky they were after all.

Let us pretend that the above is the original plot. Then let us begin the writing with haphazard dialogue and see whither it leads:

"Where was you?" asked Edith Quaver.

"To the taxidermist's," replied Dorothy Abbott.

The two girls were spending the heated term at a famous watering trough. They had just been bathing and were now engaged in sorting dental floss.

"I am getting sick in tired of this place," went on Miss Quaver.

"It is mutual," said Miss Abbott, shying a cucumber at a passing paper-hanger.

There was a rap at their door and the maid's voice announced that company was awaiting them downstairs. The two girls went down and entered the music room. Garnett Whaledriver was at the piano and the girls tiptoed to the lounge.

The big Nordic, oblivious of their presence, allowed his fingers to form weird, fantastic minors before they strayed unconsciously into the first tones of Chopin's 121st Fugue for the Bass Drum.

From this beginning, a skilled writer could go most anywheres, but it would be my tendency to drop these three characters and take up the life of a mule in the Grand Canyon. The mule watches the trains come in from the east, he watches the trains come in from the west, and keeps wondering who is going to ride him. But she never finds out.

The love interest and climax would come when a man and a lady, both strangers, got to talking together on the train going back east.

"Well," said Mrs. Croot, for it was she, "what did you think of the Canyon?"

"Some cave," replied her escort.

"What a funny way to put it!" replied Mrs. Croot. "And now play me something."

Without a word, Warren took his place on the piano bench and at first allowed his fingers to form weird, fantastic chords on the black keys. Suddenly and with no seeming intention, he was in the midst of the second movement of Chopin's Twelfth Sonata for Flute and Cuspidor. Mrs. Croot felt faint.

That will give young writers an idea of how an apparently trivial thing such as a line of dialogue will upset an entire plot and lead an author far from the path he had pointed for himself. It will also serve as a model for beginners to follow in regards to style and technic. I will not insult my readers by going on with the story to its obvious conclusion. That simple task they can do for themselves, and it will be good practice.

So much for the planning and writing. Now for the marketing of the completed work. A good many young writers make the mistake of enclosing a stamped, self-addressed envelope, big enough for the manuscript to come back in. This is too much of a temptation to the editor.

Personally I have found it a good scheme to not even sign my name to the story, and when I have got it sealed up in its envelope and stamped and addressed, I take it to some town where I don't live and mail it from there. The editor has no idea who wrote the story, so how can he send it back? He is in a quandary.

In conclusion let me warn my pupils never to write their stories—or, as we professionals call them, "yarns"—on used paper. And never to write them on a post-card. And never to send them by telegraph (Morse code).

CHAMPION [1]

MIDGE KELLY scored his first knockout when he was seventeen. The knockee was his brother Connie, three years his junior and a cripple. The purse was a half dollar given to the younger Kelly by a lady whose electric had just missed bumping his soul from his frail little body.

Connie did not know Midge was in the house, else he never would have risked laying the prize on the arm of the least comfortable chair in the room, the better to observe its shining beauty. As Midge entered from the kitchen, the crippled boy covered the coin with his hand, but the movement lacked the speed requisite to escape his brother's quick eye.

[1] From *How to Write Short Stories,* by Ring Lardner, copyright, 1924, by Charles Scribner's Sons. Reprinted by permission of the author and of the publishers.

"Watcha got there?" demanded Midge.

"Nothin'," said Connie.

"You're a one legged liar!" said Midge.

He strode over to his brother's chair and grasped the hand that concealed the coin.

"Let loose!" he ordered.

Connie began to cry.

"Let loose and shut up your noise," said the elder, and jerked his brother's hand from the chair arm.

The coin fell onto the bare floor. Midge pounced on it. His weak mouth widened in a triumphant smile.

"Nothin', huh?" he said. "All right, if it's nothin' you don't want it."

"Give that back," sobbed the younger.

"I'll give you a red nose, you little sneak! Where'd you steal it?"

"I didn't steal it. It's mine. A lady give it to me after she pretty near hit me with a car."

"It's a crime she missed you," said Midge.

Midge started for the front door. The cripple picked up his crutch, rose from his chair with difficulty, and, still sobbing, came toward Midge. The latter heard him and stopped.

"You better stay where you're at," he said.

"I want my money," cried the boy.

"I know what you want," said Midge.

Doubling up the fist that held the half dollar, he landed with all his strength on his brother's mouth. Connie fell to the floor with a thud, the crutch tumbling on top of him. Midge stood beside the prostrate form.

"Is that enough?" he said. "Or do you want this, too?"

And he kicked him in the crippled leg.

"I guess that'll hold you," he said.

There was no response from the boy on the floor. Midge looked at him a moment, then at the coin in his hand, and then went out into the street, whistling.

An hour later, when Mrs. Kelly came home from her day's work at Faulkner's Steam Laundry, she found Connie on the floor, moaning. Dropping on her knees beside him, she called him by name a score of times. Then she got up and, pale as a ghost, dashed from the house. Dr. Ryan left the Kelly abode about dusk and walked toward Halsted Street. Mrs. Dorgan spied him as he passed her gate.

"Who's sick, Doctor?" she called.

"Poor little Connie," he replied. "He had a bad fall."

"How did it happen?"

"I can't say for sure, Margaret, but I'd almost bet he was knocked down."

"Knocked down!" exclaimed Mrs. Dorgan.

"Why, who—?"

"Have you seen the other one lately?"

"Michael? No, not since mornin'. You can't be thinkin'—"

"I wouldn't put it past him, Margaret," said the doctor gravely. "The lad's mouth is swollen and cut, and his poor, skinny little leg is bruised. He surely didn't do it to himself and I think Helen suspects the other one."

"Lord save us!" said Mrs. Dorgan. "I'll run over and see if I can help."

"That's a good woman," said Doctor Ryan, and went on down the street.

Near midnight, when Midge came home, his mother was sitting at Connie's bedside. She did not look up.

"Well," said Midge, "what's the matter?"

She remained silent. Midge repeated his question.

"Michael, you know what's the matter," she said at length.

"I don't know nothin'," said Midge.

"Don't lie to me, Michael. What did you do to your brother?"

"Nothin'."

"You hit him."

"Well, then, I hit him. What of it? It ain't the first time."

Her lips pressed tightly together, her face like chalk, Ellen Kelly rose from her chair and made straight for him. Midge backed against the door.

"Lay off'n me, Ma. I don't want to fight no woman."

Still she came on breathing heavily.

"Stop where you're at, Ma," he warned.

There was a brief struggle and Midge's mother lay on the floor before him.

"You ain't hurt, Ma. You're lucky I didn't land good. And I told you to lay off'n me."

"God forgive you, Michael!"

Midge found Hap Collins in the showdown game at the Royal.

"Come on out a minute," he said.

Hap followed him out on the walk.

"I'm leavin' town for a w'ile," said Midge.

"What for?"

"Well, we had a little run-in up to the house. The kid stole a half buck off'n me, and when I went after it he cracked me with his crutch. So I nailed him. And the old lady came at me with a chair and I took it off'n her and she fell down."

"How is Connie hurt?"

"Not bad."

"What are you runnin' away for?"

"Who the hell said I was runnin' away? I'm sick and tired o' gettin' picked on; that's all. So I'm leavin' for a w'ile and I want a piece o' money."

"I ain't only got six bits," said Happy.

"You're in bad shape, ain't you? Well, come through with it."

Happy came through.

"You oughtn't to hit the kid," he said.

"I ain't astin' you who can I hit," snarled Midge. "You try to put somethin' over on me and you'll get the same dose. I'm goin' now."

"Go as far as you like," said Happy, but not until he was sure that Kelly was out of hearing.

Early the following morning, Midge boarded a train for Milwaukee. He had no ticket, but no one knew the difference. The conductor remained in the caboose.

On a night six months later, Midge hurried out of the "stage door" of the Star Boxing Club and made for Duane's saloon, two blocks away. In his pocket were twelve dollars, his reward for having battered up one Demon Dempsey through the six rounds of the first preliminary.

It was Midge's first professional engagement in the manly art. Also it was the first time in weeks that he had earned twelve dollars.

On the way to Duane's he had to pass Niemann's. He pulled his cap over his eyes and increased his pace until he had gone by. Inside Niemann's stood a trusting bartender, who for ten days had staked Midge to drinks and allowed him to ravage the lunch on a promise to come in and settle the moment he was paid for the "prelim."

Midge strode into Duane's and aroused the napping

bartender by slapping a silver dollar on the festive board.

"Gimme a shot," said Midge.

The shooting continued until the wind-up at the Star was over and part of the fight crowd joined Midge in front of Duane's bar. A youth in the early twenties, standing next to young Kelly, finally summoned sufficient courage to address him.

"Wasn't you in the first bout?" he ventured.

"Yeh," Midge replied.

"My name's Hersch," said the other.

Midge received the startling information in silence.

"I don't want to butt in," continued Mr. Hersch, "but I'd like to buy you a drink."

"All right," said Midge, "but don't overstrain yourself."

Mr. Hersch laughed uproariously and beckoned to the bartender.

"You certainly gave that wop a trimmin' tonight," said the buyer of the drink, when they had been served. "I thought you'd kill him."

"I would if I hadn't let up," Midge replied. "I'll kill 'em all."

"You got the wallop all right," the other said admiringly.

"Have I got the wallop?" said Midge. "Say, I can kick like a mule. Did you notice them muscles in my shoulders?"

"Notice 'em? I couldn't help from noticin' 'em," said Hersch. "I says to the fella settin' alongside o' me, I says: 'Look at them shoulders! No wonder he can hit,' I says to him."

"Just let me land and it's good-by, baby," said Midge. "I'll kill 'em all."

The oral manslaughter continued until Duane's closed for the night. At parting, Midge and his new friend shook hands and arranged for a meeting the following evening.

For nearly a week the two were together almost constantly. It was Hersch's pleasant rôle to listen to Midge's modest revelations concerning himself, and to buy every time Midge's glass was empty. But there came an evening when Hersch regretfully announced that he must go home to supper.

"I got a date for eight bells," he confided. "I could stick till then, only I must clean up and put on the Sunday clo'es, 'cause she's the prettiest little thing in Milwaukee."

"Can't you fix it for two?" asked Midge.

"I don't know who to get," Hersch replied. "Wait, though. I got a sister and if she ain't busy, it'll be O. K. She's no bum for looks herself."

So it came about that Midge and Emma Hersch and Emma's brother and the prettiest little thing in Milwaukee foregathered at Wall's and danced half the night away. And Midge and Emma danced every dance together, for though every little onestep seemed to induce a new thirst of its own, Lou Hersch stayed too sober to dance with his own sister.

The next day, penniless at last in spite of his phenomenal ability to make some one else settle, Midge Kelly sought out Doc Hammond, matchmaker for the Star, and asked to be booked for the next show.

"I could put you on with Tracy for the next bout," said Doc.

"What's they in it?" asked Midge.

"Twenty if you cop," Doc told him.

"Have a heart," protested Midge. "Didn't I look good the other night?"

"You looked all right. But you aren't Freddie Welsh yet by a consid'able margin."

"I ain't scared of Freddie Welsh or none of 'em," said Midge.

"Well, we don't pay our boxers by the size of their chests," Doc said. "I'm offerin' you this Tracy bout. Take it or leave it."

"All right; I'm on," said Midge, and he passed a pleasant afternoon at Duane's on the strength of his booking.

Young Tracy's manager came to Midge the night before the show.

"How do you feel about this go?" he asked.

"Me?" said Midge. "I feel all right. What do you mean, how do I feel?"

"I mean," said Tracy's manager, "that we're mighty anxious to win, 'cause the boy's got a chanct in Philly if he cops this one."

"What's your proposition?" asked Midge.

"Fifty bucks," said Tracy's manager.

"What do you think I am, a crook? Me lay down for fifty bucks. Not me!"

"Seventy-five, then," said Tracy's manager.

The market closed on eighty and the details were agreed on in short order. And the next night Midge was stopped in the second round by a terrific slap on the forearm.

This time Midge passed up both Niemann's and Duane's, having a sizable account at each place, and sought his refreshment at Stein's farther down the street.

When the profits of his deal with Tracy were gone, he learned, by first-hand information from Doc Hammond and the matchmakers at the other "clubs," that he was no longer desired for even the cheapest of preliminaries. There was no danger of his starving or dying of thirst while Emma and Lou Hersch lived. But he made up his mind, four months after his defeat by Young Tracy, that Milwaukee was not the ideal place for him to live.

"I can lick the best of 'em," he reasoned, "but there ain't no more chanct for me here. I can maybe go east and get on somewheres. And besides—"

But just after Midge had purchased a ticket to Chicago with the money he had "borrowed" from Emma Hersch "to buy shoes," a heavy hand was laid on his shoulders and he turned to face two strangers.

"Where are you goin', Kelly?" inquired the owner of the heavy hand.

"Nowheres," said Midge. "What the hell do you care?"

The other stranger spoke:

"Kelly, I'm employed by Emma Hersch's mother to see that you do right by her. And we want you to stay here till you've done it."

"You won't get nothin' but the worst of it, monkeying with me," said Midge.

Nevertheless, he did not depart for Chicago that night. Two days later, Emma Hersch became Mrs. Kelly, and the gift of the groom, when once they were alone, was a crushing blow on the bride's pale cheek.

Next morning, Midge left Milwaukee as he had entered it—by fast freight.

"They's no use kiddin' ourself any more," said Tommy Haley. "He might get down to thirty-seven in a pinch, but if he done below that a mouse could stop him. He's a welter; that's what he is and he knows it as well as I do.

He's growed like a weed in the last six mont's. I told him, I says, 'If you don't quit growin' they won't be nobody for you to box, only Willard and them.' He says, 'Well, I wouldn't run away from Willard if I weighed twenty pounds more.'"

"He must hate himself," said Tommy's brother.

"I never seen a good one that didn't," said Tommy. "And Midge is a good one; don't make no mistake about that. I wisht we could of got Welsh before the kid growed so big. But it's too late now. I won't make no holler, though, if we can match him up with the Dutchman."

"Who do you mean?"

"Young Goetz, the welter champ. We mightn't not get so much dough for the bout itself, but it'd roll in afterward. What a drawin' card we'd be, 'cause the people pays their money to see the fella with the wallop, and that's Midge. And we'd keep the title just as long as Midge could make the weight."

"Can't you land no match with Goetz?"

"Sure, 'cause he needs the money. But I've went careful with the kid so far and look at the results I got! So what's the use of takin' a chanct? The kid's comin' every minute and Goetz is goin' back faster'n big Johnson did. I think we could lick him now; I'd bet my life on it. But six mont's from now they won't be no risk. He'll of licked hisself before that time. Then all as we'll have to do is sign up with him and wait for the referee to stop it. But Midge is so crazy to get at him now that I can't hardly hold him back."

The brothers Haley were lunching in a Boston hotel. Dan had come down from Holyoke to visit with Tommy and to watch the latter's protégé go twelve rounds, or less, with Bud Cross. The bout promised little in the way of a contest, for Midge had twice stopped the Baltimore youth and Bud's reputation for gameness was all that had earned him the date. The fans were willing to pay the price to see Midge's hay-making left, but they wanted to see it used on an opponent who would not jump out of the ring the first time he felt its crushing force. But Cross was such an opponent, and his willingness to stop boxing-gloves with his eyes, ears, nose and throat had long enabled him to escape the horrors of honest labor. A game boy was Bud, and he showed it in his battered, swollen, discolored face.

"I should think," said Dan Haley, "that the kid'd do whatever you tell him after all you done for him."

"Well," said Tommy, "he's took my dope pretty straight so far, but he's so sure of hisself that he can't see no reason for waitin'. He'll do what I say, though; he'd be a sucker not to."

"You got a contrac' with him?"

"No, I don't need no contrac'. He knows it was me that drug him out o' the gutter and he ain't goin' to turn me down now, when he's got the dough and bound to get more. Where'd he of been at if I hadn't listened to him when he first come to me? That's pretty near two years ago now, but it seems like last week. I was settin' in the s'loon acrost from the Pleasant Club in Philly, waitin' for McCann to count the dough and come over, when this little bum blowed in and tried to stand the house off for a drink. They told him nothin' doin' and to beat it out o' there, and then he seen me and come over to where I was settin' and ast me wasn't I a boxin' man and I told him who I was. Then he ast me for money to buy a shot and I told him to set down and I'd buy it for him.

"Then we got talkin' things over and he told me his

name and told me about fightn' a couple o' prelims out to Milwaukee. So I says, 'Well, boy, I don't know how good or how rotten you are, but you won't never get nowheres trainin' on that stuff.' So he says he'd cut it out if he could get on in a bout and I says I would give him a chanct if he played square with me and didn't touch no more to drink. So we shook hands and I took him up to the hotel with me and give him a bath and the next day I bought him some clo'es. And I staked him to eats and sleeps for over six weeks. He had a hard time breakin' away from the polish, but finally I thought he was fit and I give him his chanct. He went on with Smiley Sayer and stopped him so quick that Smiley thought sure he was poisoned.

"Well, you know what he's did since. The only beatin' in his record was by Tracy in Milwaukee before I got hold of him, and he's licked Tracy three times in the last year.

"I've gave him all the best of it in a money way and he's got seven thousand bucks in cold storage. How's that for a kid that was in the gutter two years ago? And he'd have still more yet if he wasn't so nuts over clo'es and got to stop at the good hotels and so forth."

"Where's his home at?"

"Well, he ain't really got no home. He came from Chicago and his mother canned him out o' the house for bein' no good. She give him a raw deal, I guess, and he says he won't have nothin' to do with her unlest she comes to him first. She's got a pile o' money, he says, so he ain't worryin' about her."

The gentleman under discussion entered the café and swaggered to Tommy's table, while the whole room turned to look.

Midge was the picture of health despite a slightly colored eye and an ear that seemed to have no opening. But perhaps it was not his healthiness that drew all eyes. His diamond horse-shoe tie pin, his purple cross-striped shirt, his orange shoes and his light blue suit fairly screamed for attention.

"Where you been?" he asked Tommy. "I been lookin' all over for you."

"Set down," said his manager.

"No time," said Midge. "I'm goin' down to the w'arf and see 'em unload the fish."

"Shake hands with my brother Dan," said Tommy.

Midge shook with the Holyoke Haley.

"If you're Tommy's brother, you're O. K. with me," said Midge, and the brothers beamed with pleasure.

Dan moistened his lips and murmured an embarrassed reply, but it was lost on the young gladiator.

"Leave me take twenty," Midge was saying. "I prob'ly won't need it, but I don't like to be caught short."

Tommy parted with a twenty dollar bill and recorded the transaction in a small black book the insurance company had given him for Christmas.

"But," he said, "it won't cost you no twenty to look at them fish. Want me to go along?"

"No," said Midge hastily. "You and your brother here prob'ly got a lot to say to each other."

"Well," said Tommy, "don't take no bad money and don't get lost. And you better be back at four o'clock and lay down a w'ile."

"I don't need no rest to beat this guy," said Midge. "He'll do enough layin' down for the both of us."

And laughing even more than the jest called for, he strode out through the fire of admiring and startled glances.

The corner of Boylston and Tremont was the nearest Midge got to the wharf, but the lady awaiting him was doubtless a more dazzling sight than the catch of the luckiest Massachusetts fisherman. She could talk, too— probably better than the fish.

"O you Kid!" she said, flashing a few silver teeth among the gold. "O you fighting man!"

Midge smiled up at her.

"We'll go somewheres and get a drink," he said. "One won't hurt."

In New Orleans, five months after he had rearranged the map of Bud Cross for the third time, Midge finished training for his championship bout with the Dutchman.

Back in his hotel after the final workout, Midge stopped to chat with some of the boys from up north, who had made the long trip to see a champion dethroned, for the result of this bout was so nearly a foregone conclusion that even the experts had guessed it.

Tommy Haley secured the key and the mail and ascended to the Kelly suite. He was bathing when Midge came in, half hour later.

"Any mail?" asked Midge.

"There on the bed," replied Tommy from the tub.

Midge picked up the stack of letters and postcards and glanced them over. From the pile he sorted out three letters and laid them on the table. The rest he tossed into the waste-basket. Then he picked up the three and sat for a few moments holding them, while his eyes gazed off into space. At length he looked again at the three unopened letters in his hand; then he put one in his pocket and tossed the other two at the basket. They missed their target and fell on the floor.

"Hell!" said Midge, and stooping over picked them up.

He opened one postmarked Milwaukee and read:

DEAR HUSBAND:

I have wrote to you so manny times and got no anser and I dont know if you ever got them, so I am writeing again in the hopes you will get this letter and anser. I dont like to bother you with my trubles and I would not only for the baby and I am not asking you should write to me but only send a little money and I am not asking for myself but the baby has not been well a day sence last Aug. and the dr. told me she cant live much longer unless I give her better food and thats impossible the way things are. Lou has not been working for a year and what I make dont hardley pay for the rent. I am not asking for you to give me any money, but only you should send what I loaned when convenient and I think it amts. to about $36.00. Please try and send that amt. and it will help me, but if you cant send the whole amt. try and send me something.

Your wife,

EMMA.

Midge tore the letter into a hundred pieces and scattered them over the floor.

"Money, money, money!" he said. "They must think I'm made o' money. I s'pose the old woman's after it too."

He opened his mother's letter:

dear Michael Connie wonted me to rite and say you must beet the dutchman and he is sur you will and wonted me to say we wont you to rite and tell us about it, but I gess you havent no time to rite or we herd from you long beffore this but I wish you would rite jest a line or 2 boy becaus it wuld be better for Connie then a barl of medisin. It wuld help me to keep things going if you send me money now and then when you can spair it but if you cant send no money try and fine time to rite a letter onley a few lines and it will please Connie. jest think boy he hasent got out of bed in over 3 yrs. Connie says good luck.

Your Mother,
ELLEN F. KELLY.

"I thought so," said Midge. "They're all alike."
The third letter was from New York. It read:

HON:—This is the last letter you will get from me before your champ, but I will send you a telegram Saturday, but I can't say as much in a telegram as in a letter and I am writeing this to let you know I am thinking of you and praying for good luck.

Lick him good hon and don't wait no longer than you have to and don't forget to wire me as soon as its over. Give him that little old left of yours on the nose hon and don't be afraid of spoiling his good looks because he couldn't be no homlier than he is. But don't let him spoil my baby's pretty face. You won't will you hon.

Well hon I would give anything to be there and see it, but I guess you love Haley better than me or you wouldn't let him keep me away. But when your champ hon we can do as we please and tell Haley to go to the devil.

Well hon I will send you a telegram Saturday and I almost forgot to tell you I will need some more money, a couple hundred say and you will have to wire it to me as soon as you get this. You will won't you hon.

I will send you a telegram Saturday and remember hon I am pulling for you.

Well good-by sweetheart and good luck.

GRACE.

"They're all alike," said Midge. "Money, money, money."

Tommy Haley, shining from his ablutions, came in from the adjoining room.

"Thought you'd be layin' down," he said.

"I'm goin' to," said Midge, unbuttoning his orange shoes.

"I'll call you at six and you can eat up here without no bugs to pester you. I got to go down and give them birds their tickets."

"Did you hear from Goldberg?" asked Midge.

"Didn't I tell you? Sure; fifteen weeks at five hundred, if we win. And we can get a guarantee o' twelve thousand, with privileges either in New York or Milwaukee."

"Who with?"

"Anybody that'll stand up in front of you. You don't care who it is, do you?"

"Not me. I'll make 'em all look like a monkey."

"Well, you better lay down aw'ile."

"Oh, say, wire two hundred to Grace for me, will you? Right away; the New York address."

"Two hundred! You just sent her three hundred last Sunday."

"Well, what the hell do you care?"

"All right, all right. Don't get sore about it. Anything else?"

"That's all," said Midge, and dropped onto the bed.

"And I want the deed done before I come back," said Grace as she rose from the table. "You won't fall down on me, will you, hon?"

"Leave it to me," said Midge. "And don't spend no more than you have to."

Grace smiled a farewell and left the café. Midge continued to sip his coffee and read his paper.

They were in Chicago and they were in the middle of Midge's first week in vaudeville. He had come straight north to reap the rewards of his glorious victory over the broken-down Dutchman. A fortnight had been spent in learning his act, which consisted of a gymnastic exhibition and a ten minutes' monologue on the various excellences of Midge Kelly. And now he was twice daily turning 'em away from the Madison Theater.

His breakfast over and his paper read, Midge sauntered into the lobby and asked for his key. He then beckoned to a bell-boy, who had been hoping for that very honor.

"Find Haley, Tommy Haley," said Midge. "Tell him to come up to my room."

"Yes, sir, Mr. Kelly," said the boy, and proceeded to break all his former records for diligence.

Midge was looking out of his seventh-story window when Tommy answered the summons.

"What'll it be?" inquired his manager.

There was a pause before Midge replied.

"Haley," he said, "twenty-five per cent's a whole lot o' money."

"I guess I got it comin', ain't I?" said Tommy.

"I don't see how you figger it. I don't see where you're worth it to me."

"Well," said Tommy, "I didn't expect nothin' like this. I thought you was satisfied with the bargain. I don't want to beat nobody out o' nothin', but I don't see where you could have got anybody else that would of did all I done for you."

"Sure, that's all right," said the champion. "You done a lot for me in Philly. And you got good money for it, didn't you?"

"I ain't makin' no holler. Still and all, the big money's still ahead of us yet. And if it hadn't of been for me, you wouldn't of never got within grabbin' distance."

"Oh, I guess I could of went along all right," said Midge. "Who was it that hung that left on the Dutchman's jaw, me or you?"

"Yes, but you wouldn't been in the ring with the Dutchman if it wasn't for how I handled you."

"Well, this won't get us nowheres. The idear is that you ain't worth no twenty-five per cent now and it don't make no diff'rence what come off a year or two ago."

"Don't it?" said Tommy. "I'd say it made a whole lot of difference."

"Well, I say it don't and I guess that settles it."

"Look here, Midge," Tommy said, "I thought I was fair with you, but if you don't think so, I'm willin' to hear what you think is fair. I don't want nobody callin' me a Sherlock. Let's go down to business and sign up a contrac'. What's your figger?"

"I ain't namin' no figger," Midge replied. "I'm sayin' that twenty-five's too much. Now what are you willin' to take?"

"How about twenty?"

"Twenty's too much," said Kelly.

"What ain't too much?" asked Tommy.

"Well, Haley, I might as well give it to you straight. They ain't nothin' that ain't too much."

"You mean you don't want me at no figger?"

"That's the idear."

There was a minute's silence. Then Tommy Haley walked toward the door.

"Midge," he said, in a choking voice, "you're makin' a big mistake, boy. You can't throw down your best friends and get away with it. That damn woman will ruin you."

Midge sprang from his seat.

"You shut your mouth!" he stormed. "Get out o' here before they have to carry you out. You been spongin' off o' me long enough. Say one more word about the girl or about anything else and you'll get what the Dutchman got. Now get out!"

And Tommy Haley, having a very vivid memory of the Dutchman's face as he fell, got out.

Grace came in later, dropped her numerous bundles on the lounge and perched herself on the arm of Midge's chair.

"Well?" she said.

"Well," said Midge, "I got rid of him."

"Good boy!" said Grace. "And now I think you might give me that twenty-five per cent."

"Besides the seventy-five you're already gettin'?" said Midge.

"Don't be no grouch, hon. You don't look pretty when you're grouchy."

"It ain't my business to look pretty," Midge replied.

"Wait till you see how I look with the stuff I bought this mornin'!"

Midge glanced at the bundles on the lounge.

"There's Haley's twenty-five per cent," he said, "and then some."

The champion did not remain long without a manager. Haley's successor was none other than Jerome Harris, who saw in Midge a better meal ticket than his popular-priced musical show had been.

The contract, giving Mr. Harris twenty-five per cent of Midge's earnings, was signed in Detroit the week after Tommy Haley had heard his dismissal read. It had taken Midge just six days to learn that a popular actor cannot get on without the ministrations of a man who thinks, talks and means business. At first Grace objected to the new member of the firm, but when Mr. Harris had demanded and secured from the vaudeville people a one-hundred dollar increase in Midge's weekly stipend, she was convinced that the champion had acted for the best.

"You and my missus will have some great old times," Harris told Grace. "I'd of wired her to join us here, only I seen the Kid's bookin' takes us to Milwaukee next week, and that's where she is."

But when they were introduced in the Milwaukee hotel, Grace admitted to herself that her feeling for Mrs. Harris could hardly be called love at first sight. Midge, on the contrary, gave his new manager's wife the many times over and seemed loath to end the feast of his eyes.

"Some doll," he said to Grace when they were alone.

"Doll is right," the lady replied, "and sawdust where her brains ought to be."

"I'm li'ble to steal that baby," said Midge, and he smiled as he noted the effect of his words on his audience's face.

On Tuesday of the Milwaukee week the champion suc-

cessfully defended his title in a bout that the newspapers
never reported. Midge was alone in his room that morning
when a visitor entered without knocking. The visitor was
Lou Hersch.

Midge turned white at sight of him.

"What do you want?" he demanded.

"I guess you know," said Lou Hersch. "Your wife's
starvin' to death and your baby's starvin' to death and
I'm starvin' to death. And you're dirty with money."

"Listen," said Midge, "if it wasn't for you, I wouldn't
never saw your sister. And, if you ain't man enough
to hold a job, what's that to me? The best thing you can
do is keep away from me."

"You give me a piece o' money and I'll go."

Midge's reply to the ultimatum was a straight right to
his brother-in-law's narrow chest.

"Take that home to your sister."

And after Lou Hersch had picked himself up and
slunk away, Midge thought: "It's lucky I didn't give him
my left or I'd of croaked him. And if I'd hit him in the
stomach, I'd of broke his spine."

There was a party after each evening performance
during the Milwaukee engagement. The wine flowed freely
and Midge had more of it than Tommy Haley ever would
have permitted him. Mr. Harris offered no objection,
which was possibly just as well for his own physical
comfort.

In the dancing between drinks, Midge had his new manager's wife for a partner as often as Grace. The latter's
face as she floundered round in the arms of the portly
Harris, belied her frequent protestations that she was
having the time of her life.

Several times that week, Midge thought Grace was on the point of starting the quarrel he hoped to have. But it was not until Friday night that she accommodated. He and Mrs. Harris had disappeared after the matinee and when Grace saw him again at the close of the night show, she came to the point at once.

"What are you tryin' to pull off?" she demanded.

"It's none o' your business, is it?" said Midge.

"You bet it's my business; mine and Harris's. You cut it short or you'll find out."

"Listen," said Midge, "have you got a mortgage on me or somethin'? You talk like we was married."

"We're goin' to be, too. And tomorrow's as good a time as any."

"Just about," Midge said. "You got as much chanct o' marryin' me tomorrow as the next day or next year and that ain't no chanct at all."

"We'll find out," said Grace.

"You're the one that's got somethin' to find out."

"What do you mean?"

"I mean I'm married already."

"You lie!"

"You think so, do you? Well, s'pose you go to this here address and get acquainted with my missus."

Midge scrawled a number on a piece of paper and handed it to her. She stared at it unseeingly.

"Well," said Midge, "I ain't kiddin' you. You go there and ask for Mrs. Michael Kelly, and if you don't find her, I'll marry you tomorrow before breakfast."

Still Grace stared at the scrap of paper. To Midge it seemed an age before she spoke again.

"You lied to me all this w'ile."

"You never ast me was I married. What's more, what

the hell diff'rence did it make to you? You got a split, didn't you? Better'n fifty-fifty."

He started away.

"Where you goin'?"

"I'm goin' to meet Harris and his wife."

"I'm goin' with you. You're not goin' to shake me now."

"Yes, I am, too," said Midge quietly. "When I leave town tomorrow night, you're going to stay here. And if I see where you're goin' to make a fuss, I'll put you in a hospital where they'll keep you quiet. You can get your stuff tomorrow mornin' and I'll slip you a hundred bucks. And then I don't want to see no more o' you. And don't try and tag along now or I'll have to add another K. O. to the old record."

When Grace returned to the hotel that night, she discovered that Midge and the Harrises had moved to another. And when Midge left town the following night, he was again without a manager. and Mr. Harris was without a wife.

Three days prior to Midge Kelly's ten-round bout with Young Milton in New York City, the sporting editor of *The News* assigned Joe Morgan to write two or three thousand words about the champion to run with a picture lay-out for Sunday.

Joe Morgan dropped in at Midge's training quarters Friday afternoon. Midge, he learned, was doing road work, but Midge's manager, Wallie Adams, stood ready and willing to supply reams of dope about the greatest fighter of the age.

"Let's hear what you've got," said Joe, "and then I'll try to fix up something."

So Wallie stepped on the accelerator of his imagination and shot away.

"Just a kid; that's all he is; a regular boy. Get what I mean? Don't know the meanin' o' bad habits. Never tasted liquor in his life and would prob'bly get sick if he smelled it. Clean livin' put him up where he's at. Get what I mean? And modest and unassumin' as a school girl. He's so quiet you wouldn't never know he was round. And he'd go to jail before he'd talk about himself.

"No job at all to get him in shape, 'cause he's always that way. The only trouble we have with him is gettin' him to light into these poor bums they match him up with. He's scared he'll hurt somebody. Get what I mean? He's tickled to death over this match with Milton, 'cause everybody says Milton can stand the gaff. Midge'll maybe be able to cut loose a little this time. But the last two bouts he had, the guys hadn't no business in the ring with him, and he was holdin' back all the w'ile for the fear he'd kill somebody. Get what I mean?"

"Is he married?" inquired Joe.

"Say, you'd think he was married to hear him rave about them kiddies he's got. His fam'ly's up in Canada to their summer home and Midge is wild to get up there with 'em. He thinks more o' that wife and them kiddies than all the money in the world. Get what I mean?"

"How many children has he?"

"I don't know, four or five, I guess. All boys and every one of 'em a dead ringer for their dad."

"Is his father living?"

"No, the old man died when he was a kid. But he's got a grand old mother and a kid brother out in Chi. They're the first ones he thinks about after a match, them and his wife and kiddies. And he don't forget to send the old woman a thousand bucks after every bout. He's goin' to buy her a new home as soon as they pay him off for this match."

"How about his brother? Is he going to tackle the game?"

"Sure, and Midge says he'll be a champion before he's twenty years old. They're a fightin' fam'ly and all of 'em honest and straight as a die. Get what I mean? A fella that I can't tell you his name come to Midge in Milwaukee onct and wanted him to throw a fight and Midge give him such a trimmin' in the street that he couldn't go on that night. That's the kind he is. Get what I mean?"

Joe Morgan hung around the camp until Midge and his trainers returned.

"One o' the boys from *The News*," said Wallie by way of introduction. "I been givin' him your fam'ly hist'ry."

"Did he give you good dope?" he inquired.

"He's some historian," said Joe.

"Don't call me no names," said Wallie smiling. "Call us up if they's anything more you want. And keep your eyes on us Monday night. Get what I mean?"

The story in Sunday's *News* was read by thousands of lovers of the manly art. It was well written and full of human interest. Its slight inaccuracies went unchallenged, though three readers, besides Wallie Adams and Midge Kelly, saw and recognized them. The three were Grace, Tommy Haley and Jerome Harris and the comments they made were not for publication.

Neither the Mrs. Kelly in Chicago nor the Mrs. Kelly in Milwaukee knew that there was such a paper as the New York *News*. And even if they had known of it and that it contained two columns of reading matter about Midge, neither mother nor wife could have bought it. For *The News* on Sunday is a nickel a copy.

Joe Morgan could have written more accurately, no doubt, if instead of Wallie Adams, he had interviewed Ellen Kelly and Connie Kelly and Emma Kelly and Lou Hersch and Grace and Jerome Harris and Tommy Haley and Hap Collins and two or three Milwaukee bartenders.

But a story built on their evidence would never have passed the sporting editor.

"Suppose you can prove it," that gentleman would have said. "It wouldn't get us anything but abuse to print it. The people don't want to see him knocked. He's champion."

KONRAD BERCOVICI

FORGET THE FORMULA

I never know when an idea for a short story happens to fly past my way. I never know when an everyday occurrence strikes some reminiscent cell in my brain and begins to revolve, until something or other is evolved from it.

As far as technique is concerned, I don't know the first thing about it. The technique of the short story is studied in the short story classes of universities. I am well aware of that. But as I have never studied the short story, I don't happen to be aware of any special technique required. I am very much like the gypsy fiddler who knows how to play without ever having studied. I don't mean to advise others not to know more about technique than I do. Each creative artist has his own requirements and is law unto himself. It seems to me that each story requires a different technique. What is more necessary, however, is to have a story to tell. All the rest will take care of itself. There is no uglier thing than a consciously created beautiful one. An ugly woman may be able to dye her hair and paint her lips and rouge her cheeks, but ugliness pertains chiefly to structure and where the lines are not beautiful, no amount of paint can make them otherwise than they are.

The short story form of literature is, to my mind, the most difficult and the most artistic one. Art is organized movement. Before a short story is wrested out of the chaos created by an incident or an occurrence in one's mind, the artist proceeds in most ruthless fashion to an elimination of unessentials of the material out of which he is to build his structure; to organize movement. But all this is not done in the conscious, stilted manner taught in universities, but in the unconscious free manner dictated by one's creative impulse.

What I have said applies not only to literature, but also to other arts. You can teach a bear to dance but will he know that he is dancing unless he is moved by an inner rhythm?

THE STRANGER [1]

Close to the Dobrudjan side of the winding Danube River, there lived a tribe of gipsies known throughout Rumania as the Tziganies from Canara. The men, big, broad, and lithe, wore, in the winter, long coats made of bear-pelts, and short white lambskin jackets over large blue trousers in the summer. And the women wore dresses and shawls and kerchiefs of such gay colors that it was said of them: "When a Canara woman crosses the road, even a funeral cortège looks like a wedding procession."

And the peasant women would stop churning butter in the tall, narrow wooden pails to talk to them and ask: "What do you do to make your hair grow so long and be so soft and so glossy?" And touch their arms with the tips of their fingers and question: "What do you do to make your skin so soft and so smooth?"

And when one wanted to praise a man one had but to say: "As faithful as a Tzigany from Canara."

The whole summer to late in the fall the gipsies roved through the country, selling horses, in Moldavia, to the blue-eyed peasants along the Sereth River; buying furs from the long-haired, fierce-eyed hunters of the Carpathian Mountains; bartering, trading copper kettles for homespun, sieves for fowl, earrings for lambs; charms, necklaces, fiddles, flutes, combs, shawls. For a wagon of a Canara gipsy held no end of things. One had but to ask something and it was forthcoming.

The whole summer they traveled, but late in the fall they would cross the Danube in boats and return to their huts and fields, which had been taken care of by the older people who had remained at home. It was the only gipsy

[1] From *Pictorial Review,* July, 1923. Reprinted by permission of the author.

tribe that had settled in that way. The feast of the holy Demetrius over, toward the end of the October month, the young people threshed the wheat and oats, shucked the corn, pressed the grapes, did the fall plowing, sawed wood for the winter stove, repaired the cattle sheds; so that the Christmas snowstorm should find them ready and the freezing of the Danube should hold no terrors for them. In the Dobrudja one had to expect to spend at least four months indoors, with plenty of food and wood fire, while the wolves howled and sniffed at the doors and windows. In all, there were about a hundred straw-thatched huts, with perhaps six hundred souls in them. There was no regularity in the building of these huts. Some stood with doors to the east and others with doors to the west; and the houses themselves were built helter-skelter.

A happy and contented tribe, the gipsies of Canara. Their chief was a wise old man. Solni was his name. And so old was he, people said even death respected him, for he was older than death.

One day, early in the spring, Solni's youngest son, Naye, his pride, for he was handsomer and stronger than any of the tribe—this youngest son, having returned from a day's ride to Kara Murat, a Tatar inland marsh village, sat down at the feet of his father and said: "It is of the woman I love I want to speak to my father."

Solni stroked his long gray beard that reached to his belt; then he answered: "When you shall return from your summer travels I shall be no more, my son. The hut is yours then. You will be *barossan* [chief]. Whose daughter is she?"

"The daughter of Selim of Kara Murat, Father. And this hut shall be inhabited by another of your sons, for I shall build a hut in Kara Murat."

After a long silence, the old gipsy chief said: "Wait until the hut is yours before you begin building another. Wait until the chieftainship is yours before you abandon it. Then only will you be able to weigh your love. And if what you have is lighter than what you desire, go. Be happy."

When Naye returned home that fall, his wagon was heavy with things of silk and copper and silver he had bought for Para Selim's daughter. The hut was his. So was the chieftainship. He refused both in favor of his older brother. And the gipsies chanted the whole night long before Naye left: "Happy he who loves so well he is willing to estrange himself, to leave a crown and accept a chain."

Twelve of the best horses and four of the strongest oxen Naye drove ahead to Kara Murat and into Selim's shed. And having spread the silks and the copper on the mud floor of Selim's round hut, he said: "All this is my share of my tribe's wealth. It is mine now."

Selim, who liked the young gipsy, looked at the things before him.

"More than that has been offered me for Para, but I have made promise to you and I have had speech with her. She loves you. Yet—you are a stranger here. Your ways are not our ways. Your people are rovers. Mine have been here since the beginning of time; before the Turks had been here and long before the giaours had claimed this land as theirs. If you take Para for wife, you must remain here among us. Half of what you brought I give back to you. Build a hut. There is plenty of land, become one of us; and you can trade within a day's journey."

"What I brought here," Naye answered, "is not one-tenth of what I have abandoned because of my love for Para: my father's hut and the chieftainship of my tribe. And now I become one of your people and will do as you say."

The following day, Naye went to Ishmet, the brick-maker, and bought the flat mud bricks for the building of a hut; for a man must first have a home before a wife is given to him in marriage. While he was chopping straw to mix with the cementing clay soil Para came to see him work. It was the custom of the village. She had to pay him a visit there daily.

"Build a large hut, Naye," she advised.

"I shall make it large enough," the young Tzigany answered with a twinkle in his eye. "It shall be the largest of the village."

Para's cheek flushed and her eyelids drooped when he gazed at her.

She was a beautiful girl. Not more beautiful, true, than any of twenty of Naye's own tribe. But the gaze of a man who loves makes a woman beautiful; makes her skin radiate warm color. Loving eyes upon a woman do what the dew does to a flower. Only loved women are beautiful. Woman ages only when she is no longer loved.

After a few minutes of thought, Para spoke again. Her voice was heavy with emotion.

"Don't make it too large, Naye. Don't make it the largest of the village."

"Why?" Naye inquired, dropping the short, heavy knife upon the tree trunk that served as a chopping block.

"If you were born one of ours, it would not matter. As it is, they will say: 'Why should he, a stranger, shame us by building the largest hut?' So I ask you to make it not larger than my father's."

"There is wisdom in what you say," Naye answered sadly. "If I were to make it small, they would say: 'Why should he shame us by building a small hut in our village?'"

"But we can make it beautiful inside; as beautiful as we want, Allah be praised," Para rejoined.

"That we will do, Para," said Naye, resuming his work, "for when the hut is ready and we are married, I shall think of nothing else than making our home beautiful."

While the two young people spoke, Para's two companions stood at a distance. But they strained their ears to hear every word. In gay burnooses and large yellow pantaloons, while Para wore green clothes, those two companions were to be with her steadily to the day of marriage. It was their duty never to allow the bride out of their eyes.

Para and Naye had tried hard to outwit them, but the vigilance of the girls was heightened by the fact that the groom was a gipsy. He was not to be permitted to think that a Tatar was less than he was. The pride of the race was involved.

Usually, the male youth of the village helped the groom to outwit the bride's companions, and there was great sport until the wedding day. But no one was willing to help Naye. Para herself, knowing how clever her lover was, had told him not to try too hard; not to lower the pride of her people by outwitting them.

Before the first snow had fallen, the top bricks of the wall had been set and the places for the roof beams were scooped out. Then the whole village became busy. Seated around huge kettles in which boiled pilau, sweetened with honey and spiced with cinnamon, the women were plaiting the straw to thatch the roof with. And while the women worked, the men were listening to the stories told by the blind Kiril, Osman, who had put out the light of his eyes because of a vow he had made on his return from seeing the glories of Mekka.

When all was ready, the night before the roof was raised upon the hut, Naye was shut in alone in one hut while Para was being guarded in another.

Then all the unmarried men, dressed in their best, with copper-studded pistols in yellow sashes and white turbans over red fezzes, with long yataghans glistening bluish light in the glare of the red flames, astride the best horses, passed separately Para's window and asked: "It is the night before the roof is set upon the hut. If I were to ask thee now whether thou preferrest me under that roof, what would thine answer be, Para, daughter of Selim?"

"Not thee," Para answered without tremor, calling out his name. Then, as the man rode away and the others were laughing, the second and the third and the tenth passed by the window, each one asking the same question, each one receiving the same answer.

Then the maidens, dressed in their best, preceded by flaming torches and tambourine players, passed in front of the window behind which Naye was standing and, dancing and singing, each in her turn asked: "If I were to ask thee whether thou preferrest me under that roof, what would thine answer be, Naye, son of Solni?"

"Not thee," Naye answered, "though thou art lovely"; and they laughed and enjoyed themselves.

After the last of the maidens had asked the same question, Para was brought before Naye's window. Everybody listened.

"Is the hut, then, built for me?"

"For thee."

Then they all shouted: "The hut was built for Para, Selim's daughter," and the men fired their pistols in the air. It was an old custom of the Tatars of Kara Murat, so that it should be known by all that the choice of the young people is a voluntary one. Bride and groom were allowed to sit together for the first time while the *baya-deres* danced and the men sang, accompanying themselves on the little skin drums that rested on the rugs upon which they squatted. They were as good as married after that ceremony.

At sunrise, after prayers, the roof was set by the villagers while Naye and Para looked on. They were not allowed to help, neither were they permitted to speak to each other or answer questions put by others. Another Kara Murat custom and one affording unending little pleasures. For when they answered they were punished according to the whim of the man or woman who had succeeded in getting them off guard.

After the wedding, Naye brought forth, from a secret bottom in his tent wagon, a number of rugs and carpets he had held back from Para's father; and in the days that followed, he surprised his Tatar wife constantly with a new thing which he had kept secreted. When Selim and his friends paid the first visit on a Friday, after prayers, to the young couple's home, they were taken aback by the number of gay silks hung upon the walls and the rugs spread everywhere. And Naye had hung new golden coin necklaces on Para's neck and given her new earrings; and kettles and pans made of hammered copper and brass were nailed all about the oven, catching and reflecting the faces and the flames and the dancing lights of the sheening silks on the divans.

It was a gay hut, the gayest of all the village. The outside was no different from any other; but the gipsy loved color and light; loved his hut with the instinct of a bird feathering his nest. He had painted with blue and red the inside of the lone window, and with yellow and green and white the door; and there were sheens and colors on the beams of the ceilings and the posts of the walls.

Selim was proud; it was his daughter's hut. He had driven a good bargain. Though the gipsy had kept many a thing from him, it was as it should be. He was a good trader, Naye. And he was the husband of his daughter.

Early the following spring there arrived at Kara Murat a gang of Rumanian workmen followed by a number of low-wheeled carts heavy with machinery. A valuable limestone quarry had been discovered not more than a mile from the Tatar village, and the exploitation of it began then and there. Without haste the workmen began to build sheds and barracks for themselves and the power machines.

Apathetically, the Tatars looked on from a distance, stood in their doors, and looked and cursed. They did not understand what was going on, except that the century-old peace had been disturbed. The giaours were bringing deviltry to their doors. They looked on with dread to a new village springing up under their very noses.

Naye went over to see what was intended. While the Tatars of Kara Murat closed their ears and cursed when the log-fired engine's whistle emitted the first screech, Naye's eyes glistened with pleasure and delight. It was like music to his ears. It was life—active, feverish.

There were more than a hundred workmen; they would need many things. He was a trader. He offered to furnish them with fresh meat and milk and honey, and sell them horses and carts. Indeed, the very first day he sold them several young lambs and many other things.

"We shall get rich, Para," he told his wife, kissing her when he returned to his roof. "And I shall make this hut the most beautiful in the world."

Para was very happy. "I know you will, Naye; I know you will."

The whole day long the engine turned the screeching saw that tore into the soft limestone, cutting it into square slabs. Heavy ox-carts, driven by young boys with long sticks in their hands, carried them away. The workmen were loud-voiced, and as the quarry went deeper and deeper, the echo became stronger and stronger, so that every word, every hammer blow resounded, reëchoed, and traveled over the hills and dales. A soft white powder settled over everything within miles.

To Naye, the activity of the quarry was like life renewed. The long, silent winter had been very monotonous to him. In his tribe the winter had been gay with dances and fights. The Tatars of Kara Murat were pious Mussulmans and a very quiet people. But trade was now brisk. The workmen were noisy, singing and dancing at every occasion, laughing loudly at the slightest provocation. Some of the men had fiddles, others flutes, and many had accordions, which they played expertly.

Naye was so absorbed he did not notice how Para's people looked askance at him when they saw him go or come from the giaours' camp. He was too happy to notice anything. He even smiled when they asked more than a reasonable price for the honey and the lambs he bought from them for his customers. "Let them also feel the sudden prosperity," he said when Para protested against the high price of eggs.

As the spring advanced, more workmen arrived at the quarry. Some brought their families and proceeded to build little homes. Neat, square, green-roofed houses made of limestone, which they painted white, with blue lines about the doors and windows. Naye had to go afar from Kara Murat to get provisions for them. His own people did not have enough to sell. Never before had the Tatars seen so much gold. Never before had they received such prices for their goods. Yet they resented the intrusion of the giaours on their marshes; resented the devil that swallowed fire, spat smoke and steam, and shrieked and screamed; resented the white powder that found its way into every corner, into the food and even into the teeth. Even the children's curiosity was not stronger than their hatred for the men and the things that had disturbed their peace. And when the Rumanian workmen passed Kara Murat on Sunday, eager to see the village and to meet their neighbors, the doors were closed, the people sullen.

Only Naye and Para were happy. From every trip he brought new things. As a bird feathering a nest carries pieces of straw in its beak, he carried on every trip homeward silver and gold and copper things with which to beautify his hut. The two were indeed bent on making it the most beautiful in the world.

Then one Monday morning, when the mechanician came to start the steam engine he found the shed door broken, the transmission belts cut to shreds, and the entire machinery out of commission. A fez found on the ground indicated that the culprit was one from the Tatar village.

When Naye, wondering why he had not heard the shrill morning work whistle, had walked over to the quarry, he found out what had happened. He became so furious he was uncontrollable. Quite apart from the profit he made, he liked the noise about the quarry. The gang of workmen, too, were uncontrollable in their wrath. They recalled the sullenness of the heathen Tatars, who, after all, were only tolerated there, it being the Dobrudja, Rumanian territory. The damage done the engine meant loss of time, of wages. Naye shook his fist at every Tatar he met that day. He was angry. He was mad with anger.

That very afternoon, two mechanicians arrived from Sulina, and with them were a half-dozen gendarmes, carbines on their shoulders, headed by a gold-bespangled officer.

While the engine was being repaired, a tent was raised and the Rumanian flag was unfurled. Seating himself behind a table also covered with the red-yellow-and-blue flag, the officer opened court. Naye, who spoke the Tatar tongue, was asked to act as interpreter. The whole male population of Kara Murat, young and old, was herded together. One by one they were brought before the officer and asked whether they knew who had perpetrated the crime. The answer was as expected. No one knew.

The officer, speaking through Naye to the assembled crowd, then said that he gave them till Thursday to deliver the culprit; after which he would proceed to inflict justice as he saw fit. And he warned that he was going to be very severe, while if the culprit was delivered he would be very lenient with him.

The Tatars departed sullenly to their huts. Late in the night, the whistle of the engine shrieked triumphantly. The machine had been repaired. Naye and Para were happy to hear the piercing noise. He did not feel as his wife's people felt; he did not feel with them. He rose from his couch and went to see the engine work. He even helped with the stretching of the new belt and worked with the mechanicians the whole night long to help put the engine in shape. He did not notice, early the following morning, that his neighbors did not answer his greetings.

On the third day, the officer assembled the Tatars of Kara Murat before his hut and told them that one-twentieth of their huts were to be burned down to the ground that same evening unless the guilty ones were given up. The Tatars returned to their huts. No one knew whose house was to be burned. Some of the people emptied their huts of all the belongings to save something from the impending disaster. Others merely shut themselves in and waited for the fatal hour.

An hour before sunset, a hundred gendarmes in glittering uniforms, with drawn swords and riding spirited horses, drew up in a circle around the village. Just at the hour of prayer the bugle was blown. For the last time the officer asked of the assembled populace that the guilty ones be delivered to the law. There being no answer, five huts were chosen at random, were thoroughly soaked in kerosene, and set on fire while the soldiers kept vigil to see that this punishment was carried out fully.

At first the fires burned brightly, then they settled down to a slow smoldering and a crackling and sizzling. Para and Naye, holding on to each other, had trembled in fear lest their hut should be one of the five.

But the rising flames, instead of having the desired effect, only fanned more active hatred in the hearts of the Tatars against the intruders.

All the old Asiatic lust for destruction, all that had been asleep since the days of Tamerlane, awoke at the sight of the leaping flames and dense clouds of smoke. The naked swords of the gendarmes, instead of scaring them into submission, aroused them, stirred them, made them think of their own yataghans that hung over the fireplaces in every hut. But there were too many gendarmes. Caution was necessary.

For a full week after that night, there was no quiet. The watch around the engine room had been doubled, and it was thought that the punishment had been the very thing. And even Naye thought so, and answered the question of the officer as to what was said by the Tatars.

"They don't say anything. They do not know who did it. It's a great loss: five huts."

But the younger element of Kara Murat could not withhold their hatred any longer, for, on the eighth night after the five houses had been burned, two houses of the new Rumanian hamlet were set on fire. Naye was in great despair when he saw the white houses burning in the night. He knew what was to happen. This time there was no question and no delay. The following night, ten Tatar houses were burned down by the gendarmes. While the flames were dancing, some of the younger Tatars, unable to control themselves, fascinated by the flames, drew up their horses round the burning huts and rode at top speed round and round about them, shouting and yelling all the old-time imprecations against the giaours.

For more than a month afterward, there was quiet in Kara Murat. As the soldiers remained in the Rumanian settlement Naye had to go afar to get provisions for the two hundred and more people, including the workmen. His wife's people had little to sell, and refused to sell what they had. Such errands frequently took the young gipsy too far away; thus he was frequently compelled to stay away nights. And when he returned, he was too busy to have much time for social intercourse with his wife's people, too absorbed to understand their attitude toward himself. The beautifying of the hut was his chief concern. The more colored rugs and silks he could obtain for it, the happier he was, and the more Para loved him.

The Tatars began to look upon him as one of the enemy's camp, for was he not seen with them from early morning to sundown? And when he was away he was always working for them. Some began to say covertly that Selim was responsible for all the misfortunes; that, had he refused to give his daughter in marriage to a gipsy, had he not been so greedy for a few pieces of gold and a few rings, the Rumanians, unable then to find food and fodder, would have departed and abandoned the quarry.

Selim indirectly and Naye directly were the cause of all the misfortunes: the noise and the gritting stone powder in the pots and in the ears, the nose, and the teeth. All this was muttered silently. Neither Naye nor Para noticed the change of attitude in their neighbors. They were too happy in loving one another, feathering their mud nest with colorful things, to notice the drab, sullen faces about them.

Late one night Naye, who had gone out to see why one of the horses in the shed adjoining the hut was neighing, saw smoke rise from the Rumanian settlement. Two huddled figures were stealthily returning to the Tatar camp. In the clear, sudden light of a tongue of flame leaping in the air against the clouded sky he recognized the bearded faces of the culprits. A terrible anger against them made him want to fly at their throats, but he controlled himself and entered his hut.

"Osman and Kahlil have set fire to a giaour house," he told his wife, awakening her from her slumbers. "There will be trouble with the authorities again. Maybe they will burn the whole village this time."

"You must not tell the giaours who did it!" Para clutched at him.

Naye hid his face and sobbed, "Why do you people do such things?"

She trembled in fear as she listened to the whistle of the engine that had suddenly begun to shriek. The fire was quickly put out. But the following morning the gendarmes came and arrested the two guilty Tatars. The watchman had seen their faces in the light of the same flame in which Naye had recognized them. Twenty Tatar houses were burned that night. And the Tatars, instead of being humbled, subdued, were only aroused. A dozen of the younger men set upon two gendarmes. There was a scuffle, and blood flowed freely.

Half of Kara Murat was already destroyed by that time. For a house in the Rumanian settlement ten Tatar huts were burned. And no one knew until the last minute which of the houses would be destroyed. A few days later the watchman of the engine-shed was found stabbed. Again the gendarmes came. This time they set fire indiscriminately to house after house, driving the people out first at the point of the naked sword.

Naye and Para trembled with fear. They had worked so hard to beautify their hut. It was piled high with green-silk cushions and feathered divans and piles of Damascus and Atlases and rugs and fox-skins. And the window was painted so brightly and the door so gayly! Their hut was spared! When one of the gendarmes wanted to set fire to it the sergeant interfered. "Leave this hut. It belongs to Naye, the Tzigany." Four huts on each side had been burned to the ground.

When Naye opened his door the following morning what had been a village a few months before was only a mass of ruins. Only a dozen crooked chimneys, like beaks of crows hiding in strawstacks, were still in existence. Horses, cows, goats, and fowl of all kinds were running wild about the grounds. Sheds, stables, and granaries had been destroyed. The smoke had driven the bees back into the hives, where they ate the honey they had distilled for months.

Naye had been awake the whole night. He had been thinking searchingly. The Tatars were wrong, but the Rumanians were not doing the right thing either. He was first going to speak to his own people, to the people he had adopted as his own. He was going to explain to them that the others were the masters, the rulers; that the country belonged to them; that it was folly to fight against them. They had thousands of soldiers and gendarmes; swords and guns and cannons. Then, when he had succeeded in making that clear to them, he was going to have speech with the authority on the other side, and to him he was going to explain what the Tatars felt. And then they would establish a truce on both sides. The mud huts could be rebuilt rapidly enough. They could use broken slabs of limestone for the purpose and for the asking.

Before winter, half of the village could be restored in a more or less temporary way. People could crowd when necessary. The sheds for the animals had to be restored. Cattle had to be taken care of. He was willing to house his father-in-law with his two wives. Others could likewise with their relatives. In a short time they could again be happy. There was trade for all of them. The other settlement, the Rumanian one, was bound to grow. How he loved his hut! Coming home to it was his greatest joy.

His people, the Tziganies of Canara, half-settled rovers, loved their huts, and the homecoming had always been great joy.

Coming out of his door, Naye sought out Selim, his father-in-law, and the chief of the tribe.

"I must have speech with our people today, my father," he said as soon as he had seen him. He was excited. Fired by the importance of his self-imposed mission, his voice was masterful.

"You shall have it after sundown. I myself shall call them," Selim answered, wondering what had come over his son-in-law.

"Good! Call them all in front of my house after sundown, Father."

Then Naye went quickly to the Rumanian settlement. "I must see the officer, the captain, the general," he pleaded with the sentinel guarding the door.

"Not today, Tzigany. He is not to be disturbed. Two other officers are inside, and they are talking together. They will raze the whole Tatar village to the ground."

"Tell him that I must see him. I must, I must," Naye pleaded.

Then he went among the workmen and spoke to them. "Because two or more fools were setting fire to a few houses, it was not right to destroy a whole village," he argued.

"Look at the gipsy taking the Tatar side!" they scoffed. But he was so earnest, so persuasive, so eloquent, that some of the older workmen began to say that there was some sense in what the Tzigany spoke. The whole day long he spoke.

He cried with hot tears as he explained the Tatar side,

the impending misery of the winter, the death of horses and cows, children in the cold, death and starvation. He spoke to the men who drilled and to the men who manipulated the handsaws, to the ones who loaded the stones on the ox-pulled carts, and to the ones who chopped wood for the steam engine. At the end of the day, exhausted, feverish, hoarse, he was convinced that he had gained the others in favor of a truce. The most difficult task was accomplished. He returned home.

Entering his hut, he wondered why Para was so nervous.

"Don't worry, dear; whatever comes, they shall not destroy our nest. The whole day I have been among them to prevent the burning of our hut, and I have begged and cried for the others also"; and as he spoke his eyes embraced in a glance all that his home contained. Para did not answer.

Selim, grown considerably older, curved, bent, as if the woes of the whole world had suddenly descended upon him, unshod himself at his daughter's door, but did not dare enter. Naye waited indoors for a little while, full of buoyant expectancy at first and then wondering why the father of his wife did not appear. He opened the door.

"Why art thou waiting outside, Father?"

Selim replied, not looking at Naye, "I have called, but they will not come to listen to thee."

"Why should they refuse to listen to me when I have only good news to give them?" Naye questioned.

"It is because their faith in you, which was never very strong, has weakened even more of late."

"And why?" Naye asked, standing off so as to bring his full stature to bear upon the old man and his wife.

"It is because you are a stranger, and you see the other people too frequently. It is because my people feel that you are the friend of the others," Selim answered, and his words dragged as if they had long been imprisoned within him.

"Allah be merciful!" cried Para, as she threw herself into her husband's arms.

Naye disengaged himself from her and pushed her into her father's arms.

"Wait outside, both of you, until you see me again," he advised. Then he closed the door behind him as he entered his hut. When he was alone, he emptied the kerosene lamp, the only one in Kara Murat, upon the divans, high with cushions of silks of all colors. He tore down all the hangings, curtains of heavy Damascus cloth and rugs from Bokhara and Tientsin, and made piles of them, strewing them upon the divans. His eyes were full of tears, but his face was set with the decision he had so suddenly taken.

A match cracked. He applied the flame to the silken fringe of a divan. When Naye was certain that the fire had set in he slowly opened the door and faced his wife and her father.

"Man, what have you done?" Selim cried, seeing the bursting flames when Naye came out of the door. The old man wanted to rush inside, to put out the fire. Naye, calm and collected, barred the door.

"Now it will be light enough for me to see the faces of the men I am speaking to. Go call them outside my door. I have paid for the right to speak to them," Naye answered.

And they came. While the hut burned, Naye spoke to

the pale faces of the assembled men, who looked up to him like sinners to a saint.

Within the new year a new village was built by the Tatars. When all was restored, Naye and his wife departed to live with his own people at Canara.

In the center of Kara Murat stands a roofless ruin of a mud hut. It is known as "The Stranger's Hut."

SHERWOOD ANDERSON

WRITING CANNOT BE TAUGHT

After all—you must admit—it is a fairly large-sized order you have given here. I really cannot attempt to do it. I do not like such pawing over of my past emotions. Sometimes it is inevitable. I have put a character in a book. There is the book of mine called *A Story Teller's Story*. That isn't autobiography. It is really a novel—of the mind of a man, let us say, of a man who happened to be a writer.

You are bound to find that most of your students will be thinking of writing as a way to make a living, to attain success, attract attention to themselves. The formulas are infinitely better for them. If they follow the formulas they will be much more likely to succeed.

Of course all kinds of emotions are stirring about in them. So are they in my colored cook, in the first man I meet when I go out into the street. And I understand your feelings too. You do not like the cheap little channels into which human emotions are poured, in the ordinary conventional short story in the magazines.

You would like all of these young writers to be artists. Well, I would like all people to be lovers, but do not know how to bring it about. I suppose there are only two sorts of really nice people in the world, the lover in love or the artist at work.

You wouldn't attempt to give a course in love-making, would you, or get out a book of explanations by well-known lovers?

How am I to attempt to lay down a formula for the channeling of the emotions of these young people?

Let us say I am in love. God knows I have been many times. I see or meet some woman who is beautiful to me. I want her. How am I to get her? Well, I send her flowers and candy. I go to see her. Alas, this is a test for me. Am I up to it? Many doubts assail me. I walk with her under trees. It may be that I manage to get her off somewhere where we can be alone together. This might be difficult. . . .

But be that as it may, let us say I have pulled this matter off. I have got my lady to the seashore and am walking with her. On a certain afternoon, when I am with her, the matter between us is decided.

I come home from there, my dear man, and you take me aside. "I want you to tell my students just how it was done. What did you say to her? Repeat your words. Perhaps it was something in your eyes. Make your eyes look as they did at that moment. My students are worthy young men and women. They want to succeed in love. At the critical moment did you feel a certain emotion? Please feel it again now. My students want to see how you look when you feel it."

You see the probabilities are that Komroff, Frank and Miss Zona Gale were talking nonsense. When they really do it they cannot tell how they do it. Their explanations are as likely to be wrong as right.

You know that is one thing I like about painters. Most of them let some one else do the explaining. They paint. Ask one of them to tell you how he felt at a certain moment, how he held the brush in his hand, etc., and he would tell you to go to Pittsburgh.

And he would do it for just the reasons suggested above.

For each man and woman his own reactions to life, and life happens to be the writer's materials. If you are to have any individuality as a workman you have to go alone through the struggle to find expression for what you feel. You have of course to train your hand and your eye. Just because you ache to do something is no sign you can do it. Talent is given you. You have it or you haven't. A real writer shows himself a writer in every sentence he writes.

The training is another matter. It is a question of how keen is the desire, how much patience and perseverance there is. Sometimes I think it largely a matter of physical strength. How much disappointment can you stand before you throw up the sponge?

Right now, at this moment, I have a hundred stories in me I am not man enough to write as they should be written. How am I to tell another how to do what I cannot myself do?

WHAT MAKES A BOY AFRAID [1]

WHEN Tar Moorehead was sick that time there was an old man, a doctor, used to come to the house. He had a good deal to do with straightening the Mooreheads out. What was wrong with Tar's mother, Mary, was that she was almost too good.

If you are too good you think— "Well now, I'll be patient and kind. I won't scold, whatever happens." In the saloons sometimes when Tar's father, Dick, was spending money he should have taken home he heard other men speaking of their wives. Most men are afraid of their wives.

A man in the saloon used to say things. "I don't want the old woman on my neck." That was just a way of speaking. He meant he would get Hail Columbia when he got home and Dick Moorehead never got Hail Columbia. Dr. Reefy said he should get it sometimes.

In the Moorehead house things changed, got better. Not that Dick became good. Well, no one expected that.

Dick stayed more at home, brought more of his money home. Neighbors came in more. Dick could tell his war stories on the front porch in the presence of neighbor men, a drayman, a man who was section boss on the Wheeling railroad.

Tar's mother had a way she always kept, of knocking the props out from under people sometimes with little side remarks but she held herself back more and more. There are some people that when they smile make the whole house smile. When they freeze up every one around freezes up. Robert Moorehead got to be a good deal like his

[1] From *Woman's Home Companion*, January, 1927. Reprinted by permission of the author.

mother when he grew older. John was the steady one. The youngest one of all, little Will Moorehead, was to be the artist of the family. Later he was what people call a genius and had a hard time making a living.

After his childhood was over and after she had died Tar thought his mother must have been smart. He was in love with her all his life. It may be that you are most likely to love some one you can't possibly be like. After Dr. Reefy began coming to the Moorehead house Mary Moorehead changed but not so much. She went to the children's room after they had gone to bed and kissed them all. She was like a young girl about it, did not seem able to caress them in the daylight. None of her children ever saw her kiss Dick and the sight would have startled them.

If you have a mother like Mary Moorehead and she is lovely to look at—or you think she is, which is the same thing—and she dies when you are young, what you do all your life afterward is to use her as material for dreams. It is unfair to her but you do it.

Very likely you make her sweeter than she was, kinder than she was, wiser than she was. What's the harm?

You are always wanting some one almost perfect to think about because you know that you can't be that way yourself. If you ever do try you give up after a time.

Tar's mother was sick. John Moorehead had taken a job in a factory and Tar was selling papers. The mother's illness was not thought very alarming. Yet it was. She worked as always but often when she was cooking or washing clothes she had to quit suddenly and go sit in a chair. She sat with her eyes closed or if she opened them there was such a queer far-away look. It made you sick to see it. Well, if one of the children happened to be in the house she managed to smile. "It isn't anything. I'll be all right in a minute."

That sort of talk from the mother. Tar's father was seldom at home. Dr. Reefy came to the house and said nothing. Children cannot get information out of a doctor.

Tar went selling his papers. John now seemed almost a man. Margaret wasn't big but she had seemed to get older all of a sudden.

One evening when Tar had been busy distributing papers he went home late and there were his father and mother in their bedroom. He was barefooted and so they did not hear him when he went around the house and the window was open. There was a lamp burning and Dick was talking while his wife lay in bed listening and looking very tired and worn out.

What gave Tar the willies was that Dick wasn't talking about anything important. He had been in some sort of discussion with some man downtown and had got the best of it, or thought he had. What did it matter? It was about the war of course. . . . A lot of people killed in a battle, away off somewheres long ago. Who was to blame? Well, they're dead, eh? Maybe Tar's mother was being killed now—talked to death maybe. It might even be that Dick did not know how pale and worn she looked. You get all indignant inside but what are you going to do?

Tar marched in and told his mother she had better go to sleep. He hadn't exactly told Dick to shut up but that was what he meant and Dick understood. "You look tired, Mother. You'd better go to sleep." If you say words like that, what you are really doing is to say to your own father, "Shut up now and let Mother sleep." It's hard. The words hurt your throat and you want to cry but you don't. You don't really blame Dick, he's what he is—can't help it. Give him a chance and he will understand. "Sure, you're right. Mother does look rather worn out," he says. He hadn't noticed before.

After that happened Tar went upstairs and to bed. The trouble with him was that when he did any little thing like that it made him tremble all over. He felt as he did that time when he butted Henry Fuller off the bridge.

He went selling papers and thinking. Now he was thirteen years old and getting big. He still went to Tom Whitehead's stable and stood about listening to the men. The little incident with his father had made him look at men more closely, listen more closely to their talk.

In a town there are certain men other men always speak of as "well-informed." It means they know a lot, have been to a lot of places, read a lot of books. Will Truesdale was a well-informed man but not so much so as Judge Blair. It was because the judge had traveled in foreign places and Will had not.

Once Judge Blair took Tar for a walk. It did not take very long. Tar was at Tom Whitehead's stable when the judge came in and none of the others were there. There were only the stablemen and the judge never paid any attention to them.

"Come on, young man," the judge said, addressing Tar as if he were a grown man. It was just as if he had said, "Well, come on. I want company and you'll have to do." Tar could have taken it as a compliment if he had wanted to but he didn't. He thought he would have been a fool if he had.

Tar and the judge walked down by Waterworks Pond. It was an odd affair, that walk. If the judge had wanted to talk with Tar he changed his mind. They just walked down to Waterworks Pond and stayed for a time watching the fish swim around. There was a swarm of minnows in near the shore and the judge poked his cane down among them. They would all light out into the deep water and then when he took his cane out would come back. Maybe the judge had wanted to talk to Tar about his mother but when it came right down to it hadn't the nerve. What you find out later is that if kids are afraid of grown people sometimes grown people are afraid of kids too. They are afraid to hurt them, maybe. Kids can stand more than grown people think they can.

Anyway it was a queer way for the judge to act—taking Tar away from the stable that way and then not talking to him. He poked his stick in among the minnows several times and then turned to Tar and said, "Well, boy," he said, "I expect you want to run and play." After he said it he just stood looking out over the pond and Tar made a sneak. There wasn't anything else to do he could think of at the time.

Tar's father was what he was. He could not help it. Dr. Reefy liked and respected Tar's mother and he liked Dick, but not in the same way. If he came to the house and Dick was there he acted something like Judge Blair that time he took Tar for a walk. It wasn't exactly looking down on Dick, that wasn't the point. He acted a little (not knowing it) as if he and Mary Moorehead were grown people and Dick only a boy.

If Mary Moorehead had been a man—well, Tar knew she would have been Dr. Reefy's friend, Will Truesdale's friend, Judge Blair's friend, maybe.

What makes a boy more afraid than anything is something happening to his mother. It's a thing he doesn't dare to think about but Tar had to.

He had been noticing things. Nowadays Mary Moorehead went around the house the same as she always did and of course she was always at work but she was pale. Sometimes when she was at work—maybe she was ironing or getting supper—she stopped suddenly and went to sit in a chair. If you asked her if there was anything the matter she said no. Dick Moorehead was being pretty steady and brought more money home than he used to and John's earnings with Tar's, selling newspapers and other jobs, helped a lot but things cost more all the time. Mary Moorehead had begun to take in washing and ironing. Tar and Margaret went and got the clothes and took them home, usually in the evening after dark, and there was something—Tar did not know why it was true —they never spoke of it. . . . Well, they were both a little ashamed—for Dick maybe.

No one would have dared say it to Mary Moorehead. She would have taken his head off. Maybe there are a lot of things in every family no one dares say, even to others in the family.

It's fun having a dad who can tell stories and all that but . . .

Why do you feel some men are solid and others as wobbly as calves?

When Mary Moorehead got pale that way it made Tar all shivery inside. A cold place came that would not get warm. She just sat in the chair awhile and there was a funny gone look in her eyes and if any of the children were around she managed to laugh. It had never happened when Dick was at home. He was away a lot. "Liked to be away," Tar thought.

Tar's mother had that funny gone look in her eyes and she was gentle as she never used to be. Nowadays she did not caress the children any more than she ever did but sometimes when they were in the house with her they felt her looking at them and when one of them turned around and faced her there was something in her eyes. It was as if she saw them in danger of some kind and did not know what to do about it.

Was Tar's mother trying to say something to him and the others at home, something she dared not put into words? Things going on in a family and no one letting on. A father maybe who all his life has been fooling himself. Sometimes nowadays Tar could sit at home and feel all right. He could tell himself that the secret fears he had were not true.

At night after dark was the worst. If you went upstairs and to bed with John and Robert you couldn't say a word.

Ghostly fears, little creeping fears.

There isn't anything to make you afraid but something terrible happening. You don't dare think about it but such a creepy feeling comes. It makes you want to crawl close to something solid, something maybe you can hold onto a bit.

Tar had the feeling one evening going home from his paper-selling and went and crept into the yard of Judge Blair's house and concealed himself under a bush to be near a man who, if trouble came, might be of help to himself and the others.

Nothing happened. The judge was in the library reading a book. After a time Dr. Reefy came. The two men talked for half an hour and then came out to the porch.

From where he lay concealed by a bush Tar might have reached out and touched them with his hands.

The two men stood together a moment looking at the stars, and Judge Blair put his arm on Dr. Reefy's shoulder. Then in a moment Dr. Reefy went away.

Tar also went. He went home. When he got there he did not go in at once.

Creeping around the house he went to the window of his mother's room. It was all dark inside. It was early, but nowadays his mother always went to bed early and, to keep the house quiet, so did the children.

Tar thought his mother might be in her bed, asleep and all right.

But on the other hand she might be—

Why nowadays did Tar always have the feeling something dreadful was about to happen?

He crept indoors and upstairs to his room.

How very silent the house was. John was out somewhere and had not yet come home.

Margaret was in her room.

When Tar got into bed he lay on his back and closed his eyes and when he opened them the walls, the ceiling, the floor of the room in which he lay all seemed to have floated away.

It was like that time when he was sick. Everything floated away from him. If there were only some one now he could get hold of. If only his father, Dick Moorehead, were more like Dr. Reefy or Judge Blair—well, not always but now and then. If even Margaret were more grown up.

Tar lay for a long time in the bed like that, the house silent, that queer feeling of being isolated from every living thing in the world playing over him like a wind.

It was a feeling he would have to fight all his life. Maybe all people have to fight it a good deal.

It was a thing that almost made him want to die while it lasted and it was on him often just before his mother's death, but being a boy with a boy's body and spending the day as he did out of doors the blessing was that when the feeling was worst the good angel of sleep came and passed her hand over his eyes.

The coming of death to Tar's mother was without special dramatic interest. She died in the night and only Dr. Reefy was in the room with her. There was no death-bed scene, the husband and children gathered about, a few last courageous words, a struggle and then the soul taking flight. For a long time Dr. Reefy had been expecting her death and was not surprised. Having been summoned to the house and the children having been sent upstairs to bed he sat down to talk with Mary Moorehead.

There were words said that Tar lying awake in a room above could not hear. As he afterward became a writer he often reconstructed in his imagination the scene in the room below. Well, there had always been some kind of understanding between Dr. Reefy and his mother. The man never became his own friend, never talked intimately to him as Judge Blair did later, but he liked to think that the last talk of the man and woman in the little frame house in the Ohio town was full of significance to them both.

Voices in a room downstairs in a small frame house. Dick Moorehead, the husband, was away in the country on a painting job. What do two grown people talk about at such a time? The man and woman in the room below now and then laughed softly. After the doctor had been there for some time Mary Moorehead went quietly to sleep and died in her sleep.

The doctor did not awaken the children but went out of the house and got a neighbor to drive off to the country for Dick and then, coming back, sat down.

Mary Moorehead died during a night in the fall. Tar was then selling papers and John had gone to the factory. When Tar got home in the early evening his mother was not at table and Margaret said she was not feeling well. It was raining outside. The children ate in silence, the depression that always came with one of Mother's bad times hanging over them. Depression is something on which the imagination also feeds. When the meal was over Tar helped Margaret wash the dishes.

The children sat around. The mother had said she did not want anything to eat. John, who had just begun his work at the factory, went off early to bed and so also did Robert and Will.

Neither Tar nor Margaret was a bit sleepy. Margaret made the others go upstairs softly so as not to disturb the mother—if she was asleep. The two children got their school lessons, then Margaret and Tar got out the dominoes.

When Mary Moorehead was having one of her bad times she breathed irregularly. Her bedroom was right next the kitchen and at the front of the house was the parlor where the funeral was afterward held. When you wanted to go upstairs to bed you had to go right into the mother's bedroom but there was an offset in the wall and if you were careful you could go up without being seen. Mary Moorehead's bad times were coming more and more regularly now. You almost got used to them. When Margaret had got home from school the mother was in bed and looking very pale and weak and Margaret wanted to send Robert off for the doctor at once but the mother said, "Not yet."

A grown person like that, and your mother . . . when they say "no" what are you going to do?

Now and then either Margaret or Tar went to put a stick of wood in the stove. Outside the house it rained and the wind came in through a crack under the door. There were always holes like that in the houses the Mooreheads lived in. You could throw a cat through the cracks. In the winter Mary Moorehead and John went around and nailed strips of wood and pieces of cloth over the cracks. It kept out some of the cold.

Time passed, perhaps an hour. It seemed longer. The fears Tar had been having for a year John and Margaret also had. You go along thinking you are the only one who thinks and feels things but if you do you're a fool. Others are thinking the same thoughts.

All of a sudden, that night when Mary Moorehead died, Margaret did something. As Margaret and Tar sat playing dominoes they could hear the mother's breathing in the next room. It was soft and irregular. Margaret got up in the middle of a game and tiptoed softly into the next room. She stayed there awhile, hidden so the mother couldn't see, then she came back into the kitchen and made a sign to Tar.

She had got all worked up just sitting there. That was it.

It was raining outside and her coat and hat were upstairs but she did not go up. Tar wanted her to take his cap but she wouldn't.

The two children got outside the house and Tar knew at once what was up. They went along the street to Dr. Reefy's office without saying a word to each other.

Dr. Reefy wasn't there. There was a slate on the door and on it was written, "Back at ten o'clock." It might have been there for two or three days. A doctor like that, who hadn't much practice and didn't want much, was pretty careless.

"He might be at Judge Blair's," Tar said and they went there.

On a night like that when you are afraid something is going to happen what you do is to remember other times when you were scared and everything turned out all right. It is the best way.

On a night like that, when you are going for the doctor and your mother is going to die although you don't know it yet, other people you meet in the street go along just as they always do.

Margaret and Tar got to Judge Blair's house and sure enough the doctor was there. It was warm and bright inside but they did not go in. The judge came to the door and Margaret said, "Tell the doctor please that mother's sick," and she had hardly got the words said when out the doctor came. He went right along with the two children and when they were leaving the judge's house the judge came out and patted Tar on the back. "You're soaked," he said. He never spoke to Margaret at all.

The children took the doctor home with them and then went upstairs. They wanted to pretend to the mother that the doctor had just come by accident—to make a call.

They went up the stairs as softly as they could and when Tar got into the room where he slept with John and

Robert he undressed and got into dry clothes. He put on his Sunday suit. It was the only one he had that was dry.

Downstairs he could hear his mother and the doctor talking. He did not know that the doctor was telling his mother about the trip in the rain. What happened was that Dr. Reefy came to the foot of the stairs and called him down. No doubt he intended to call both children. He made a little whistling sound and Margaret came out of her room dressed in dry clothes just as Tar was. She also had to put on her best clothes. None of the other children heard them at all.

They went down and stood by the bed and their mother talked a little. "I'm all right. Nothing's going to happen. Don't worry," she said. She meant it too. She must have thought she was all right up to the last. It was a good thing, if she had to go, that she could go like that, just slip off during her sleep.

She said she would not die but she did. When she had spoken a few words to the children they went back upstairs but for a long time Tar did not sleep. Neither did Margaret. Tar never asked her afterward but he knew she didn't.

That night, now and then, Tar thought he heard his mother and the doctor talking. He couldn't just tell. It might only have been the wind outside the house. Once he was quite sure he heard the doctor run across the kitchen floor. Then he thought he heard a door open and close softly.

The worst of all for Tar and Margaret and John and all of them was the next day and the next and the next. A house full of people, a sermon to be preached, the man coming with the coffin, the trip to the graveyard. Margaret got out of it the best. She worked around the house.

They couldn't make her stop. A woman said, "No, let me do it," but Margaret did not answer. She was white and kept her lips tightly closed together. She went and did it herself.

People came to the house Tar had never seen, worlds of people.

The queerest thing was what happened to Tar on the day after the burial.

He was going along a street, coming from school. School was out at four and the train with his papers did not come until after five. He was going along the street and had got to the vacant lot by the Wilder's barn and there, in the lot, were some of the kids playing ball. Clark Wilder was there and the Richmond kid and a lot of others. When your mother dies you do not play ball for a long, long time. It isn't showing the proper respect. Tar knew that. The others knew it too.

Tar did stop. The queer thing that happened was that he played ball that day just as if nothing had happened. Well, not like that either. He never intended to play at all. What he did surprised him and the others. Of course they all knew about the death of his mother.

The boys were playing three-old-cat and Bob Mann was pitching. He had an out-curve and an in-shoot and a lot of speed for a twelve-year-old.

Tar just climbed over the fence and walked across the field and right up to the batter and took the bat out of his hand. At any other time there would have been a row over his doing that. When you play three-old-cat first you have to field, then hold base, then pitch, then catch before you can bat.

Tar didn't care. He took the bat out of Clark Wilder's hands and stood up at the plate. He began to taunt Bob

Mann. "Let's see you put her over. Let's see what you got."

Bob threw one and then another and Tar soaked the second one. It was a home run and when he got around the bases he took the bat right up and soaked another, although it wasn't his turn. The others let him. They never said a word.

Tar yelled, he taunted the others, he acted crazy but nobody cared. When he had kept it up for maybe ten minutes he left just as suddenly as he had come.

He went, after he had acted like that on the very day after his mother's funeral, down to the depot. Well, the train wasn't in.

There were some empty box cars on a railroad siding over by Sid Gray's elevator near the depot and going over there he crawled into one of the cars.

At first he thought he would like to be in a car like that and be carried away, he didn't care where, and then he thought of something else. The cars were to have grain loaded in them. They stood right near the elevator and also near a shed in which there was an old blind horse that went round and round in a circle and kept the machinery going that lifted the grain up to the top of the building.

The grain was lifted up and then run down through a shoot. They could fill a car in just a little while. All they had to do was to pull a lever and down the grain came.

It would be nice, Tar thought, to lie still in the car and be buried under the grain. It wouldn't be like being buried under the ground. Grain was nice stuff, it felt nice in the hand. It was golden yellow stuff and would run down like rain and would bury you deep down where you could not breathe and you would die.

For what seemed to him a long time he lay on the floor of the car thinking of such a death for himself and then, rolling over on his side, he saw the old horse in his shed. The horse was looking out at him with blind eyes.

Tar looked at the horse and the horse looked at him. He heard the train that had brought his papers come in but did not stir. Now he was crying so that he was himself almost blind. It was as well, he thought, to do his crying where none of the other Moorehead children and none of the kids around town could see. The Moorehead children all felt something like that. At such a time you can't go making a show of yourself.

Tar lay in the car until the train came and went and then, drying his eyes, crawled out.

The people who had been down to meet the train were walking away up the street. Now in the Moorehead house Margaret would be home from school and would be doing her housework. John was at the factory. It was no special fun for John but he stuck to his job just the same.

As for the people walking away up the street—it might be that some of them would be wanting a paper.

A kid if he is any good has to be tending up to his job. He has to get up a hustle. It is a good thing he can't be blubbering away his time lying in an empty box car. What he has to do is bring into the family all the money he can. Heavens knows they need it all. He has got to tend up to his job.

These the thoughts in Tar Moorehead's head as he grabbed his bundle of newspapers and wiping his eyes on the back of his hand raced away up the street.

Although he did not know it Tar was at that very moment racing away out of childhood. Who knows when one thing ends and another begins?

MORLEY CALLAGHAN

CAN ONE EXPLAIN?

I chose the short story because it is more immediate than any other kind of prose. It is a pattern you can get under your eye. At one time I used to read all the short-story writers and admire them. I began writing short stories in an effort to prove to myself that I could write real short stories. But I was not in the competitive business. I felt there weren't many good short-story writers in America. In college the idea prevailed that America was the home of the short story. I discovered that it was the home of the machine-made short story.

I didn't send anything to the magazines for years. My writing was a very personal thing. The stories didn't seem to matter. The important thing to me was not so much to sell my stories as to get them before those who would like them.

I have never done anything that has been indifferent to me. I am trying for sincere, cautious and fresh expression.

Your writing should be your own growth. You can't help but add a modern world consciousness to your own growth. I have written only of things around me. I don't want to write about anything I can't handle perfectly.

As for the "genesis" of one of my stories, that is a rather difficult matter. I try to be honest, to give an insight or illumination of the character, to place the character in life, to give a kind of higher truth to it (the story) in terms of my own emotion for the character. This may not mean much. As a matter of fact, an explanation that sounds good today sounds rotten tomorrow. There was an article about my work in the New York *Sunday World* that touched upon the short story, and may make the thing a bit clearer. I daresay that you know as well as I do that most explanations of the genesis of a story are the bunk, at least I've always thought so. One can give a kind of historical sketch of the notions accompanying events that became the material for a short story, but I don't believe that much is really explained, do you?

A GIRL WITH AMBITION [1]

After leaving public school when she was sixteen Mary Ross worked for two weeks with a cheap chorus at the old La Plazza, quitting when her stepmother heard the girls were a lot of toughs. Mary was a neat clean girl with short fair curls and blue eyes, looking more than her age because she had very good legs and knew it. She got another job as cashier in the shoe department of Eaton's Store after a row with her father and a slap on the ear from her stepmother.

She was marking time in the store of course, but it was good fun telling the girls about imaginary offers from big companies. The older salesgirls sniffed and said her hair was bleached. The salesmen liked fooling around her cage, telling jokes, but she refused to go out with them; she didn't believe in running around with fellows working in the same department. Mary paid her mother six dollars a week for board and always tried to keep fifty cents out. Mrs. Ross managed to get the fifty cents, insisting every time that Mary would come to a bad end.

Mary met Harry Brown when he was pushing a truck on the second floor of the store, returning goods to the department. Every day he came over from the mail order building, stopping longer than necessary in the shoe department, watching Mary in the cash cage out of the corner of his eye while he fidgeted in his brown wicker truck. Mary found out that he went to high school and worked in the store for the summer holidays. He hardly spoke to her, but once when passing, he slipped a letter written on wrapping paper under the cage wire. It was such a nice letter that she wrote a long one the next morning and dropped it in his truck when he passed. She

[1] From *This Quarter*, No. 2. Reprinted by permission of the author.

liked him because he looked neat and had a serious face
and wrote a fine letter with big words that was hard to
read.

In the morning and early afternoons they exchanged
wise glances that held a secret. She imagined herself talking very earnestly, all about getting on. It was good having some one to talk to like that because the neighbors
on her street were always teasing about going on the
stage. If she went to the corner butcher to get a pound of
round steak cut thin, he saucily asked how was the village
queen and the actorine. The lady next door, who had a
loud voice and was on bad terms with Mrs. Ross, often
called her a stage hussy, saying she should be spanked for
staying out so late at night, waking decent people when
she came in.

Mary liked to think that Harry Brown knew nothing
of her home or street, for she looked up to him because
he was going to be a lawyer. Harry admired her ambition but was a little shy. He thought she knew too much
for him.

In the letters she called herself his sweetheart but never
suggested they meet after work. Her manner implied it
was unimportant that she was working in the store.
Harry, impressed, liked to tell his friends about her, showing off the letters, wanting them to see that a girl who
had a lot of experience was in love with him. "She's got
some funny ways but I'll bet no one gets near her," he
often said.

They were together the first time the night she asked
him to meet her downtown at 10.30 p.m. He was at the
corner early and didn't ask where she had been earlier
in the evening. She was ten minutes late. Linking arms
they walked east along Queen Street. He was self-con-

scious. She was trying to be very practical though pleased to have on her new blue suit with the short stylish coat.

Opposite the Cathedral at the corner of Church Street, she said, "I don't want you to think I'm like the people you sometimes see me with, will you now?"

"Gee no, I think you away ahead of the girls you eat with at noon hour."

"And look, I know a lot of boys, but that don't mean nothing. See."

"Of course, you don't need to fool around with tough guys, Mary. It won't get you anywhere," he said.

"I can't help knowing them, can I?"

"I guess not."

"But I want you to know that they haven't got anything on me," she said, squeezing his arm.

"Why do you bother with them?" he said, as if he knew the fellows she was talking about.

"I go to parties, Harry. You got to do that if you're going to get along. A girl needs a lot of experience."

They walked up Parliament and turned east, talking confidentially as if many things had to be explained before they could be satisfied with each other. They came to a row of huge sewer pipes along the curb for a hundred yards to the Don Bridge. The city was repairing the drainage. Red lights were about fifty feet apart on the pipes. Mary got up on the pipes and walked along, supporting herself with a hand on Harry's shoulder, while they talked in a silly way, laughing. A night watchman came along and yelled at Mary, asking if she wanted to knock the lights over.

"Oh, have an apple," Mary yelled back at him.

"You better get down," Harry said, very dignified.

"Aw, let him chase me," she said. "I'll bet he's got a

wooden leg," but she jumped down and held on to his arm.

For a time they stood on the bridge, looking beyond the row of short poplars lining the river bank to the undulating line of street lights on the hill in the good district on the other side of the park. Mary asked Harry if he didn't live over there, wanting to know if they could see his house from the bridge. They watched the lights on a street car moving slowly up the hill. She felt he was going to kiss her. He was looking down at the slow-moving water wondering if she would like it if he quoted some poetry.

"I think you are swell," he said finally.

"I'll let you walk home with me," she said.

"Gee, I wish you didn't want to be an actress," he said.

They retraced their steps until a few blocks from her home. They stood near the police station in the shadow of the fire hall. He coaxed so she let him walk just one block more. In the light from the corner butcher store keeping open, they talked for a few minutes. He started to kiss her. "Oh, the butcher will see us," she said, but didn't care for Harry was very respectable looking and she wanted to be kissed. Harry wondered why she wouldn't let him go to the door with her. She left him and walked ahead, turning to see if he was watching her. It was necessary she walk a hundred yards before Harry went away. She turned and walked back home, one of a row of eight dirty frame houses jammed under one long caving roof.

She talked a while with her father but was really liking the way Harry had kissed her and talked to her and the very respectable way he had treated her all evening. She hoped he wouldn't meet any boys who would say bad things about her.

She might have been happy if Harry had worked on in the store. It was the end of August and his summer holidays were over. The last time he pushed his wicker truck over to the cash cage, she said he was to remember she would always be a sincere friend and would write often. They could have seen each other for he wasn't leaving the city, but they took it for granted they wouldn't.

Every week she wrote to him about offers and rehearsals that would have made a meeting awkward. She liked to think of him not because of being in love but because he seemed so respectable. Thinking of how he liked her made her feel a little better than the girls she knew.

When she quit work to spend a few weeks up at Georgian Bay with a girl friend, Hilda Heustis, who managed to have a good time without working, she forgot about Harry. Hilda had a party in a cottage on the beach and they came home the night after. It was cold and it rained all night. One of Hilda's friends, a fat man with a limp, had chased her around the house and down to the beach, shouting and swearing, and into the bush, limping and groaning. She got back to the house all right. He was drunk. A man in pajamas from the cottage to the right came and thumped on the door, shouting that they were a pack of strumpets, hussies and rotters and if they didn't clear out he would have the police on them before they could say Tom Thumb. He was shivering and looked very wet. Hilda, a little scared, said they ought to clear out next day.

Mary returned to Toronto and her stepmother was waiting, very angry because Mary had left her job. They had a big row. Mary left home, slamming the door. She went two blocks north to live with Hilda.

It was hard to get a job and the landlady was nasty. She tried to get work in a soldiers' company touring the province with a kind of musical comedy called "Mademoiselle from Courcelette," but the manager, a nice young fellow with tired eyes, said she had the looks but he wanted a dancer. After that Mary and Hilda every night practiced a step dance, waiting for the show to return.

Mary's father one night came over to the boarding house and coaxed her to come back home because she was really all he had in the world and he didn't want her to turn out to be a good for nothing. He rubbed his brown face in her hair. She noticed for the first time that he was getting old and was afraid he was going to cry. She promised to live at home if her stepmother would mind her own business.

Now and then she wrote to Harry just to keep him thinking of her. His letters were sincere and free from slang. Often he wrote, "What is the use of trying to get on the stage?" She told herself he would be astonished if she were successful, would look up to her. She would show him.

Winter came and she had many inexpensive good times. The gang at the east end roller rink knew her and she occasionally got in free. There she met Wilfred Barnes, the son of a grocer four blocks east of the fire hall, who had a good business. Wilfred had a nice manner but she never thought of him in the way she thought of Harry. He got fresh with little encouragement. Sunday afternoons she used to meet him at the rink in Riverdale Park where a bunch of the fellows had a little fun. Several times she saw Harry and a boy friend walking through the park, and leaving her crowd, she would talk to him for a few minutes. He was shy and she was a little ashamed of her crowd that whistled and yelled while she was talking. These chance meetings got to mean a good deal, helping her to think a lot about Harry during the first part of the week.

In the early spring "Mademoiselle from Courcelette" returned to Toronto. Mary hurried to the man that had been nice to her and demonstrated the dance she had practiced all winter. He said she was a good kid and should do well, offering her a try out at thirty dollars a week. Even her stepmother was pleased because it was a respectable company that a girl didn't need to be ashamed of. Mary celebrated by going to a party with Wilfred and playing strip poker until 4 A.M. She was getting to like being with Wilfred.

When it was clear she was going on the road with the company she phoned Harry and asked him to meet her at the roller rink.

She was late. Harry was trying to roller skate with another fellow, fair haired, long legged, wearing large glasses. They had never roller skated before but were trying to appear unconcerned and dignified. They looked very funny because every one else on the floor was free and easy, willing to start a fight. Mary got her skates on but the old music box stopped and the electric sign under it flashed, reverse. The music started again. The skaters turned and went the opposite way. Harry and his friend skated off the floor because they couldn't cut corners with the left foot. Mary followed them to a bench near the soft-drink stand.

"What's your hurry, Harry?" she yelled.

He turned quickly, his skates slipping and would have fallen but his friend held his arm.

"Look here, Mary, this is the damnedest place," he said.

His friend said roguishly, "Hello, I know you because Harry has told me a lot about you."

"Oh, well, it's not much of a place but I know the gang," she said.

"I guess we don't need to stay here," Harry said.

"I'm not fussy, let's go for a walk, the three of us," she said.

Harry was glad his friend was noticing her classy blue coat with the wide sleeves and her light brown fur. Taking off his skates he tore loose a leather layer on the sole of his shoe.

They left the rink and arm in arm the three walked up the street. Mary was eager to tell about "Mademoiselle from Courcelette." The two boys were impressed and enthusiastic.

"In some ways I don't like to think of you being on the stage, but I'll bet a dollar you get ahead," said Harry.

"Oh, Baby, I'll knock them dead in the hick towns."

"How do you think she'll do, Chuck?" said Harry.

The boy with the glasses could hardly say anything, he was so impressed. "Gee whiz," he said.

Mary talked seriously. She had her hand in Harry's coat pocket and kept tapping his fingers. Harry gayly beat time as they walked, flapping the loose shoe leather on the sidewalk. They felt that they should stay together after being away for a long time. When she said that it would be foolish to think she would cut up like some girls in the business did, Harry left it to Chuck if a fellow couldn't tell a mile away that she was a real good kid.

The lighted clock in the tower of the firehall could be seen when they turned a bend in the street. Then they could make out the hands on the clock. Mary, leaving them, said she had had a swell time, she didn't know just why. Harry jerked her into the shadow of the side door of the police station and kissed her, squeezing her tight. Chuck leaned back against the brick wall, wondering what to do. An automobile horn hooted. Mary, laughing happily, showed the boys her contract and they shook their heads earnestly. They heard footfalls around the corner. "Give Chuck a kiss," said Harry suddenly, generously. The boy with the glasses was so pleased he could hardly kiss her. A policeman appeared at the corner and said, "All right, Mary, your mother wants you. Beat it."

Mary said, "How's your father?" After promising to write Harry she ran up the street.

The boys, pleased with themselves, walked home. "You want to hang on to her," Chuck said.

"I wonder why she is always nice to me just when she is going away," Harry said.

"Would you want her for a girl?"

"I don't know. Wouldn't she be a knock-out at the school dance? The old ladies would throw a fit."

Mary didn't write to Harry and didn't see him for a long time. After two weeks she was fired from the company. She wasn't a good dancer.

Many people had a good laugh and Mary stopped talking about her ambitions for a little while. And though usually careful and fairly strict, she slipped into easy, careless ways with Wilfred Barnes. She never thought of him as she thought of Harry, but he won her and became important to her. Harry was like something she used to pray for when a little girl and never really expected to get.

It was awkward when Wilfred got into trouble for tampering with the postal pillars that stood on the street corners. He had discovered a way of getting all the pennies people put in the slots for stamps. The police found a big pile of coppers hidden in his father's stable. The judge sent him to jail for only two months because his parents were very respectable people. He promised to marry Mary when he came out.

One afternoon in the late summer they were married by a Presbyterian minister. Mrs. Barnes made it clear that she didn't think much of the bride. Mr. Barnes said Wilfred would have to go on working in the store. They took three rooms in a big rooming house on Berkley Street.

Mary cried a little when she wrote to tell Harry she was married. She had always been too independent to cry in that way. She would be his sincere friend and still intended to be successful on the stage, she said. Harry wrote that he was surprised that she had married a fellow just out of jail even though he seemed to come from respectable people.

In the dancing pavilion at Scarboro Beach, a month later, she talked to Harry for the last time. The meeting was unexpected and she was with three frowsy girls from a circus that was in the east end for a week. Mary had on a long blue knitted cape that the stores were selling cheaply. Harry turned up his nose at the three girls but talked cheerfully to Mary. They danced together. She said that her husband didn't mind her taking another try at the stage and he wondered if he should say that he had been to the circus. Giggling and watching him closely, she said she was working for the week in the circus, for the experience. He gave her to understand that always she would do whatever pleased her and shouldn't try for a thing that wasn't natural to her. He wasn't enthusiastic when she offered to phone him, just curious about what she might do.

Late in the fall a small part in a local company at the La Plazza for a week was offered to her. She took the job because she detested staying around the house. She wanted Harry to see her really on the stage so she phoned and asked if he would come to the La Plazza on Tuesday night. Good-humoredly, he offered to take her dancing afterwards. It was funny, he said laughing, that she should be starting all over again at the old La Plazza.

But Harry sitting solemnly in the theater, watching the ugly girls in tights on the stage, couldn't pick her out. He wondered what on earth was the matter when he waited at the stage door and she didn't appear. Disgusted, he went home and didn't bother about her because he had a nice girl of his own. She never wrote to tell him what was the matter.

But one warm afternoon in November, Mary took it into her head to sit on the front seat of the rig with Wilfred, delivering groceries. They went east through many streets until they were in the beach district. Wilfred was telling jokes and she was laughing out loud. Once he stopped his wagon, grabbed his basket and went running along a side entrance yelling, grocer. Mary sat on the wagon seat. Three young fellows and a woman were sitting up on a veranda opposite the wagon. She saw Harry looking at her and vaguely wondered how he got there. She didn't want him to see that she was going to have a baby. Leaning on the veranda rail, he saw that her slimness had passed into the shapelessness of her pregnancy and he knew why she had been kept off the stage that night at the La Plazza. She sat erect and strangely dignified on the seat of the grocery wagon, uncomfortable when he was looking at her but very angry when he turned away. They didn't speak. She made up her mind to be hard up for some one to talk to before she bothered him again, as if without going any further she wasn't as good as he was. She smiled sweetly at Wilfred when he came running out of the alley and jumped on the seat, shouting, "Gidup," to the horse. They drove on to a customer further down the street.

ERNEST HEMINGWAY

WHO KNOWS HOW?

For the guidance of your classes, the way in which I wrote a story called "The Undefeated" was as follows:

I got the idea of writing it while on an AE bus in Paris just as it was passing the Bon Marché (a large department store on the Boulevard Raspail). I was standing on the back platform of the bus and was in a great hurry to get home to start writing before I would lose it. I wrote all during lunch and until I was tired. Each succeeding day I went out of the house to a café in the morning and wrote on the story. It took several days to finish it. I do not remember the names of the cafés.

I wrote a story called "The Killers," in Madrid. I started it when I woke up after lunch and worked on it until supper. At supper I was very tired and drank a bottle of wine and read *La Voz, El Heraldo, Informaciones, El Debate* so as not to think about the story. After supper I went out for a walk. I saw no one I knew and went back to bed. The next morning I wrote a story called "Today Is Friday." I forget what we had for lunch. That afternoon it snowed.

My other stories have mostly been written in bed in the morning. If the above is not practical for the pupils perhaps they could substitute Fifth Avenue bus for AE bus; Saks for the Bon Marché; drug store for café—I believe there would be little difference except that they might not be permitted to write in a drug store.

THE KILLERS [1]

THE door of Henry's lunch-room opened and two men came in. They sat down at the counter.

"What's yours?" George asked them.

"I don't know," one of the men said. "What do you want to eat, Al?"

"I don't know," said Al. "I don't know what I want to eat."

[1] From *Men Without Women*, by Ernest Hemingway. Copyright, 1927, by Charles Scribner's Sons. Reprinted by permission of the author and of the publishers.

121

Outside it was getting dark. The street-light came on outside the window. The two men at the counter read the menu. From the other end of the counter Nick Adams watched them. He had been talking to George when they came in.

"I'll have a roast pork tenderloin with apple sauce and mashed potatoes," the first man said.

"It isn't ready yet."

"What the hell do you put it on the card for?"

"That's the dinner," George explained. "You can get that at six o'clock."

George looked at the clock on the wall behind the counter.

"It's five o'clock."

"The clock says twenty minutes past five," the second man said.

"It's twenty minutes fast."

"Oh, to hell with the clock," the first man said. "What have you got to eat?"

"I can give you any kind of sandwiches," George said. "You can have ham and eggs, bacon and eggs, liver and bacon, or a steak."

"Give me chicken croquettes with green peas and cream sauce and mashed potatoes."

"That's the dinner."

"Everything we want's the dinner, eh? That's the way you work it."

"I can give you ham and eggs, bacon and eggs, liver—"

"I'll take ham and eggs," the man called Al said. He wore a derby hat and a black overcoat buttoned across the chest. His face was small and white and he had tight lips. He wore a silk muffler and gloves.

"Give me bacon and eggs," said the other man. He was about the same size as Al. Their faces were different, but they were dressed like twins. Both wore overcoats too tight for them. They sat leaning forward, their elbows on the counter.

"Got anything to drink?" Al asked.

"Silver beer, bevo, ginger-ale," George said.

"I mean you got anything to *drink?*"

"Just those I said."

"This is a hot town," said the other. "What do they call it?"

"Summit."

"Ever hear of it?" Al asked his friend.

"No," said the friend.

"What do you do here nights?" Al asked.

"They eat the dinner," his friend said. "They all come here and eat the big dinner."

"That's right," George said.

"So you think that's right?" Al asked George.

"Sure."

"You're a pretty bright boy, aren't you?"

"Sure," said George.

"Well, you're not," said the other little man. "Is he, Al?"

"He's dumb," said Al. He turned to Nick. "What's your name?"

"Adams."

"Another bright boy," Al said. "Ain't he a bright boy, Max?"

"The town's full of bright boys," Max said.

George put the two platters, one of ham and eggs, the other of bacon and eggs, on the counter. He set down two side-dishes of fried potatoes and closed the wicket into the kitchen.

"Which is yours?" he asked Al.

"Don't you remember?"

"Ham and eggs."

"Just a bright boy," Max said. He leaned forward and took the ham and eggs. Both men ate with their gloves on. George watched them eat.

"What are *you* looking at?" Max looked at George.

"Nothing."

"The hell you were. You were looking at me."

"Maybe the boy meant it for a joke, Max," Al said. George laughed.

"*You* don't have to laugh," Max said to him. "*You* don't have to laugh at all, see?"

"All right," said George.

"So he thinks it's all right." Max turned to Al. "He thinks it's all right. That's a good one."

"Oh, he's a thinker," Al said. They went on eating.

"What's the bright boy's name down the counter?" Al asked Max.

"Hey, bright boy," Max said to Nick. "You go around on the other side of the counter with your boy friend."

"What's the idea?" Nick asked.

"There isn't any idea."

"You better go around, bright boy," Al said. Nick went around behind the counter.

"What's the idea?" George asked.

"None of your damn business," Al said. "Who's out in the kitchen?"

"The nigger."

"What do you mean the nigger?"

"The nigger that cooks."

"Tell him to come in."

"What's the idea?"

"Tell him to come in."

"Where do you think you are?"

"We know damn well where we are," the man called Max said. "Do we look silly?"

"You talk silly," Al said to him. "What the hell do you argue with this kid for? Listen," he said to George, "tell the nigger to come out here."

"What are you going to do to him?"

"Nothing. Use your head, bright boy. What would we do to a nigger?"

George opened the slit that opened back into the kitchen. "Sam," he called. "Come in here a minute."

The door to the kitchen opened and the nigger came in. "What was it?" he asked. The two men at the counter took a look at him.

"All right, nigger. You stand right there," Al said. Sam, the nigger, standing in his apron, looked at the two men sitting at the counter. "Yes, sir," he said. Al got down from his stool.

"I'm going back to the kitchen with the nigger and bright boy," he said. "Go on back to the kitchen, nigger. You go with him, bright boy." The little man walked after Nick and Sam, the cook, back into the kitchen. The door shut after them. The man called Max sat at the counter opposite George. He didn't look at George but looked in the mirror that ran along back of the counter. Henry's had been made over from a saloon into a lunch-counter.

"Well, bright boy," Max said, looking into the mirror, "why don't you say something?"

"What's it all about?"

"Hey, Al," Max called, "bright boy wants to know what it's all about."

"Why don't you tell him?" Al's voice came from the kitchen.

"What do you think it's all about?"

"I don't know."

"What do you think?"

Max looked into the mirror all the time he was talking.

"I wouldn't say."

"Hey, Al, bright boy says he wouldn't say what he thinks it's all about."

"I can hear you, all right," Al said from the kitchen. He had propped open the slit that dishes passed through into the kitchen with a catsup bottle. "Listen, bright boy," he said from the kitchen to George. "Stand a little further along the bar. You move a little to the left, Max." He was like a photographer arranging for a group picture.

"Talk to me, bright boy," Max said. "What do you think's going to happen?"

George did not say anything.

"I'll tell you," Max said. "We're going to kill a Swede. Do you know a big Swede named Ole Andreson?"

"Yes."

"He comes here to eat every night, don't he?"

"Sometimes he comes here."

"He comes here at six o'clock, don't he?"

"If he comes."

"We know all that, bright boy," Max said. "Talk about something else. Ever go to the movies?"

"Once in a while."

"You ought to go to the movies more. The movies are fine for a bright boy like you."

"What are you going to kill Ole Andreson for? What did he ever do to you?"

"He never had a chance to do anything to us. He never even seen us."

"And he's only going to see us once," Al said from the kitchen.

"What are you going to kill him for, then?" George asked.

"We're killing him for a friend. Just to oblige a friend, bright boy."

"Shut up," said Al from the kitchen. "You talk too goddam much."

"Well, I got to keep bright boy amused. Don't I, bright boy?"

"You talk too damn much," Al said. "The nigger and my bright boy are amused by themselves. I got them tied up like a couple of girl friends in the convent."

"I suppose you were in a convent."

"You never know."

"You were in a kosher convent. That's where you were."

George looked up at the clock.

"If anybody comes in you tell them the cook is off, and if they keep after it, you tell them you'll go back and cook yourself. Do you get that, bright boy?"

"All right," George said. "What you going to do with us afterward?"

"That'll depend," Max said. "That's one of those things you never know at the time."

George looked up at the clock. It was a quarter past six. The door from the street opened. A street-car motor-man came in.

"Hello, George," he said. "Can I get supper?"

"Sam's gone out," George said. "He'll be back in about half an hour."

"I'd better go up the street," the motorman said. George looked at the clock. It was twenty minutes past six.

"That was nice, bright boy," Max said. "You're a regular little gentleman."

"He knew I'd blow his head off," Al said from the kitchen.

"No," said Max. "It ain't that. Bright boy is nice. He's a nice boy. I like him."

At six-fifty-five George said: "He's not coming."

Two other people had been in the lunch-room. Once George had gone out to the kitchen and made a ham-and-egg sandwich "to go" that a man wanted to take with him. Inside the kitchen he saw Al, his derby hat tipped back, sitting on a stool beside the wicket with the muzzle of a sawed-off shotgun resting on the ledge. Nick and the cook were back to back in the corner, a towel tied in each of their mouths. George had cooked the sandwich, wrapped it up in oiled paper, put it in a bag, brought it in, and the man had paid for it and gone out.

"Bright boy can do everything," Max said. "He can cook and everything. You'd make some girl a nice wife, bright boy."

"Yes?" George said. "Your friend, Ole Andreson, isn't going to come."

"We'll give him ten minutes," Max said.

Max watched the mirror and the clock. The hands of the clock marked seven o'clock, and then five minutes past seven.

"Come on, Al," said Max. "We better go. He's not coming."

"Better give him five minutes," Al said from the kitchen.

In the five minutes a man came in, and George explained that the cook was sick.

"Why the hell don't you get another cook?" the man asked. "Aren't you running a lunch-counter?" He went out.

"Come on, Al," Max said.

"What about the two bright boys and the nigger?"

"They're all right."

"You think so?"

"Sure. We're through with it."

"I don't like it," said Al. "It's sloppy. You talk too much."

"Oh, what the hell," said Max. "We got to keep amused, haven't we?"

"You talk too much, all the same," Al said. He came out from the kitchen. The cut-off barrels of the shotgun made a slight bulge under the waist of his too tight-fitting overcoat. He straightened his coat with his gloved hands.

"So long, bright boy," he said to George. "You got a lot of luck."

"That's the truth," Max said. "You ought to play the races, bright boy."

The two of them went out the door. George watched them, through the window, pass under the arc-light and cross the street. In their tight overcoats and derby hats they looked like a vaudeville team. George went back through the swinging-door into the kitchen and untied Nick and the cook.

"I don't want any more of that," said Sam, the cook. "I don't want any more of that."

Nick stood up. He had never had a towel in his mouth before.

"Say," he said. "What the hell?" He was trying to swagger it off.

"They were going to kill Ole Andreson," George said. "They were going to shoot him when he came in to eat."

"Ole Andreson?"

"Sure."

The cook felt the corners of his mouth with his thumbs.

"They all gone?" he asked.

"Yeah," said George. "They're gone now."

"I don't like it," said the cook. "I don't like any of it at all."

"Listen," George said to Nick. "You better go see Ole Andreson."

"All right."

"You better not have anything to do with it at all," Sam, the cook, said. "You better stay way out of it."

"Don't go if you don't want to," George said.

"Mixing up in this ain't going to get you anywhere," the cook said. "You stay out of it."

"I'll go see him," Nick said to George. "Where does he live?"

The cook turned away.

"Little boys always know what they want to do," he said.

"He lives up at Hirsch's rooming-house," George said to Nick.

"I'll go up there."

Outside the arc-light shone through the bare branches of a tree. Nick walked up the street beside the car-tracks and turned at the next arc-light down a side-street. Three houses up the street was Hirsch's rooming-house. Nick walked up the two steps and pushed the bell. A woman came to the door.

"Is Ole Andreson here?"

"Do you want to see him?"

"Yes, if he's in."

Nick followed the woman up a flight of stairs and back to the end of a corridor. She knocked on the door.

"Who is it?"

"It's somebody to see you, Mr. Andreson," the woman said.

"It's Nick Adams."

"Come in."

Nick opened the door and went into the room. Ole Andreson was lying on the bed with all his clothes on. He had been a heavyweight prizefighter and he was too long for the bed. He lay with his head on two pillows. He did not look at Nick.

"What was it?" he asked.

"I was up at Henry's," Nick said, "and two fellows came in and tied up me and the cook, and they said they were going to kill you."

It sounded silly when he said it. Ole Andreson said nothing.

"They put us out in the kitchen," Nick went on. "They were going to shoot you when you came in to supper."

Ole Andreson looked at the wall and did not say anything.

"George thought I better come and tell you about it."

"There isn't anything I can do about it," Ole Andreson said.

"I'll tell you what they were like."

"I don't want to know what they were like," Ole Andreson said. He looked at the wall. "Thanks for coming to tell me about it."

"That's all right."

Nick looked at the big man lying on the bed.

"Don't you want me to go and see the police?"

"No," Ole Andreson said. "That wouldn't do any good."

"Isn't there something I could do?"

"No. There ain't anything to do."

"Maybe it was just a bluff."

"No. It ain't just a bluff."

Ole Andreson rolled over toward the wall.

"The only thing is," he said, talking toward the wall, "I just can't make up my mind to go out. I been in here all day."

"Couldn't you get out of town?"

"No," Ole Andreson said. "I'm through with all that running around."

He looked at the wall.

"There ain't anything to do now."

"Couldn't you fix it up some way?"

"No. I got in wrong." He talked in the same flat voice. "There ain't anything to do. After a while I'll make up my mind to go out."

"I better go back and see George," Nick said.

"So long," said Ole Andreson. He did not look toward Nick. "Thanks for coming around."

Nick went out. As he shut the door he saw Ole Andreson with all his clothes on, lying on the bed looking at the wall.

"He's been in his room all day," the landlady said down-stairs. "I guess he don't feel well. I said to him: 'Mr. Andreson, you ought to go out and take a walk on a nice fall day like this,' but he didn't feel like it."

"He doesn't want to go out."

"I'm sorry he don't feel well," the woman said. "He's an awfully nice man. He was in the ring, you know."

"I know it."

"You'd never know it except from the way his face is," the woman said. They stood talking just inside the street door. "He's just as gentle."

"Well, good night, Mrs. Hirsch," Nick said.

"I'm not Mrs. Hirsch," the woman said. "She owns the place. I just look after it for her. I'm Mrs. Bell."

"Well, good night, Mrs. Bell," Nick said.

"Good night," the woman said.

Nick walked up the dark street to the corner under the arc-light, and then along the car-tracks to Henry's eating-house. George was inside, back of the counter.

"Did you see Ole?"

"Yes," said Nick. "He's in his room and he won't go out."

The cook opened the door from the kitchen when he heard Nick's voice.

"I don't even listen to it," he said and shut the door.

"Did you tell him about it?" George asked.

"Sure. I told him but he knows what it's all about."

"What's he going to do?"

"Nothing."

"They'll kill him."

"I guess they will."

"He must have got mixed up in something in Chicago."

"I guess so," said Nick.

"It's a hell of a thing."

"It's an awful thing," Nick said.

They did not say anything. George reached down for a towel and wiped the counter.

"I wonder what he did?" Nick said.

"Double-crossed somebody. That's what they kill them for."

"I'm going to get out of this town," Nick said.

"Yes," said George. "That's a good thing to do."

"I can't stand to think about him waiting in the room and knowing he's going to get it. It's too damned awful."

"Well," said George, "you better not think about it."

WILBUR DANIEL STEELE

OUT OF WHOLE CLOTH

I'm sorry to say that the question you have put to me—as to the genesis and development of my stories—is one which I have never been able to answer. Almost invariably they are made out of whole cloth, so to say, and once the thing has gotten itself together in my head the preceding stages seem in some automatic way to be wiped out of my memory.

And that's all I can tell you.

THE MAN WHO SAW THROUGH HEAVEN [1]

PEOPLE have wondered (there being obviously no question of romance involved) how I could ever have allowed myself to be let in for the East African adventure of Mrs. Diana in search of her husband. There were several reasons. To begin with, the time and effort and money weren't mine; they were the property of the wheel of which I was but a cog, the Society through which Diana's life had been insured, along with the rest of that job-lot of missionaries. The "letting in" was the firm's. In the second place, the wonderers have not counted on Mrs. Diana's capacity for getting things done for her. Meek and helpless. Yes, but God was on her side. Too meek, too helpless to move mountains herself, if those who happened to be handy didn't move them for her then her God would know the reason why. Having dedicated her all to making straight the Way, why should her neighbor cavil at giving a little? The writer for one, a colonial governor general for another, railway magnates, insurance managers, *safari* leaders, the ostrich-farmer of Ndua, all these and a dozen others in their turns have felt the hundred-ton

[1] From *Harper's Magazine*, September, 1925. Reprinted by permission of the author.

weight of her thin-lipped meekness—have seen her in
metaphor sitting grimly on the doorsteps of their souls.

A third reason lay in my own troubled conscience.
Though I did it in innocence, I can never forget that it
was I who personally conducted Diana's party to the observatory on that fatal night in Boston before it sailed.
Had it not been for that kindly intentioned "hunch" of
mine, the astounded eye of the Reverend Hubert Diana
would never have gazed through the floor of Heaven, and
he would never have undertaken to measure the Infinite
with the foot-rule of his mind.

It all started so simply. My boss at the shipping-and-
insurance office gave me the word in the morning. "Bunch
of missionaries for the *Platonic* tomorrow. They're on our
hands in a way. Show 'em the town." It wasn't so easy
when you think of it: one male and seven females on their
way to the heathen; though it was easier in Boston than it
might have been in some other towns. The evening looked
the simplest. My friend Krum was at the Observatory that
semester; there at least I was sure their sensibilities would
come to no harm.

On the way out in the street car, seated opposite to
Diana and having to make conversation, I talked of Krum
and of what I knew of his work with the spiral nebulae.
Having to appear to listen, Diana did so (as all day long)
with a vaguely indulgent smile. He really hadn't time for
me. That night his life was exalted as it had never been,
and would perhaps never be again. Tomorrow's sailing,
the actual fact of leaving all to follow Him, held his
imagination in thrall. Moreover, he was a bridegroom of
three days with his bride beside him, his nerves at once
assuaged and thrilled. No, but more. As if a bride were

not enough, arrived in Boston, he had found himself surrounded by a very galaxy of womanhood gathered from
the four corners; already within hours one felt the chaste
tentacles of their feminine dependence curling about the
party's unique man; already their contacts with the world
of their new lives began to be made through him; already
they saw in part through his eyes. I wonder what he would
have said if I had told him he was a little drunk.

In the course of the day I think I had got him fairly
well. As concerned his Church he was at once an asset and
a liability. He believed its dogma as few still did, with a
simplicity, "the old-time religion." He was born that kind.
Of the stuff of the fanatic, the reason he was not a fanatic
was that, curiously impervious to little questionings, he
had never been aware that his faith was anywhere at-
tacked. A self-educated man, he had accepted the necessary smattering facts of science with a serene indulgence,
as simply so much further proof of what the Creator
could do when He put His Hand to it. Nor was he conscious of any conflict between these facts and the fact
that there existed a substantial Heaven, geographically
up, and a substantial Hot Place, geographically down.

So, for his Church, he was an asset in these days. And
so, and for the same reason, he was a liability. The Church
must after all keep abreast of the times. For home con-
sumption, with modern congregations, especially urban
ones, a certain streak of "healthy" skepticism is no longer
amiss in the pulpit; it makes people who read at all more
comfortable in their pews. A man like Hubert Diana is
more for the cause than a hundred. But what to do with
him? Well, such things arrange themselves. There's the
Foreign Field. The blacker the heathen the whiter the

light they'll want, and the solider the conception of a God the Father enthroned in a Heaven of which the sky above them is the visible floor.

And that, at bottom, was what Hubert Diana believed. Accept as he would with the top of his brain the fact of a spherical earth zooming through space, deep in his heart he knew that the world lay flat from modern Illinois to ancient Palestine, and that the sky above it, blue by day and by night festooned with guiding stars for wise men, was the nether side of a floor on which the resurrected trod. . . .

I shall never forget the expression of his face when he realized he was looking straight through it that night. In the quiet dark of the dome I saw him remove his eye from the eye-piece of the telescope up there on the staging and turn it in the ray of a hooded bulb on the demon's keeper, Krum.

"What's that, Mr. Krum? I didn't get you!"

"I say, that particular cluster you're looking at—"

"This star, you mean?"

"You'd have to count awhile to count the stars describing their orbits in that 'star,' Mr. Diana. But what I was saying—have you ever had the wish I used to have as a boy—that you could actually look back into the past? With your own two eyes?"

Diana spoke slowly. He didn't know it, but it had already begun to happen; he was already caught. "I have often wished, Mr. Krum, that I might actually look back into the time of our Lord. Actually. Yes."

Krum grunted. He was young. "We'd have to pick a nearer neighbor than *Messier 79* then. The event you see when you put your eye to that lens is happening much too far in the past. The light-waves thrown off by that particular cluster on the day, say of the Crucifixion—*you* won't live to see them. They've hardly started yet—a mere twenty centuries on their way—leaving them something like eight hundred and thirty centuries yet to come before they reach the earth."

Diana laughed the queerest catch of a laugh. "And— and there—there won't be any earth here, then, to welcome them."

"*What?*" It was Krum's turn to look startled. So for a moment the two faces remained in confrontation, the one, as I say, startled, the other exuding visibly little sea-green globules of sweat. It was Diana that caved in first, his voice hardly louder than a whisper.

"W-w-will there?"

None of us suspected the enormousness of the thing that had happened in Diana's brain. Krum shrugged his shoulders and snapped his fingers. Deliberately. *Snap!* "What's a thousand centuries or so in the cosmic reckoning?" He chuckled. "We're just beginning to get out among 'em with *Messier*, you know. In the print room, Mr. Diana, I can show you photographs of clusters to which, if you cared to go, traveling at the speed of light—"

The voice ran on; but Diana's eye had gone back to the eye-piece, and his affrighted soul had reëntered the big black tube sticking its snout out of the slit in the iron hemisphere. . . . "At the speed of light!" . . . That unsuspected, that wildly chance-found chink in the armor of his philosophy! The body is resurrected and it ascends to Heaven instantaneously. At what speed must it be borne to reach instantaneously that city beyond the ceiling of the sky? At a speed inconceivable, mystical. At, say (as he had often said to himself), *the speed of light.*

. . . And now, hunched there in the trap that had caught him, black rods, infernal levers and wheels, he was aware of his own eye passing vividly through unpartitioned emptiness, *eight hundred and fifty centuries at the speed of light!*

"And still beyond these," Krum was heard, "we begin to come into the regions of the spiral nebulae. We've some interesting photographs in the print room, if you've the time."

The ladies below were tired of waiting. One had "lots of packing to do." The bride said, "Yes, I do think we should be getting along. Hubert, dear, if you're ready—"

The fellow actually jumped. It's lucky he didn't break anything. His face looked greener and dewier than ever amid the contraptions above. "If you—you and the ladies, Cora—wouldn't mind—if Mr.—Mr.—(he'd mislaid my name) would see you back to the hotel—" Meeting silence, he began to expostulate. "I feel that this is a rich experience. I'll follow shortly; I know the way."

In the car going back into the city Mrs. Diana set at rest the flutterings of six hearts. Being unmarried, they couldn't understand men as she did. When I think of that face of hers, to which I was destined to grow only too accustomed in the weary, itchy days of the trek into Kavirondoland, with its slightly tilted nose, its irregular pigmentation, its easily inflamed lids, and long moist cheeks, like a hunting dog, glorying in weariness, it seems incredible that a light of coyness could have found lodgment there. But that night it did. She sat serene among her virgins.

"You don't know Bert. You wait; he'll get a perfectly wonderful sermon out of all that tonight, Bert will."

Krum was having a grand time with his neophyte. He

would have stayed up all night. Immured in the little print room crowded with files and redolent of acids, he conducted his disciple "glassy-eyed" through the dim frontiers of space, holding before him one after another the likenesses of universes sister to our own, islanded in immeasurable vacancy, curled like glimmering crullers on their private Milky Ways, and hiding in their wombs their myriad "coal-pockets," star-dust foetuses of which—their quadrillion years accomplished—their litters of new suns would be born, to bear their planets; to bear their moons in turn.

"And beyond these?"

Always, after each new feat of distance, it was the same. "And beyond?" Given an ell, Diana surrendered to a pop-eyed lust for nothing less than light-years. "And still beyond?"

"Who knows?"

"The mind quits. For if there's no end to these nebu-lae—"

"But supposing there is?"

"An end? But, Mr. Krum, in the very idea of an end-ing—"

"An end to what we might call this particular category of magnitudes. Eh?"

"I don't get that."

"Well, take this—take the opal in your ring there. The numbers and distances inside that stone may conceivably be to themselves as staggering as ours to us in our own system. Come! that's not so far-fetched. What are we learning about the structure of the atom? A nucleus (call it a sun) revolved about in eternal orbits by electrons (call them planets, worlds). Infinitesimal; but after all, what are bigness and littleness but matters of comparison? To eyes on one of those electrons (don't be too sure there aren't any) its tutelary sun may flame its way across a heaven a comparative ninety million miles away. Impossible for them to conceive of a boundary to their billions of atomic systems, molecular universes. In that category of magnitudes its diameter is infinity; once it has made the leap into our category and become an opal it is merely a quarter of an inch. That's right, Mr. Diana, you may well stare at it: between *now* and *now* ten thousand histories may have come and gone down there. . . . And just so the diameter of our own cluster of universes, going over into another category, may be—"

"May be a—a ring—a little stone—in a—a—a—ring."

Krum was tickled by the way the man's imagination jumped and engulfed it.

"Why not? That's as good a guess as the next. A ring, let's say, worn carelessly on the—well, say the tentacle—of some vast organism—some inchoate creature hobnobbing with its cloudy kind in another system of universes—which in turn—"

It is curious that none of them realized next day that they were dealing with a stranger, a changed man. Why he carried on, why he capped that night of cosmic debauch by shaving, eating an unremarkable breakfast, packing his terrestrial toothbrush and collars, and going up the gangplank in tow of his excited convoy to sail away, is beyond explanation—unless it was simply that he was in a daze.

It wasn't until four years later that I was allowed to know what had happened on that ship, and even then the tale was so disjointed, warped, and opinionated, so darkly seen in the mirror of Mrs. Diana's orthodoxy, that I had almost to guess what it was *really* all about.

"When Hubert turned irreligious. . . ." That phrase, recurrent on her tongue in the meanderings of the East African quest to which we were by then committed, will serve to measure her understanding. Irreligious! Good Lord! But from that sort of thing I had to reconstruct the drama. Evening after evening beside her camp fire (appended to the Mineral Survey Expedition Toward Uganda through the kindness—actually the worn-down surrender—of the Protectorate government) I lingered awhile before joining the merrier engineers, watched with fascination the bumps growing under the mosquitoes on her forehead, and listened to the jargon of her mortified meekness and her scandalized faith.

There had been a fatal circumstance, it seems, at the very outset. If Diana could but have been seasick, as the rest of them were (horribly), all might still have been well. In the misery of desired death, along with the other contents of a heaving midriff, he might have brought up the assorted universes of which he had been led too rashly to partake. But he wasn't. As if his wife's theory was right, as if Satan was looking out for him, he was spared to prowl the swooping decks immune. Four days and nights alone. Time enough to digest and assimilate into his being beyond remedy that lump of whirling magnitudes and to feel himself surrendering with a strange new ecstasy to the drunkenness of liberty.

Such liberty! Given Diana's type, it is hard to imagine it adequately. The abrupt, complete removal of the toils of reward and punishment; the withdrawal of the surveillance of an all-seeing, all-knowing Eye; the windy assurance of being responsible for nothing, important to no one, no longer (as the police say) "wanted"! It must have been beautiful in those few days of its first purity, before it began to be discolored by his contemptuous pity for others, the mask of his inevitable loneliness and his growing fright.

The first any of them knew of it—even his wife—was in mid-voyage, the day the sea went down and the seven who had been sick came up. There seemed an especial Providence in the calming of the waters; it was Sunday morning and Diana had been asked to conduct the services.

He preached on the text: "For of such is the kingdom of Heaven."

"If our concept of God means anything it means a God *all*-mighty, Creator of *all* that exists, Director of the *infinite,* cherishing in His Heaven the saved souls of *all space and all time*."

Of course; amen. And wasn't it nice to feel like humans again, and real sunshine pouring up through the lounge ports from an ocean suddenly grown kind. . . . But— then—*what* was Diana *saying?*

Mrs. Diana couldn't tell about it coherently even after a lapse of fifty months. Even in a setting as remote from that steamer's lounge as the equatorial bush, the ember-reddened canopy of thorn trees, the meandering camp fires, the chant and tramp somewhere away of Kikuyu porters dancing in honor of an especial largesse of fat zebra meat—even here her memory of that impious outburst was too vivid, too aghast.

"It was Hubert's look! The way he stared at us! As if you'd said he was licking his chops! . . . That '*Heaven*' of his!"

It seems they hadn't waked up to what he was about until he had the dimensions of his sardonic Paradise irreparably drawn in. The final haven of all right souls. Not alone the souls released from this our own tiny earth. In the millions of solar systems we see as stars how many millions of satellites must there be upon which at some time in their histories conditions suited to organic life subsist? Uncounted hordes of wheeling populations! Of men? God's creatures at all events, a portion of them reasoning. Weirdly shaped, perhaps, but what of that? And that's only to speak of our own inconsiderable cluster of universes. That's to say nothing of other systems of magnitudes, where God's creatures are to our world what we are to the world's in the atoms in our finger-rings. (He had shaken *his*, here, in their astounded faces.) And all these, all the generations of these enormous and microscopic beings harvested through a time beside which the life-span of our earth is as a second in a million centuries: all these brought to rest for an eternity to which time itself is a watch-tick—all crowded to rest pellmell, thronged, serried, packed, packed to suffocation in layers unnumbered light-years deep. This must needs be our concept of Heaven if God is the God of the Whole. If, on the other hand—

The other hand was the hand of the second officer, the captain's delegate at divine worship that Sabbath day. He at last had "come to."

I don't know whether it was the same day or the next; Mrs. Diana was too vague. But here's the picture. Seven women huddled in the large stateroom on B-deck, conferring in whispers, aghast, searching one another's eyes obliquely even as they bowed their heads in prayer for some light—and of a sudden the putting back of the door and the in-marching of the Reverend Hubert. . . .

As Mrs. Diana tried to tell me, "You understand, don't

you, he had just taken a bath? And he hadn't—he had forgotten to—"

Adam-innocent there he stood. Not a stitch. But I don't believe for a minute it was a matter of forgetting. In the high intoxication of his soul-release, already crossed (by the second officer) and beginning to show his zealot claws, he needed some gesture stunning enough to witness to his separation, his unique rightness, his contempt of match-flare civilizations and infinitesimal taboos.

But I can imagine that stateroom scene: the gasps, the heads colliding in aversion, and Diana's six weedy feet of birthday-suit towering in the shadows, and ready to sink through the deck, I'll warrant, now the act was irrevocable, but still grimly carrying it off.

"And if, on the other hand, you ask me to bow down before a God peculiar to this one earth, this one grain of dust lost among the giants of space, watching its sparrows fall, profoundly interested in a speck called Palestine no bigger than the quadrillionth part of one of the atoms in the ring here on my finger—"

Really scared by this time, one of the virgins shrieked. It was altogether too close quarters with a madman.

Mad? Of course there was the presumption: "Crazy as a loon." Even legally it was so adjudged at the *Platonic's* first port-of-call, Algiers, where, when Diana escaped ashore and wouldn't come back again, he had to be given over to the workings of the French Law. I talked with the magistrate myself some forty months later, when, "let in" for the business as I have told, I stopped there on my way out.

"But what would you?" were his words. "We must live in the world as the world lives, is it not? Sanity? Sanity is what? Is it, for example, an intellectual clarity, a balanced perception of the realities? Naturally, speaking out of court, your friend was of a sanity—of a sanity, sir—" Here the magistrate made with thumb and fingers the gesture only the French can make for a thing that is matchless, a beauty, a transcendent instance of any kind. He himself was Gallic, rational. Then, with a lift of shoulder, "But what would you? We must live in the world that seems."

Diana, impounded in Algiers for deportation, escaped. What, after all, are the locks and keys of this pinchbeck category of magnitudes? More remarkable still, there in Arab Africa, he succeeded in vanishing from the knowledge and pursuit of men. And of women. His bride, now that their particular mission had fallen through, was left to decide whether to return to America or to go on with two of the company, the Misses Brookhart and Smutts, who were bound for a school in Smyrna. In the end she followed the latter course. It was there, nearly four years later, that I was sent to join her by an exasperated and worn-out Firm.

By that time she knew again where her husband-errant was—or where at least, from time to time in his starry dartings over this our mote of dust, he had been heard of, spoken to, seen.

Could we but have a written history of those years of his apostolic vagabondage, a record of the towns in which he was jailed or from which he was kicked out, of the ports in which he starved, of the ships on which he stowed away, presently to reveal himself in proselyting ardor, denouncing the earthlings, the fatelings, the dupes of bugaboo, meeting scoff with scoff, preaching the new revelation red-eyed, like an angry prophet. Or was it, more simply, like a man afraid?

Was that the secret, after all, of his prodigious restless-
ness? Had it anything in common with the swarming of
those pale worms that flee the Eye of the Infinite around
the curves of the stone you pick up in a field? Talk of the
man without a country! What of the man without a universe?

It is curious that I never suspected his soul's dilemma
until I saw the first of his mud-sculptures in the native
village of Ndua in the province of Kasuma in British East.
Here it was, our objective attained, we parted company
with the government *safari* and shifted the burden of
Way-straightening to the shoulders of Major Wyeside,
the ostrich-farmer of the neighborhood.

While still on the *safari* I had put to Mrs. Diana a
question that had bothered me: "Why on earth should
your husband ever have chosen this particular neck of the
woods to land up in? Why Kavirondoland?"

"It was here we were coming at the time Hubert turned
irreligious to found a mission. It's a coincidence, isn't it?"

And yet I would have sworn Diana hadn't a sense of
humor about him anywhere. But perhaps it *wasn't* an
ironic act. Perhaps it was simply that, giving up the
struggle with a society blinded by "a little learning" and
casting about for a virgin field, he had remembered this.

"I supposed he was a missionary," Major Wyeside told
us with a flavor of indignation. "I went on that. I let him
live here—six or seven months of it—while he was learning the tongue. I was a bit nonplussed, to put it mildly,
when I discovered what he was up to."

What things Diana had been up to the Major showed
us in one of the huts in the native kraal—a round dozen
of them, modeled in mud and baked. Blackened blobs of
mud, that's all. Likenesses of nothing under the sun, for-

tuitous masses sprouting haphazard tentacles, only two among them showing pustules that might have been experimental heads. . . . The ostrich-farmer saw our faces.

"Rum, eh? Of course I realized the chap was anything but fit. A walking skeleton. Nevertheless, whatever it is about these beasties, there's not a nigger in the village has dared set foot inside this hut since Diana left. You can see for yourselves it's about to crash. There's another like it he left at Suki, above here. Taboo, no end!"

So Diana's "hunch" had been right. He had found his virgin field indeed, fit soil for his cosmic fright. A religion in the making, here before our eyes.

"This was at the very last before he left," Wyeside explained. "He took to making these mud-pies quite of a sudden; the whole lot within a fortnight's time. Before that he had simply talked, harangued. He would sit here in the doorway of an evening with the niggers squatted around and harangue 'em by the hour. I knew something of it through my house-boys. The most amazing rot. All about the stars to begin with, as if these black baboons could half grasp *astronomy!* But that seemed all proper. Then there was talk about a something a hundred times as big and powerful as the world, sun, moon, and stars put together—some perfectly enormous stupendous awful being—but knowing how mixed the boys can get, it still seemed all regular—simply the parson's way of getting at the notion of an Almighty God. But no, they insisted, there wasn't any God. That's the point, they said; there *is no* God. . . . Well, that impressed me as a go. That's when I decided to come down and get the rights of this star-swallowing monstrosity the beggar was feeding my labor on. And here he sat in the doorway with one of these beasties—here it is, this one—waving it furiously in the niggers' benighted faces. And do you know what he'd done?—you can see the mark here still on this wabble-leg, this tentacle-business—he had taken off a ring he had and screwed it on just here. His finger ring, my word of honor! And still, if you'll believe it, I didn't realize he was just daft. Not until he spoke to me. 'I find,' he was good enough to enlighten me, 'I find I have to make it somehow concrete.' . . . 'Make what?' . . . 'Our wearer.' . . . 'Our *what, where?*' . . . 'In the following category.' . . . His actual words, honor bright. I was going to have him sent down-country where he could be looked after. He got ahead of me though. He cleared out. When I heard he'd turned up at Suki I ought, I suppose, to have attended to it. But I was having trouble with leopards. And you know how things go."

From there we went to Suki, the Major accompanying. It was as like Ndua as one flea to its brother, a stockade inclosing round houses of mud, wattles, and thatch, and full of naked heathen. The Kavirondo are the nakedest of all African peoples and, it is said, the most moral. It put a great strain on Mrs. Diana; all that whole difficult anxious time, as it were detachedly, I could see her itching to get them into Mother Hubbards and cast-off Iowa pants.

Here, too, as the Major had promised, we found a holy of holies, rather a dreadful of dreadfuls, "taboo no end," its shadows cluttered with the hurlothrumbos of Diana's artistry. What puzzled me was their number. Why this appetite for experimentation? There was an uncertainty; one would think its effect on potential converts would be bad. Here, as in Ndua, Diana had contented himself at first with words and skyward gesticulations. Not for so long, however. Feeling the need of giving his concept of the cosmic "wearer" a substance much earlier, he had shut himself in with the work, literally—a fever of creation. We counted seventeen of the nameless "blobs," all done, we were told, in the seven days and nights before their maker had again cleared out. The villagers would hardly speak of him; only after spitting, their eyes averted, and in an undertone, would they mention him: "He of the Ring." Thereafter we were to hear of him only as "He of the Ring."

Leaving Suki, Major Wyeside turned us over (thankfully, I warrant) to a native who told us his name was Charlie Kamba. He had spent some years in Nairobi, running for an Indian outfitter, and spoke English remarkably well. It was from him we learned, quite casually, when our modest eight-load *safari* was some miles on its way, that the primary object of our coming was non-existent. Hubert Diana was dead.

Dead nearly five weeks—a moon and a little—and buried in the mission church at Tara Hill.

Mission church! There was a poser for us. *Mission church?*

Well, then, Charlie Kamba gave us to know that he was paraphrasing in a large way suitable to our habits of thought. We shouldn't have understood *his* informant's "wizard house" or "house of the effigy."

I will say for Mrs. Diana that in the course of our halt of lugubrious amazement she shed tears. That some of them were not tears of unrealized relief it would be hardly natural to believe. She had desired loyally to find her husband, but when she should have found him—what? This problem, sturdily ignored so long, was now removed.

Turn back? Never! Now it would seem the necessity for pressing forward was doubled. In the scrub-fringed ravine of our halt the porters resumed their loads, the dust stood up again, the same caravan moved on. But how far it was now from being the same.

From that moment it took on, for me at least, a new character. It wasn't the news especially; the fact that Diana was dead had little to do with it. Perhaps it was simply that the new sense of something aimfully and cumulatively dramatic in our progress had to have a beginning, and that moment would do as well as the next.

Six villages: M'nann, Leika, Leikapo, Shamba, Little Tara, and Tara, culminating in the apotheosis of Tara Hill. Six stops for the night on the road it had cost Diana as many months to cover in his singular pilgrimage to his inevitable goal. Or in his flight to it. Yes, his stampede. Now the pipers at that four-day orgy of liberty on the *Platonic's* decks were at his heels for their pay. Now that his strength was failing, the hosts of loneliness were after him, creeping out of their dreadful magnitudes, the hounds of space. Over all that ground it seemed to me we were following him not by the world of hearsay but, as one follows a wounded animal making for its earth, by the droppings of his blood.

Our progress had taken on a pattern; it built itself with a dramatic artistry; it gathered suspense. As though it were a story at its most breathless places "continued in our next," and I a reader forgetting the road's weariness, the dust, the torment of insects never escaped, the inadequate food, I found myself hardly able to keep from running on ahead to reach the evening's village, to search out the inevitable repository of images left by the white stranger who had come and tarried there awhile and gone again.

More concrete and ever more concrete. The immemorial

compromise with the human hunger for a symbol to see with the eyes, touch with the hands. Hierarchy after hierarchy of little mud effigies—one could see the necessity pushing the man. Out of the protoplasmic blobs of Ndua, Suki, even M'nann, at Leikapo Diana's concept of infinity (so pure in that halcyon epoch at sea), of categories nested within categories like Japanese boxes, of an over-creature wearing our cosmos like a trinket, unawares, had become a mass with legs to stand on and a real head. The shards scattered about in the filth of the hut there (as if in violence of despair) were still monstrosities, but with a sudden stride of concession their monstrousness was the monstrousness of lizard and turtle and crocodile. At Shamba there were dozens of huge-footed birds.

It is hard to be sure in retrospect, but I do believe that by the time we reached Little Tara I began to see the thing as a whole—the foetus, working out slowly, blindly, but surely, its evolution in the womb of fright. At Little Tara there was a change in the character of the exhibits; their numbers had diminished, their size had grown. There was a boar with tusks and a bull the size of a dog with horns, and on a tusk and on a horn an indentation left by a ring.

I don't believe Mrs. Diana got the thing at all. Toward the last she wasn't interested in the huts of relics; at Little Tara she wouldn't go near the place; she was "too tired." It must have been pretty awful, when you think of it, even if all she saw in them was the mud-pie play of a man reverted to a child.

There was another thing at Little Tara quite as momentous as the jump to boar and bull. Here at last a mask had been thrown aside. Here there had been no pretense of proselyting, no astronomical lectures, no doorway harangues. Straightway he had arrived (a fabulous figure already, long heralded), he had commandeered a house and shut himself up in it and there, mysterious, assiduous, he had remained three days and nights, eating nothing, but drinking gallons of the foul water they left in gourds outside his curtain of reeds. No one in the village had ever seen what he had done and left there. Now, candidly, those labors were for himself alone.

Here at last in Tara the moment of that confession had overtaken the fugitive. It was he, ill with fever and dying of nostalgia—not these naked black baboon men seen now as little more than blurs—who had to give the Beast of the Infinite a name and a shape. And more and more, not only a shape, but a *shapeliness*. From the instant when, no longer able to live alone with nothingness, he had given it a likeness in Ndua mud, and perceived that it was intolerable and fled its face, the turtles and distorted crocodiles of Leikapo and the birds of Shamba had become inevitable, and no less inevitable the Little Tara boar and bull. Another thing grows plain in retrospect: the reason why, done to death (as all the way they reported him) he couldn't die. He didn't dare to. Didn't dare to close his eyes.

It was at Little Tara we first heard of him as "Father Witch," a name come back, we were told, from Tara, where he had gone. I had heard it pronounced several times before it suddenly obtruded from the native context as actually two English words. That was what made it queer. It was something they must have picked up by rote, uncomprehending; something then they could have had from no lips but his own. When I repeated it after them with a better accent they pointed up toward the

north, saying "Tara! Tara!"—their eagerness mingled
with awe.

I shall never forget Tara as we saw it, after our last
blistering scramble up a gorge, situated in the clear air on
a slope belted with cedars. A mid-African stockade left
by some blunder in an honest Colorado landscape, or a
newer and bigger Vermont. Here at the top of our journey, black savages, their untidy *shambas*, the very
Equator, all these seemed as incongruous as a Gothic cathedral in a Congo marsh. I wonder if Hubert Diana
knew whither his instinct was guiding him on the long
road of his journey here to die. . . .

He had died and he was buried, not in the village, but
about half a mile distant, on the ridge; this we were given
to know almost before we had arrived. There was no need
to announce ourselves, the word of our coming had outrun
us; the populace was at the gates.

"Our Father Witch! Our Father Witch!" They knew
what we were after; the funny parrot-wise English stood
out from the clack and clatter of their excited speech.
"Our Father Witch! Ay! Ay!" With a common eagerness
they gesticulated at the hilltop beyond the cedars.

Certainly here was a change. No longer the propitia-
tory spitting, the averted eyes, the uneasy whispering al-
lusion to him who had passed that way: here in Tara they
would shout him from the housetops, with a kind of civic
pride.

We learned the reason for this on our way up the hill.
It was because they were his chosen, the initiate.

We made the ascent immediately, against the village's
advice. It was near evening; the return would be in the
dark; it was bad lion country; wouldn't tomorrow morn-

ing do? . . . No, it wouldn't do the widow. Her face was set. . . . And so, since we were resolved to go, the village went with us, armed with spears and rattles and drums. Charlie Kamba walked beside us, sifting the information a hundred were eager to give.

These people were proud, he said, because their wizard was more powerful than all the wizards of all the other villages "in the everywhere together." If he cared to he could easily knock down all the other villages in the "everywhere," destroying all the people and all the cattle. If he cared to he could open his mouth and swallow the sky and the stars. But Tara he had chosen. Tara he would protect. He made their mealies to grow and their cattle to multiply.

I protested, "But he is *dead* now!"

Charlie Kamba made signs of deprecation. I discerned that he was far from clear about the thing himself.

Yes, he temporized, this Father Witch was dead, quite dead. On the other hand, he was up there. On the other hand, he would never die. He was longer than for ever. Yes, quite true, he was dead and buried under the pot.

I gave it up. "How did he die?"

Well, he came to this village of Tara very suffering, very sick. The dead man who walked. His face was very sad. Very eaten. Very frightened. He came to this hill. So he lived here for two full moons, very hot, very eaten, very dead. These men made him a house as he commanded them, also a stockade. In the house he was very quiet, very dead, making magic two full moons. Then he came out and they that were waiting saw him. He had made the magic, and the magic had made him well. His face was kind. He was happy. He was full fed. He was full fed, these men said, without any eating. Yes, they carried up

to him very fine food, because they were full of wonder
and some fear, but he did not eat any of it. Some
water he drank. So, for two days and the night between
them, he continued sitting in the gate of the stockade,
very happy, very full fed. He told these people very much
about their wizard, who is bigger than everywhere and
longer than for ever and can, if he cares to, swallow the
sky and stars. From time to time, however, ceasing to talk
to these people, he got to his knees and talked in his own
strange tongue to Our Father Witch, his eyes held shut.
When he had done this just at sunset of the second day
he fell forward on his face. So he remained that night.
The next day these men took him into the house and buried him under the pot. On the other hand, Our Father
Witch is longer than for ever. He remains there still. . . .

The first thing I saw in the hut's interior was the
earthen pot at the northern end, wrong-side-up on the
ground. I was glad I had preceded Mrs. Diana. I walked
across and sat down on it carelessly, hoping so that her
afflicted curiosity might be led astray. It gave me the odd-
est feeling, though, to think of what was there beneath
my nonchalant sitting-portion—aware as I was of the
Kavirondo burial of a great man—up to the neck in
mother earth, and the rest of him left out in the dark of
the pot for the undertakings of the ants. I hoped his
widow wouldn't wonder about that inverted vessel of clay.

I needn't have worried. Her attention was arrested oth-
erwheres. I shall not forget the look of her face, caught
above me in the red shaft of sundown entering the western
door, as she gazed at the last and the largest of the Reverend Hubert Diana's gods. That long, long cheek of hers,
buffeted by sorrow, startled now, and mortified. Not till
that moment, I believe, had she comprehended the steps of

mud images she had been following for what they were, the steps of idolatry.

For my part, I wasn't startled. Even before we started up the hill, knowing that her husband had dared to die here, I could have told her pretty much what she would find.

This overlord of the cosmic categories that he had fashioned (at last) in his own image sat at the other end of the red-streaked house upon a bench—a throne?—of mud. Diana had been no artist. An ovoid two-eyed head, a cylindrical trunk, two arms, two legs, that's all. But indubitably man, man-size. Only one finger of one of the hands had been done with much care. It wore an opal, a two-dollar stone from Mexico, set in a silver ring. This was the hand that was lifted, and over it the head was bent.

I've said Diana was no artist. I'll take back the words. The figure was crudeness itself, but in the relation between that bent head and that lifted hand there was something which was something else. A sense of scrutiny one would have said no genius of mud could ever have conveyed. An attitude of interest centered in that bauble, intense and static, breathless and eternal all in one—penetrating to its bottom atom, to the last electron, to a hill upon it, and to a two-legged mite about to die. Marking (yes, I'll swear to the incredible) the sparrow's fall.

The magic was made. The road that had commenced with the blobs of Ndua—the same that commenced with our hairy ancestors listening to the night wind in their caves—was run.

And from here Diana, of a sudden happy, of a sudden looked after, "full fed," had walked out—

But no; I couldn't stand that mortified sorrow on the

widow's face any longer. She had to be made to see. I said it aloud:

"From here, Mrs. Diana, your husband walked out—"

"He had sunk to idolatry. *Idolatry!*"

"To the bottom, yes. And come up its whole history again. And from here he walked out into the sunshine to kneel and talk with 'Our Father Which—' "

She got it. She caught it. I wish you could have seen the light going up those long, long cheeks as she got it:

"Our Father which art in Heaven, Hallowed be Thy Name!"

We went down hill in the darkness, convoyed by a vast rattling of gourds and beating of goat-hide drums.

RICHARD MATTHEWS HALLET

STORIES EVERYWHERE

A man writing about the genesis of his stories is pretty
certain to get into a snarl, as Mr. Poe did, when he told us
so glibly how "The Raven" came to be written inevitably in the
form it now has. That article of Poe's is pretty egregious
rationalizing; and if I tried the thing in any detail, I should
fall into the same trap. In general, I can say that I am like
the man in Kipling's recent story in *McCall's*, of whom Kipling
says, "Given written or verbal outlines of a plot, he was useless; but with a half dozen pictures to write his story around,
he could astonish."

I had forgotten the word astonish was in there until I ticked
it out, and had better take back what I said about being like
that man—but the general proposition fits my case. I get at
a story from pictures, scenes, groupings of characters, con-
trasts, glimpses, even rag-ends of conversation that may any
or all of them have the fertile germ lost in their folds. My
story "Foot-loose" in the current *Saturday Evening Post*
(March 10) was first a picture of the old man standing in his
cleared fields on Sunday morning, the opposite of the foot-
loose man, he suggests him, the new character is implied, the
problem then is to take the foot-loose man in the midst of his
intolerance and contempt for the fixed, the stationary, and catch
him in their toils. The simple devices of the story follow: and
the old man who started it practically disappeared out of it.

Arthur Sullivant Hoffman of *Adventure* published some
years ago *Fiction Writing by Fiction Writers* (Bobbs-Merrill)
a questionnaire to living authors on methods of work. Had you
seen that? If the questionnaire could have been put the dead
as well as the living, the returns would have been more fruitful; but I found in a course I gave at Bowdoin College that
the book had interest for the men there.

FOOT-LOOSE [1]

T OM MURCHISON went ashore from the ketch *Aileen* with a big bundle over his shoulder, and his Arctic dog, Dusky, rambling ahead through the Inlet's single twisting street. He had left Charles Tobin, his cook and foremast hand, behind in the ketch's cabin to get supper for himself. After a stormy voyage from Hudson Bay, the old fellow was glad enough to find himself at the wharf side, and Tom left him to his seagoing pea soup with a piece of pork shoulder in it for a stiffener.

Young Murchison himself was going to have supper in his own house, but first he looked in on Jeremy Potts to make sure he was expected. He had written Jeremy to have a woman in to open the house, air the bed, and have a fire going in the kitchen stove.

"Well, if here isn't the skipper of the good ship *Aileen*," Jeremy said when he opened the house door. "Where are you from?"

"From Hudson Bay."

"Had good weather?"

"Lumpy weather all the way."

"Why a little boat like that doesn't roll the bones out through your skin is a mystery to me," Jeremy said, and took a pinch out of his silver snuffbox.

"She's comfortable as an old shoe."

"She's got no legs to her."

"She's got legs enough. . . . Did you get my letter from Wolf Trap?"

"Yes. I've got a woman for you on the premises."

"Who's the woman you've got?"

"Ellen Pitcairn," the little man answered innocently,

[1] From *The Saturday Evening Post,* March 10, 1928. Reprinted by permission of the author.

and snapped to the cover of his snuffbox. Tom's jaw dropped. "Why, isn't she a capable girl?" Jeremy asked.

"Capable enough," Tom said.

"I knew she needed work," Jeremy elaborated. "Joe Pitcairn, her father, is laid up. He's had hard luck. He backed the town horses off a wharf into the harbor this spring and drowned them. His wife brought him twins the next day, but they couldn't take the place of horses. And it wasn't over a week later he fell off a ladder and broke his arm."

Tom Murchison knit his brows. Here it was again, the old tale of hardship. The place was full of disasters—people falling sick or having twins. He had better be on his guard against this little man, he thought. Jeremy loved humanity and the combinations of humanity. He had rather make a marriage than a convert to the faith, and having been a foot-loose man himself, he disapproved of foot-loose men.

"When you're settled, come round by here and have a cider shandy," Jeremy said. "Dodge in any time."

Tom nodded, but in everything but body he was out of the house already. Ellen Pitcairn worried him. They had been in school together, thick as thieves one day and off the hooks the next. She had been a year older than he in years and a thousand years in knowledge. Once, to complete his shame, she had even outrun him in the field back of the Murchison house. He had grown tall all in one rush, and the process had taken all the gimp out of him. He had got too big, in school, for any of those desks screwed to the floor, and they had made him up a desk at the back of the room out of a bread board laid across two saw-horses. And that had given the relentless Ellen the whip hand of him.

And now here she was getting supper for him. Well, times had changed; she couldn't fluster him now. He was a little toplofty with all his adventures, and he had the sea king's contempt for the land. Going up Hobart's hill, he looked in through the front windows of Ed Hulsc's place. Ed was a photographer, and there he was, against a background of gray-painted screens with ominous cloud shadows rolling up on them. He was sitting there retouching a plate, with a green shade over his eyes.

Tom Murchison took a deep breath. Nothing had changed. The white houses were as quiet as cattle driven down to drink; the rocks hadn't been displaced, hadn't been chipped; the trees were rooted in dumb soil. He was in front of his own house now, and sighting along the north side of it, over a meadow full of young frogs, to a certain dark ridge, he saw a big hemlock tree standing up there, with a brushy top and one limb pointing to the east. It was a witness tree, marking the northeast corner of the Murchison property, and according to tradition, that bound had been established by combat in the old days— by a knockdown fight between a Pitcairn and a Murchison. "There's no law until the lawyers come" had been the rule then; and fighting it out, if men were fairly matched, was as sensible a way of determining rights as any other. The witness tree was an old haunt of his and Ellen Pitcairn's.

Well, here the house was again, foursquare, assertive; but it looked grayer, grimmer. It was losing heart, departing from the plumb. The woodpile had tumbled over. Tom fixed his eye on that yellow flame in a hand lamp, showing over the sinkboard in the kitchen window. Ellen was at the sink, dipping dusty dishes one by one into hot water and wiping them and putting them back on a shelf level with her head. When she stopped to dash the hair out of her face with the back of her hand, she seemed to look straight at Tom, but it was too dark outside now for her actually to see him. The same Ellen, but she had grown older. Her cheek was not so full, her mouth was not so gay, and the earrings were gone out of her ears. Her eyes looked for that second, wide, speculative, apprehensive.

He opened the kitchen door and let Dusky through ahead of him. The big dog had a black head and a white body, and paws as big as a horse's hoof. He brushed against Ellen in a friendly way and Tom dropped his bundle down back of the stove.

"Mercy, what a dog," Ellen protested. "He's brought mud in on my clean floor."

Tom went back to the little rug by the door and wiped his feet.

"I guess it's pretty cozy here," he said.

"How does it seem to be home again?"

"Good! Finest place on the planet earth!" Tom shouted louder than there was any need of. They shook hands.

"Still a little of it seems to go a long way with you," the girl said. "I never saw a man more foot-loose."

"If you don't see the world when you're young, you never will," Tom argued, just remembering to take off his cap. He looked at his hands, and Ellen poured hot water for him into an agate basin.

He washed, toweled his head and neck vigorously, picked a comb off the mantelpiece and dragged it through his hair.

"Sit right down. I've got supper ready for you," Ellen said.

Tom, sitting in the red-painted wooden chair, felt a touch of that old devilish powerlessness in her presence stream through his veins. She put his supper down before him—tea and toast and creamed finnan haddie, hot out of the oven. The little clock on the mantelpiece that played a tune on the quarter hours struck up its tinkling melody. She hadn't overlooked a thing; she had started everything up, brought the house to life, and now she sat down across the table from him. She put her elbows on the table edge and pushed her chin up with both fists.

"What's the matter with your eating something?" Tom asked.

"I had my supper at the other house when I put the kids to bed. . . . Shall you sleep here tonight?"

"Sure."

"I thought you might. I've made up a bed and put a shingle fire in the air-tight stove there to take the edge off the dampness."

Tom was outraged by that precaution.

"I've slept right out in the snow; funny if a damp sheet will put a crimp into me. I tell you I've slept in a trench in the snow with a fire going at either end, and nothing to eat but the cold marrow out of moose's bones."

"Oh, my Lord," Ellen Pitcairn said.

"In a sleeping bag," Tom triumphed; "and wake up with an eighth of an inch of white frost on the outside of the bag. I had to chew my boots to get 'em soft enough to shove my feet into 'em."

"That must have been pleasant," Ellen said archly. "I've heard before that boots do have nourishment as a last resort. What were you doing?"

"Trapping foxes. . . . Here, I've got something for you!" he shouted, jumping up. He opened his pack, tumbled out three or four blue-fox skins on the floor, picked one up, stroked it and, with a quick move, rounded it about her neck.

"There you are. That's for you," he said.

"However did you get possession of it?" Ellen gasped, and moved a little to look at herself in the mirror which hung over the roller towel.

"Trapped it. That's nothing. Look here."

He seized up the enormous pelt of a polar bear and shook it out flat. It filled the whole kitchen. Dusky growled and pawed at it.

"Did you trap him too?" Ellen cried, still holding the fox skin round her neck.

"Him? It's a her. It's a she bear. I did lay a trap for her, yes. I had a walrus cache under the rocks and she got into it. So I took a twelve-gauge automatic and lashed it to a box the height of a polar bear's shoulder, see, and I filled the box with rocks. About six inches of barrel stuck out, and I hung a piece of seal meat down over that and carried the string back through the eyebolt in the stock of the gun and forward again to the trigger. I figured when she came and pulled the meat off, she would pull the trigger at the same time."

"And did she?"

"She did not. She must have been too clever for me. All the same, a day or two later I caught sight of her, and her cub with her. They began to run away."

"They were afraid of you," Ellen said.

"I'm not saying they were. I don't know whether they were educated to a gun or not. Anyway they ran—and these polar bears can run. They can go up anywhere— right up over an iceberg as smooth as your shoulder and not slip. I saw where they were headed, and I went back to the ship and threw a dory off into clear water—what they call a tickle. It's a narrow waterway between two mountains where the tide runs hard, and keeps ice off till way into December.

"Well, this bear came over the mountain and jumped into the tickle, and her cub with her. She gave the cub a clout with her paw and knocked him down, end for end, into the tickle, and then dove herself, with her paws spread. Maybe that wasn't exciting. Say, I fired five shots and still she was alive and kicking. She stuck out her lower lip and fetched a 'Whir-r' out of her and shouldered the ship right at the water line, enough to rock her. I fired my last shot right then, and cut the neck bone through; and then, mind you, I had to shove an oar down her throat and keep her head under water till she drowned."

"Oh," Ellen cried in a protesting voice, and narrowing her shoulders.

"Well, I'm stating facts. That was the how of it. You asked me, didn't you? I got a piece of six thread round her hind leg and ran it through the dory's becket and towed her in to the ship—we had drifted some—and then Tobin and I hoisted her on deck with some purchases we had."

"I've heard enough," Ellen shuddered.

"You haven't heard about the cub," Tom pursued her. "That cub was a whole menagerie in himself. First off, when his mother'd dive he'd grab her by the tail and follow under. He was still hanging around when I got the big one on deck, and I got back into the dory and managed to get a loop over his head and tailed out thirty fathom or so. We wore him out and hoisted him aboard and lashed him with nine thread, forepaws and hind paws.

What followed was plain works. Maybe his mother's blood running under him on the decks made him wild. He got the ropes off, drove the dog into the dory, and me into the rigging. I tell you, he just took possession. Upshot was we had to shoot him. Tobin's got his skin."

Ellen's eyes were getting rounder and darker, and Tom looked at her just in time to catch her swaying. She had got up abruptly out of her chair.

"What's up?" he cried, with an arm across her shoulders.

"It must be what you said about—mother's blood," she whispered. "I can't—it's silly—just the thoughts of blood—"

She was getting dangerously limp.

"Look here! Look up!" Tom yelled in a panic. She was growing heavy, sinking through his arms, her lashes fluttering and falling.

"Get me out into the air if you can," she muttered.

Tom picked her up, appalled, and ran outdoors with her. There he tried to stand her on her own legs, and didn't succeed any more than as if she had been a doll with the sawdust spilling out of her. It wouldn't do to put her on the ground. He stood muted, with Ellen Pitcairn's body clasped against him, his chin on the crown of her head.

"I guess I overdid it," he said awkwardly. "I guess I upset the apple cart that time. How are you now? Here, brace up! You coming out of it?"

Ellen Pitcairn breathed out of nowhere, "Aren't men detestable?" and he continued to support her. They must both have been looking across the stone wall at the back end of the Pitcairn house, fifty yards away, since both of them started when the back door opened and the figure of a big man was outlined in that oblong orange blot.

"My soul, that's Ed Hulse," Ellen said. "He's come to take me to the movies. I guess he'd think this was a little compromising."

"You're better now?"

"I'm all right. If there's anything you want tomorrow, just call on me. I'm never far away."

She twisted out of his arms; he heard her running low under the apple trees, and then the Pitcairn kitchen door opened and banged shut again. Tom followed more slowly and got close enough to look in at the window.

It was a sight to give any man a jolt who had been holding Ellen Pitcairn in his arms. The kitchen was alive with yellow-headed children—Joe Pitcairn's, all of them —and Joe himself was sitting in a corner cutting off tobacco with his poor crippled hands. He was the kind of man to whom accidents are always happening. When he worked in a sawmill he lost fingers, and when he went to sea, wire poisoning or sleeping sickness afflicted him. Going round the Horn in his youth, he had got in the way of a staysail sheet just as it snapped under strain, and the block, going wild, had fetched him a clip over the ear that sent him half the length of the ship. Some people thought he had never got over the effects of that.

Nobody who glimpsed him now, huddled in his corner, could doubt the truth of that pronouncement that destiny is nothing but the shadow cast by character. Heavy weather had beaten his lobster traps to splinters, and all winter there had been nothing to eat, probably, but slack-salted cod, pork and molasses. Winter had pulled him down—not a doubt of it. It had pulled Ellen down, magnificent as she was in the body; it had pulled the children down, and pulled poor Mrs. Pitcairn down pitiably.

The little black house had an ice pond at its back; a body could jump into the pond out of the kitchen window, and Mrs. Pitcairn had threatened to do it, but nobody would take her seriously.

What under heaven had Joe Pitcairn meant, Tom wondered, by assembling such a brood around him? Nobody but an African dodger had any business setting up on land. . . . Tom's eye rested on Ellen. The girl had her back against the south wall; her head was dipped forward and the face looked actually pinched. It might have been an imperfection in the glass that gave her that wild look, as of a trapped thing still protesting.

By moving a foot or two to the left, Tom could see that she was talking to Ed Hulse with her hands on the back of his chair. Things must have gone seriously wrong when a woman like Ellen Pitcairn would go out of her way to conciliate a man like that—heavy, slow, with nothing to look forward to but a life of bone labor.

Tom felt his dog's nose thrust into his hand. The nose was hot. The heat was already beginning to affect the poor creature, and the beautiful white hide was showing mangy patches.

"Got to get you out of this, old fellow," Tom muttered. He turned away guiltily from the Pitcairn house. It was a mercy there was nobody dependent on him. He recalled Jeremy's complaint about the ketch *Aileen*—her lacking legs. Well, say she did; say she foundered, better to go down in a thousand fathoms and let the fishes pick your bones clean rather than wait for death to come in one of these ground-floor bedrooms. And yet he had let that girl bully him into being ashamed of his activities.

He went to see Jeremy Potts. The little man led him out into the dining room and put a mug of cider on the arm of his chair. Tom stole glimpses at the photographs of robustious African women on the walls. It was no good bragging about his bear to a man who had shot lions, who had gone into the jungle at the head of fifty porters, gun bearers and the like.

"Housekeeper satisfactory?" Jeremy asked.

"All right till she fainted on my hands," Tom answered.

"Fainted?" Jeremy Potts got out of his chair, full of concern.

"All but dead away, yes. I got her into the air and brought her to."

"She give you any intimation what the matter was?"

"I was telling her how I killed a bear. It was too gory for her, she said."

"The chances are she hadn't eaten a morsel today," Jeremy announced. "She's a proud woman. I've been afraid she wouldn't eat food bought with that money."

"That money? What money?"

Little Jeremy opened his silver snuffbox and put a pinch of snuff in either nostril. Tom Murchison should have taken warning; the little man took snuff to stimulate the brain. The little red devil that ruins the world, his wife called it, but Jeremy knew how to build on ruins.

"What money? Don't you know they've gone round with a paper for Joe Pitcairn?"

"Don't tell me it's come to that," Tom said.

"It has, though. Joe broke his arm early in the winter —that was after he lost the town horses—everything piled up, and there they were, twins and all, and the mother flat on her back. Ellen couldn't leave the house, and Joe called on the town. He didn't have any other course open to him."

Tom drank thirstily out of the fluted glass.

"I wouldn't believe it," he whispered. "She held her head high enough with me."

"She's a monument for pride. I wouldn't wonder if Eddie Hulse married her. He's the only man around here that wouldn't balk at shouldering the Pitcairns. The pity of it, man. There's genius in her. She's got a singing voice, my friend Adamson tells me. It ought to be cultivated, and who's going to pay for that if Ed Hulse marries her?"

"Not Ed," Tom said.

"She'll be going around for Ed, hauling seaweed to bank the foundations of the house against the wind, just the way she's doing for the Pitcairns. They calked the doors and windows with newspapers last winter. You couldn't get in the back door without a rain of paper strips falling on your head."

"No?" said Tom.

"Fact," said Jeremy, and filled both glasses again. "Well, dear me, it's a sad subject. Let's change it. How long are you staying with us this time home?"

"That I can't say. Feels good to be here."

"Finest place on the planet earth," Jeremy affirmed.

"The dog's making heavy weather of it, though. Won't eat. I guess I'm only waiting for a slant of wind to carry him back north again. We've had contrary winds lately."

"Here's a proverb for you," Jeremy laughed: "To a crazy ship all winds are contrary."

Tom Murchison's face burned a little. He knew the little man's thought. After ten years away from home— a perfect Odyssey—he had got no further than to contract an obligation to a dog. He stood up and the little man reached up a friendly hand to his shoulder.

"You used to sing for me," Jeremy said. "Come sit in my choir."

Tom went to church early and looked in back of the organ at the bellows. That had been his job as a boy, bowing over a crooked iron bar like a boat's tiller—only the motion was vertical—pulling open the wheezy bellows, with a load of brick on top to sink them again. The bar was still there, so was the artistry on the walls—the sketch of the organist in a scrubby hat.

Then he heard Ellen coming in with Ed Hulse, and strolled round the corner of the organ. The girl was in a black dress with a hint of perfume, and the raven's shadow was still across her white cheek. Her eyes were calm and undramatic. They took their places and the service began. He had barely exchanged nods with her, not feeling habituated to the celestial machinery. Yet the very tack heads in the rumpled carpet held him in the vise of the familiar. He heard her voice during the responsive reading. A sentence brushed him, paralyzed him: "My soul thirsteth after thee like thirsty land." It was spoken as if in his very ear. He turned his head, but she was looking straight ahead, and Ed Hulse's big body was slumped down just beyond her.

When she stood to sing her solo, Tom watched the song swelling in her white throat. Potts' friend was right. She had a voice, round and full; it was like a rush of wings in the air over his head; it was a song with a whisper in it, but that possibly was the whisper of the bellows.

Tom Murchison felt the surge of a wave, a green comber, under him; the thought, half born, if it expanded more, would tear the top of his head off. Something was on the very tip of his tongue—the secret, that something as unsurprisable as the back of his neck. He remembered joining a lodge when he was just of age, and somebody— a fellow citizen—at some point of the rites, had whispered the secret of the lodge to him—it was comprised in one word—and in his nervousness he couldn't catch that word. The man had repeated it time after time, but it was a queer word, and still Tom couldn't really grasp it. He had finally pretended that he had and let it go at that.

He felt now as if something had been offered to him which was going to slip through his fingers through sheer clumsiness on his part. He stared at the colored window, showing doves feeding on a cathedral roof, and then, lifting startled eyes, he saw Charles Tobin in an end seat halfway down the aisle. The little cooky had his wrinkled head cocked over on one side, his blue eyes had an amazing life, a vituperative summons. "Look out, you're a goner" Charles Tobin seemed to be saying to him from some other world, as if one of them had died and they could no longer talk back and forth.

A goner? Nonsense. What had he to fear? He was older than when he had sat here last—ten years older. These added years, considering the use he had made of them, ought to stand him in good stead. He hadn't gone back, surely. He was as supple as ever, he could lift as big a weight off the ground, polar bears were child's play to him. Nevertheless, a subtle and moving sense of dereliction drifted through his veins.

When the service was over, with the last word of the benediction, Tom and Ellen got up together, and he said, "You forgot your blue fox."

"That? Oh, I couldn't really take it," Ellen said. "You didn't think, I hope—"

"I brought it to you," he insisted deliberately, for Ed Hulse's benefit.

"I couldn't take anything like that—of value," Ellen repeated. "Thank you just the same."

Disconcerted, he walked out of the church through the vestry. Charley Tobin and the horse doctor were stooping over Dusky, who had been lying on the bell rope.

"He's getting poor," Tobin said. "You can take his whole backbone in your thumb and finger now."

"It's too hot for him here," said the horse doctor.

"I'll get him back where he belongs," Tom cut in. "Only waiting for a slant of wind."

But the next day he began to reshingle the L of his house. He ripped off a lot of the shingles while waiting for the kettle to boil, and after breakfast he slipped on a carpenter's apron, with the nail pockets full of shingle nails. When he went outdoors, Ellen Pitcairn was just walking out with a pail of feed for the hens. Even in the full sunlight that shadow of want was on her cheek, and Tom felt the walls of his heart pinch together; but she had the whip hand still. Over there, where a load of herring heads had been plowed under the soil, the June grass was dark green. The beeches had light yellow leaves, which even the direct rays of the sun could hardly yellow more. The dew-pointed shingles of the Pitcairn barn were like gray satin, with here and there a black one.

Tom sipped at his pipe, and then, reaching in under the apron, brought out a crumpled ten-dollar bill. He picked up Ellen's cold hand and doubled the fingers over this. She opened her hand and made up a funny mouth.

"What's this for?" she inquired.

"For services rendered," Tom said. "For getting the house opened, and one thing and another."

Ellen laughed, and tossed the bill back at him as if it were no more than a dead leaf.

"You must have a fine opinion of your neighbors," she said scornfully. "Dear boy, you can't pay me for anything like that. I suppose next you will be trying to pay me for fainting on your hands."

"Look here—I tell you—holy mackerel, I—"

She mocked his stuttering with her mouth. "No, I tell you. I was glad to do it. It's what any woman would expect to do when she's neighboring a bachelor. Holy mackerel, are you one of these men that can't rest under a favor?"

He stood there, beautifully baffled; the sun was getting higher and burning his neck, forcing Ellen to flicker her lids and turn her head a little away.

That night he took her to the movies. They went in late, after the lights were out, but Charles Tobin had seen them go in. He came to Tom in the morning to ask what to do about an offer he had had to go mate of a three-master—the *Anson B. Whitehead*.

"You tired of your present job?" Tom asked him.

"No. Looks like it might vanish into thin air," Charles Tobin said, in his high chest tones—"by what I hear, that is."

"What do you hear?"

"Talk is you've cut Ed Hulse out with his girl. He was there after she got back last night, and they had it hot and heavy, I hear."

"Why doesn't he come out in the open then?" Tom flashed.

"I guess he's declared himself as far as in him lies," Charles Tobin said insinuatingly.

And there was no reasonable doubt that Ed Hulse had declared himself. He had had the fish hooked and had been standing ready with the gaff, Tobin averred. Tom knew that, but he didn't like to see a fine girl like Ellen Pitcairn bound over to a man like Hulse, when it was nothing but her need that drove her to it. After the day's shingling he looked in on Jeremy Potts. The talk got round to Ellen—his neighbor, Jeremy called her.

"If she starves," Tom said, "she's only got herself to thank for it. She won't take money even when she's earned it."

Jeremy asked for details and got them.

"I wouldn't like to see it come to marriage with this man Hulse," Jeremy said soberly, "but it will, if something isn't done about it."

"They'd have another Pitcairn establishment piled on top of the present one in five years," Tom argued. "Well, here, I've got a thousand or so lying idle right now, it so happens. I won't be using it. All right. Saying there was such a thing as my leaving that money in your hands, Mr. Potts—sort of a fund. Couldn't you put it up to her to go away and educate her voice? You could say the money was coming from a—from a fund."

"From a fund, sure enough," Jeremy beamed. He turned the snuffbox end for end.

"That would cook Hulse's goose, wouldn't it? She couldn't be away from here a year and come back and see him in the same light, could she?"

"Doesn't seem as if. Wouldn't do to mention your name, would it?" Jeremy suggested, and flashed the young man a marvelously subtle look.

"Lord, no. She wouldn't take anything from me, where we were children together and all. She'd have a feeling about that."

"I suppose she would," Jeremy agreed. "I'll tell her the money's from a fund—tell her it's put up by a Mr. Smith, say, who used to live here and took an interest in music."

They struck hands on that and Jeremy went down into

the cellar after cider. Mr. Smith sat with his knees together and his feet wide apart. He stared at the Potts ceiling, with a wonderful foot-loose feeling through him. He had no ties except to a dog, and that was why he could make his benefactions of some service to the world at large. Ellen would be a great singer; nothing could hold her back or down but the incompetence of Ed Hulse, and that danger was averted—as good as averted—by the mythical Mr. Smith. And say the secret did leak out years later, when Ellen was a famous woman—well, say it did—

Something warm and comfortable—rapturous, actually —went through his frame, but the splendid reverie was shivered into nothing by an ominous howl outside the house. It was out of Dusky's throat, and Tom jumped up. He had left the dog with his muddy paws outside; and now Tom, opening Jeremy's front door, saw that a dozen men had collected in the road, springing up from nowhere. There was a dog fight going on. Dusky had a big hound dog on his back in the middle of the road. It looked desperate and the onlookers were holding off. Sam Pennell, from the far side of his fish cart, was urging somebody to go after a sponge and a bottle of ammonia.

Tom Murchison sprang in, throwing men right and left to get at the dogs. He tore them apart savagely, and the hound went whimpering away.

A voice said, "That North Pole dog ought to be shot."

Tom, still crouching with one hand on Dusky, recognized Ed Hulse. He looked straight at the big photographer, and shouted out, "Wasn't there anybody here man enough to pull a couple of dogs apart? Stand there like a lot of wooden men and watch 'em chew each other up! If I thought any of you egged them on to this—"

He kept looking square into Ed Hulse's slow-thinking,

brooding face. The photographer's arms hung at his sides; he had looked at first a little sheepish, but he was now livid, rigid with anger.

"Don't you accuse me of sicking them dogs onto each other!" Hulse yelled. "Don't you do it, mister!"

"You couldn't think of anything better to do than stand and watch them tear each other's throats out. I know that!" Tom cried.

"Maybe I've got something more to do with my hands than keep dogs from fighting," Hulse shouted in a trembling voice. "Maybe I got somebody depending on me! You show me where humans are in trouble, maybe I'll take risks with anybody!"

"Maybe you think I wouldn't!" Tom shouted back, and Hulse replied: "I know you wouldn't!"

There was later a conflict of testimony as to which of the two had struck the first blow, and probably the principals themselves couldn't have told you which of them had lashed out first. The only light was furnished by a lantern hanging off the tail of Sam Pennell's cart. They were about a match—Hulse, if anything, was heavier, but he had spent his time retouching plates while Tom was killing polar bears. It was a bare-fisted, bloody business, and couldn't last.

Suddenly, after a smacking impact, an excited cry went up, the little huddle of men yielded, and somebody elbowed the lantern off the cart. Sam snatched it off the ground. Tom Murchison, standing in the middle of things, saw out of the tail of his eye that Charles Tobin was holding Dusky by the neck. The unlucky Hulse was flat on his back, but immediately he began rolling over and getting to his knees. The crowd swarmed round him and closed him off.

"Somebody's going to get killed out of this," Sam Pennell said seriously. "Keep those men apart, some one."

Already, some of the younger men, on either side of Hulse, had him by the arms, holding him back. Ordinarily the mildest of the mild, his infuriated eyes now looked wild under the matted red hair. He lunged right and left, dragging them along with him, and only came to himself when somebody shouted in his ear:

"Here comes Mr. Potts!"

That scattered them. They didn't want a superior man like Mr. Potts to be getting acquainted with this sort of thing. Hulse's friends dragged him one way and Tom Murchison went just as fast the other. He felt like a fool —certainly not in a mood to face Jeremy. At the end of the street Charles Tobin, with Dusky, overtook him.

"Hulse is back there swearing the girl egged you on to polish him off," Tobin said. "He won't have it any other way, and he swears she's double-crossed him and he's done with her for good." Tom stared at him and stopped in his tracks. He had never been so bitterly ashamed of himself. Charles Tobin continued: "I got the water tanks full this afternoon, and sixty more gallons of gas on the starboard side. Looks like the wind's coming fair to be gone in the morning."

"Southwest, is it?" Tom muttered.

"Southwest, yes."

Tobin was right, the wind was southwest all next day, but Tom didn't take advantage of it. He didn't, in fact, stir away from the house. He felt bound, hand and foot, gagged, and worse than that. He kept seeing Ed Hulse lying sprawled there pathetically in the dust, and he asked himself how under heaven he had allowed himself to get embroiled. Was it just Ed's clamoring to have the dog shot? Was it? He misdoubted it was not. The thing had been like a wind at his back shoving him along, a hand at his neck—something outside him altogether, taking him by surprise. Some kind of red devil that kept out of sight through all the havoc, and that was keeping out of sight now.

He couldn't round on it; and then, early in the afternoon, he saw Jeremy Potts knocking on the Pitcairns' front door, with another little man in tow—a funny little round-headed man in black, with a square-blocked black hat, and a black manuscript bag in his hand.

They were inside the house perhaps half an hour. Jeremy must be arguing the case for Mr. Smith, Tom thought hopefully. Ellen herself let them out and went with them as far as the road. She stood staring after them, hugging her arms against her body, her head a little on one side, the very pose suggesting, as it often did, the presence of some valiant force within. She was the man of the family, Tom had more than once heard Jeremy say. It was Ellen who would hold the Pitcairns to the mark after Joe had had the ground struck out from under his heels. It was that quality of superiority, a sort of foreshadowing of her powers, that had kept most of the eligible young men from paying more attention to her. They didn't stand the comparison, Tom thought. She was just too calm and cool, and had that way of looking through them and beyond them.

What answer had she given Jeremy? Tom didn't for an instant doubt that the little man had put his proposition, but the Pitcairn house didn't give an inkling of the answer. It looked as dejected, as haggard, as broken backed, as ever. Joe Pitcairn crept out into the back yard and began feebly splitting wood. That was about the extent of the poor man's usefulness. He had had a prop, or the prospect of a prop, in Ed Hulse, and now Tom had knocked that prop away; sledged it down with just his fist.

Tom didn't venture out till after dark; and then, when he was throwing fish over the hen-yard fence to the penned-in Dusky, he heard Ellen's voice behind him.

"Mr. Tobin tells me you're on the point of leaving," the girl said.

"Looks like it," Tom answered, and didn't take his eyes off Dusky.

"I suppose it's got so now with you, you can't be in any one place three days together."

"I'm always wondering what's round the corner, yes," Tom said.

"Is it so different when you do find out?"

"Not so different, no."

Ellen laughed. "Well, if I don't see you again," she said, "remember your failings."

His failings. He wasn't likely to forget those in a hurry. He stood bolt upright and there was a faint ringing, as of whippoorwill music, inside his head—a swarm of abrupt little imperatives: "Tell her this, tell her that; squirm, twist, wiggle; get down on your knees." He did nothing of the sort. He said nothing, dipped his hands in the water barrel. Ellen was only a couple of feet away. It was Tuesday night and the church bell was tolling people to a meeting in the vestry.

The girl broke the spell by asking casually, "Do you remember Arthur Gillispie?"

"The singing teacher?"

"Yes. Well, he came to see me today with Mr. Potts. He's grown awfully rotund. He's still a bachelor, it seems, and goes to Europe every summer. That's on the money it would cost to keep a wife, he told Jeremy. He just loves Europe, I suppose. I told him that. It's just as easy to disconcert him as it ever was. Tom, do you remember what a scream he used to be? You can't have forgotten that time the school was singing in assembly hall, and Mr. Gillispie went round with his head down listening for mutes, and stumbled on you. Do you remember? You hadn't opened your mouth, and never did. You just lolled in a back seat making funny knots in the window cord."

"That's right," Tom said, moistening his lips.

"So then he told you to sing alone, and you sat there perfectly mum until I tipped you the wink, and then you sang it right through from start to finish. Weren't you an odd stick? But you always would do anything under heaven for me, from a little thing."

"Would I though?"

"Yes. Maybe it was malicious animal magnetism on my part. Mr. Potts will bear me out. Well, you'll never guess what my two visitors had come about."

Tom felt the scurrying of a wild alarm from his heels into his throat, and he could feel the little fiends of fear trampling his eyeballs.

"Well, what had they?"

"To get me to take singing lessons."

"You ought not to need any urging," Tom said gruffly.

"That's a back-handed compliment, if ever there was one."

"Well, now, what I mean—I guess you know as well as I do I was only—"

Ellen's cool palm was laid expertly across his lips.

"Now don't tear your shirt," she said, smoothly if

a little inelegantly. "Can't I have my little joke? Mr. Gillispie has a limited few he gives lessons to, more to have something to do than because he needs the money. He isn't rich, but he has enough for his needs, and Mr. Potts told me his house is full of the most interesting things—books and objects of art that he's picked up in his travels. He tested my chest tones—"

"Tested them?"

"Yes. It's like seeing if a horse is sound in wind and limb really. You'd laugh. And then he straightened up and said, 'Mr. Potts, there is a voice in there.' And Mr. Potts said, 'Let's get it out.' You'd think they were talking about buried treasure. Well, there they had settled that, and then the question came up about where the money was coming from that was supposed to pay for all these lessons. Whether he needs money or not, Mr. Gillispie doesn't work for love."

"I imagine money can be found," Tom said, his voice no more than a croak.

"Found? Picked up in the road? I wish you'd point it out to me. Mr. Potts, it seems, has got a fund for just such purposes, but I wouldn't lisen to having it applied to me, because it's anonymous. I think an anonymous fund is almost as contemptible as an anonymous letter. It's sure to come out in the end who the donor is, and his modesty really is just a form of bragging. Modesty is—too much of it. So, don't you see, I couldn't obligate myself like that —just let my whole life hinge on some dreadful somebody I didn't know, who just wanted to lurk in the background—just any Mr. Smith. I couldn't. Suppose he should pop up with his claims just at the psychological moment, when perhaps I—and there I would be, wouldn't I, powerless, or just as good as?"

"He won't pop up," Tom croaked. "A man like that wouldn't."

"How can you guarantee me that?" Ellen Pitcairn asked.

Well, how could he? Words stuck in his throat. There was Ellen's head ink-black against two or three fiercely burning stars, frogs were shrilling, the church bell went on tolling. There was a threat in the air, like a wolf's head looking round a rock and vanishing.

"Well, how could you guarantee it?" Ellen repeated, swaying on her heels.

"There was no string tied to it," Tom Murchison brought out with extreme difficulty, like a small boy caught red-handed.

"So it was you, then," Ellen announced calmly. "I knew it—I knew it. Who else could it have been? So you're Mr. Smith."

"Did I say it was me?"

"Will you deny it?"

He couldn't deny it; he felt as if the jaws of some small but serviceable vise had closed on him; and Ellen cried: "You dear boy, did you think I wouldn't get to the bottom of it? Did you think that even Jeremy Potts' craft would be enough? Did you?"

"I thought," Tom mumbled, "as long as my name didn't come into the transaction—"

"Your name—you thought— As if any other man on God's green earth—I don't care who—would be guilty of flinging money around like that for just—for just what—"

It couldn't be that there were tears in that self-possessed young woman's throat. If her voice trembled—and he thought it did—then it must be with secret laughter.

A puff of wind touched his face—the favoring southwest wind, with a breath of burning scent in it from the field beyond the garden patch. His father, Lem Murchison, if he were alive, would be placidly trying to sniff rain on that wind, hoping for an end of this dry weather which was burning everything up. Old Murchison had cleared that field himself, stumped it, drained it, hauled the stones away on a stone boat. First and last, the old man had plowed tons of rotten herring heads under the soil, and on Sunday mornings he had never missed standing there in the thick of the daisies and the wild vetch, pondering the fruitful hollow, breathing in the seedling dreams, listening for beans to crack the sod in growing, expecting that familiar promise of the soil to whisper fulfillment into his ear. The field made a never-ending demand upon the old man's soul; it had a fixed insistent natural appeal. Old Murchison had never seen the need of being foot-loose.

Suddenly Tom said, "It's dry as tinder. We need rain." With an absurd sense that he had been put to flight by Ellen's forces, when he had meant, at all hazards, to stand his ground.

"In other words, let's change the subject," Ellen said with a little laugh. "Agreed."

What next? He had a sense of perilous check after rapid unfoldment. He stared at the dim shape of the frenzied old dead apple tree, which still clawed for holds, though it had put forth no leaves this spring. He had a dismal sense that no matter what he said, or if he said nothing, he would soon enough be dangling in a noose of his own making.

"You'd better reconsider," he heard himself saying— "I mean, about this fund. You won't need a guaranty from me about not popping up at awkward times. Or if you do, I can give you one in black and white."

"Don't be childish," the girl whispered, dwelling on that last word with a high, outraged intonation. "There are other considerations. Suppose I did accept, what would my friend Mr. Hulse say, for one?"

"Hulse? What could he say?"

"Plenty."

"Hulse," Tom repeated stupidly—"Ed Hulse."

"Well?"

"Look here, that's a clincher. Hulse—I hadn't alluded to it, and where you haven't been over town today you may not have heard of it, but I—I had an argument with Hulse last night."

"An argument?"

"It ended in a free-for-all. I happened to catch him just right and he went down like a bottle pin. I learned later that he thinks you put me up to that, see? He saw us together at the movies and didn't like that, and then— the other coming on top of that—well, he's made up his mind to stay away from you."

"Oh, I see," Ellen said quite calmly. "So then it oc- curred to you that you could substitute a lump sum in place of Ed. Is that it? Damages?"

"He wasn't the man for you!" burst from Tom's throat. He knew the crying absurdity of the words as soon as they were out. They were the living truth, but that didn't help them any.

"Isn't that for me to say?" Ellen cried. She was getting actually fierce. "Oh, this is worse than anything. You stood there and battered him down because you didn't think he was the man for me? Had I ever said he was? Had he ever?"

"It wasn't that," Tom groaned. "No. He wanted to have a bullet put into my dog. That started it. I owe my life to that dog. He was king dog of my team. More than once he's run me back to the ship's side when I didn't know where I was from Adam. In a snowstorm say, with me lying face down on the sledge and not knowing my right hand from my left, about as much good as a lump of wood—"

His voice died. He seemed to see himself lost in that white wilderness, going heaven knew where, the dogs running close against the deepening snow, plunging at their breast straps. Where had they been taking him, and why? He hadn't known top from bottom, or whether he was running into danger or out of it. All he knew now was that he had hung by his eyelashes and that the dogs had saved him. Had it been a flight or a quest? He couldn't say. If it had been flight, Ellen Pitcairn had drawn up abreast of him, after all his trying to outstrip her.

"I see," she was saying now, quite her calm self again, "it was really a case of 'Love me, love my dog,' wasn't it? You great sillies." Her voice was entirely friendly now, interested in that glimpse of his romantic hardships. She didn't seem to want to touch on Hulse again. They dropped him out like a kind of foreign object. "When you tell me about places you've been," Ellen told Tom, "you seem to me just like a man of fifty. You have had experiences. I don't see how you survived at all. I truly don't. How strange it must seem to you to be here, out of harm's way, with just the green earth under you, and all these old trees and houses just as you remember them. And all the time you can think back to when—well, I don't wonder that people over town take you with a grain of salt. It doesn't seem possible that any human being—"

"A man never knows where his fate will overtake him," Tom soberly declared. "He doesn't know which way to go to get away from it, and he might as well give up trying. I offered young Martin a chance to come with me this last trip and his people wouldn't listen to it. Thought it was too dangerous. I was actually offering him life, it turned out, and he had to pass it up. He stayed home and fell off a hen-pen roof and cracked his skull. All I lost was a couple of toes."

Ellen drew in her breath in a little sympathetic hiss.

"You did lose toes?"

"I don't advertise it. It's no great harm. I kept some. I don't limp, but I can't run quite as fast as I did."

He heard the church bell still tolling, as if tireless in the effort to pound one iron word into his brain.

Ellen was saying, "You never did set the world on fire as a runner. I could beat you when I was just a fat little girl."

"Maybe you think you could repeat?" Tom said, and everything he wanted to say slid away through the dark.

"I don't know why not. Tom, let's try."

"Oh, well, come now."

"You suggested it. It would be cowardly to back out now." She took him by the shoulders and faced him about. "From here to the hemlock—the witness tree—across the old field. The first to touch the tree wins—and no alibis."

There they were running together. It was bizarre, exciting. Ellen was in the path between the stone wall and the long patch of plowed land ending in a lot of last year's cornstalks. Tom, forced into this patch, slipped and sank in the oozy soil. By the time he was abreast of her again, they had got through the break in the stone wall and were in the old field. He was wondering whether to let her win or win himself, but only by a nose, and he was half laughing at the desperateness of her running. She touched him, shouldered him, breathing very hard, and he felt a kind of weakness in his legs, under his ribs. A feeling that he was nowhere, everywhere; that he had got out of his own skin, out of space, out of time.

They ran down into the vapory bottom of the meadow. The turf was spongy here; right and left the young frogs were whistling and shrieking. The ground was lumpier and more uneven here, but Ellen didn't slacken her pace. She stumbled into him though, and he gave ground, thinking she was avoiding some inequality in the turf. Instantly he pitched forward to the ground. He had tripped over a sprawling pine root.

He picked himself up slowly and the frogs gave their watery shrieks. He heard Ellen's smothered laughing, and walked forward into the darkness of the pines and hemlocks with his two arms out before him. She had tricked him, jostled him deliberately into that root, which he had forgotten. She knew how to make familiar things work her will. He felt senseless childish anger boil in his throat; he took another step or two, his arms still extended, guarding him against the dark's mischief, and the tips of his fingers touched her. Then he had her in his arms.

"You forelaid for that," he muttered.

"Look out. I lost off my slipper in the mud," she gasped. "I can't put my foot down anywhere."

"Well?"

"Well?"

They swayed and breathed hard. He saw that he didn't mean to let her abash him, put him off, outskill him any more. Nothing but a bludgeon stroke would bring her down.

Dusky's mournful howl afflicted his ears. He would have to send the dog back by another hand. The master was implicated here, but it was makeshift, a temporary measure. Gillispie would have his chance at Ellen; in a little while her name would be in everybody's mouth; she wouldn't need Tom then, and he could pick up the trail where he was abandoning it.

The church bell dropped out one last languid note.

" 'My soul—thirsteth after thee like thirsty land,' " he whispered.

It was as if he had shot her through and through by the force of these words which were not his. But he knew their truth. Her head came slowly, very slowly back, touched him, transported him. There was something fatal about it, like a landslip; he had a panicky notion that she was fainting on his hands again; but then he could see that her eyes were open wide on him. They flooded him with a dark, fixed, rapt light.

"That's not original with you," she said, but he could not mistake the fact that her heart was beating faster than his own.

"We can have you performing prodigies," he babbled, after an indefinite time when they shared the world only with the frogs, the whippoorwills.

Ellen said faintly, "Possibly."

"What do you mean by possibly?" he questioned.

"What do you mean by prodigies? Tom, there'll be one saving—have you thought of that? You won't have to part with any hard-earned cash to Mr. Gillispie. There's been a total change in my ambitions. . . . Do see if you can find my slipper."

On his knees, groping for the slipper, the foot-loose man didn't notice that a little wind—the favorable southwest wind—was stirring the brushy top of the witness tree that had been chosen to keep the Murchisons and the Pitcairns from overstepping bounds.

RUTH SUCKOW

AWAY FROM ACTUALITY

I have thought about your question, but I find it impossible to answer it definitely. In fact, I do not like to go back over the specific processes of writing a story. It seems to me that in work of this kind, a balance of the conscious and unconscious must always be kept, otherwise the result is cold.

But I can say this: that I would never trust any story whose genesis was a good title from which the rest was to be worked out, or an actual incident to be slightly veiled and disarranged in fiction, or an intellectual idea or thesis primarily.

THE MAN OF THE FAMILY [1]

FLOYD OBERHOLZER was just opening up the drug-store when Gerald came.

"Hello, Gerald. Want something?"

"I come to start in working."

"This morning!" Floyd was startled. "Why, school can't be over yet, is it? What is this—Wednesday?"

"Yes, but we got done with our tests yesterday, all but arithmetic, and I didn't have to take that."

"Oh, you didn't have to take that?" Floyd repeated vaguely. "Well, you come into the store and we'll see what there is for you to do."

Gerald followed him into the drug-store.

Floyd looked around somewhat helplessly. It was only a few months since he and Lois had bought this little business in Independenceville. They knew what to do themselves, but it was a different matter setting some one else to work. They hadn't expected Gerald so soon, or wanted him. Two or three months ago, he had come into the store

---

[1] From *The American Mercury*, December, 1926. Reprinted by permission of the author.

to ask if he couldn't have a job, and because they hated to turn the kid away—it wasn't very long after the accident in which his father had been killed—Floyd had told him: "Well, you come around when school's out. Maybe we can find something then." And now he was here.

"Well, you're starting in early," Floyd said to him. "You've beat my wife—she isn't in the store yet. Well, I don't know, Gerald—I guess you might as well sweep out, the first thing." He remembered then that Lois had swept the store before they closed last night; the boys had left so many cigarette stubs around. But he guessed it could stand it again. It would keep Gerald busy while Floyd decided what to have him do.

"All right," Gerald answered soberly. "Where do you keep your broom?"

"Right out there in the back, Gerald. See—I'll show you. Then you'll know where it is."

Gerald started in to sweep the wooden floor with awkward, scowling concentration. His back was stooped and intent. He took long hard strokes, trying to do a good job of it. Floyd looked at him, and then turned and went scuttling up the stairs.

"Hey—Lois!" he called softly.

" 'Smatter, pop?"

Lois, still in her bungalow apron, came to the door of the kitchen. The Oberholzers were living over the drugstore.

"Say, that kid's here."

"What kid?"

"Gerald Rayburn. He's come to start in working. Seems awful anxious to begin. What in the dickens shall I have him do?"

"You're a fine boss!" Lois began to laugh. "What's he

doing now—standing in the middle of the floor and suck-
ing his thumb?"

"I've got him sweeping."

"Why, I swept last night, you idiot!"

"Well, I know you did, but I forgot it. I didn't want to
tell him to stand around. He goes at it like a little beaver.
You ought to watch him. Oh, I suppose the kid *is* anxious
to start in earning."

Lois didn't know what to say.

"You come down," said Floyd, "and tell him about the
soda-fountain. That's your end of the business."

"Oh, it is, is it? All right, I'll come down and give the
boss's orders since he doesn't know what they are himself," she replied with mock commiseration, and pinched
Floyd's ear.

"Well, gosh, I didn't expect that kid the minute school
let out! Most kids aren't that anxious to go to work.
Isn't this the day they have the school picnic? Why, sure
—that's why we got that pop."

He started down the stairs and then went back to the
next-to-the-top step and stood frowning uncertainly.

"Think we can really use him, Lois?"

"Well, I guess we've got him, anyway!"

"I know we'll have to have somebody, but he's such a
kid. I don't know—"

Lois said hastily: "Oh, well, let's try him. You told him
he could come. I feel so sorry for that family."

"Well, so do I. But then . . . Well, all right. . . ."

Floyd left it at that, and scuttled down the stairs again.
Lois went back to the kitchen which she herself had
painted blue and white, with figured curtains, changing it
from the gloomy old hole that the Tewkesburys had left
it, to a gay new room. She hated to leave this beloved

little place to go and help Floyd in the store. Now that they had hired just a little boy to help them for the Summer, she supposed she would have to be downstairs most of the time. She almost wished she hadn't told Floyd to keep Gerald. Well, if Gerald couldn't do the work, he'd have to go, that was all.

"All right, Gerald," Floyd went into the store saying loudly and cheerfully. "Finished that? Well, then, I guess you'd better—" His eyes, quickly roving, caught sight of the magazine rack. "I guess you'd better straighten up those magazines. Folks take 'em out and read 'em all through and then put 'em back."

"All right."

Floyd whistled as he took the long gray cambric covers off the tables in the middle of the room, where boxes of gilt-edged correspondence cards and leather-bound copies of the works of Edgar Guest had to be displayed until the graduating exercises were over. Gerald went at his work with such silent concentration that it almost embarrassed Floyd.

"What do you want I should do next?"

"Oh, well . . . Guess maybe I better show you about these cigarettes and tobacco. That's probably what they'll be after first. I'll show you how we've got things marked."

"All right."

Lois came down. Floyd gave her an expressive look and nodded toward Gerald. "He's right at it!" Certainly the boy seemed to be trying hard. His freckled face with the crop of red hair was surly with concentration. Floyd couldn't help remembering that he was just a kid and too young to be starting in to work in earnest. He was quite willing to give up his charge and let Lois initiate him into the mysteries of the new white soda-fountain which they had installed in place of the cracked, lugubrious onyx splendor of an earlier day. Gerald stood silently beside Lois, bashfully aware of her bobbed hair and her plump white arms, answering dutifully: "Yes, ma'am."

"You can watch me this morning, Gerald, and run some errands, maybe. Wash up the glasses. Do the dirty work —how's that?"

"Yes, ma'am."

He was a little clumsy, partly out of bashfulness, but so serious and determined that Lois thought: "Goodness, I wonder if it'll last!" She wanted to give him all the help he needed, but she didn't quite know what to make of his surly little face. He hated to ask her questions, and several times she had to say, "Oh, not like that, Gerald!"

II

"Gee, that was an awful thing to happen to that family!" Floyd said to Lois in the back room of the store, where he had gone to look for a special package of hog medicine ordered by old Gus Reinbeck. "I think this kid kind of realizes, don't you?"

"Have they got anything, do you suppose?"

"A little insurance, they say, and that house, but not much more than to keep them until this boy can start earning."

"The mother can earn something herself, I should think," Lois said rather defiantly. *She* worked.

"Yes, but with three kids to look after. . . . And anyway, what is there for a woman to do in a burg like this except take in washing?"

"Well, maybe."

Back door and front of the store were open, and through the shimmery blackness of the back screen the garden was green and fresh. A tin cup hung on an old-fashioned pump under the vines. Gerald looked longingly at the boards of the platform, wet with spilled water. There was city water in the soda-fountain, but the pump looked so much cooler out there. "Run out and get a drink if you want to, Gerald," Lois told him. "I always go out there for my water. It's fun to work the pump." Boys never could see a pump or a drinking fountain or even a hydrant without being consumed with thirst, she knew. Lois liked boys. Gerald made her think of her kid brother. It was a shame he had to go to work. She wanted to reassure him somehow, to rumple his red hair or pat his shoulder. But she must remember that they were hiring him. They couldn't afford to keep him out of pity. Beside, he seemed determined to evade all personal advances and stuck doggedly to work. Maybe the kid was miserable at missing that picnic.

It was getting hot in town. Cars began to rattle and whir down the street, and in a few moments Louie Grossman's big red truck drove up to the side door of the drugstore.

"Hey, Floyd! Got the pop?"

"Got the pop? You bet I've got the pop. You want it now?"

"Sure do, if it's goin' on this picnic."

"All right, sir! Want to come and help me take it out, Gerald?"

"All right."

Gerald went with Floyd into the back room of the store, bright and cool and scattered with light from the green leaves outside. He tugged at one end of the big pop case, and helped Floyd carry it outside and shove it into the truck.

"Now, another one, Gerald."

"All right."

"Well, the kids oughtn't to get thirsty today," Floyd said.

"No, they sure got plenty. What are you doing, Gerald?" Louie asked. "Ain't you going to the picnic?"

"I got to work," Gerald answered.

He went back into the store. The two men looked after him.

"He workin' for you now, Floyd?"

"Guess so. It looks like it. He came this morning."

"Goes at it pretty good, don't he?"

"Yes, he seems to be willing. He's pretty young, but then . . . Where they going for the picnic today, Louie?"

"Out to Bailey's Creek. You ever been there?"

"Not yet. Mighty pretty place, I guess," he added.

"Yes, but it ain't much of a road."

"Well, don't tip 'em out, Louie."

"No, I'll try and keep the old bus in her tracks."

Louie started the noisy engine of the big truck. It went roaring up the street between green lawns and white houses and pink peonies, to where the school children, boys in freshly ironed blouses and girls in summery dresses, waited in a flock under the elms of the school-yard . . . then out, spinning down the graveled highway between freshly planted fields, turning into the little woods road, narrow and rutted, where the children had to bend their heads under the switch of honey locusts that left small white petals in their sun-warmed hair . . . on into the depths of green woods through the heart of which the shining creek was flowing . . .

Lois had come to the doorway to watch the truck leave.

"I wouldn't mind going to a picnic myself on a day like this," she murmured.

When she went back into the store, she looked curiously at Gerald. It gave her a guilty feeling, wholly unreasonable, to have him at work in their store today when it was a holiday for all the other children. But he had come of his own accord. They hadn't told him to do it.

"Did your sisters go on the picnic, Gerald?" she asked.

"Yes, *they* went," he answered, rather slightingly.

"How many have you, Gerald? Just Juanita and Betty?"

"Yes, ma'am."

"And you're the only boy?"

"Yes, ma'am."

"You could have started in tomorrow just as well, Gerald."

He did not answer.

III

The bright morning grew hotter and hotter, until to enter the drug-store from the glaring cement outside was like going into a cool, clean-scented cavern. The regular set of loafers drifted in, asked for tobacco, and stayed, sitting on the white-topped stools at the soda fountain and trying to be facetious with Gerald. "Well, you got a new clerk?" every one who came in demanded. It was a new joke every time. In an interval of no customers, Lois stooped down and drew out a pale green bottle frosted over with cold moisture from the case under the counter. It was still a treat to her to think she owned a store.

"I'm going to try some of this new lime stuff," she said. "See how it tastes. Don't you want the other straw, Gerald?"

"No, I guess not," he answered bashfully.

There was a glint of longing and reluctance in his eyes. But Lois thought: Maybe I oughtn't to start offering him things and being too easy with him. After all, Floyd was paying him to help them, and it wasn't her fault that his father had been killed. They were doing the best they could for him by letting him have a job. When, later, she decided to try one of those chocolates Floyd had ordered from a new traveling man, she turned her back while she nibbled it and wiped her fingers on the scrap of oiled paper in which it had been wrapped. Running the business all by themselves was still an adventure to the young Oberholzers; but even now they had run up against the fact more than once that it wasn't just a game. They had halfway discovered the meaning of that term—"If you want to do business—" Lois couldn't pick out from the traveling man's stock the delicately scented toilet waters that she herself liked, but had to choose the red and green brands with big gaudy flowers on the labels that the girls here in town would buy—the kind that "went." She had had to freeze out old Bart Bailey who came in every morning to read the paper and the detective magazines he had no money to buy, and left dirty thumb marks on all the pages.

Noon came with the shriek of the whistle from the power-house, with the noise of cars being started and of the men driving home to dinner.

"When does your mamma expect you home for dinner, Gerald?" Lois asked.

"Oh, I guess it don't matter," Gerald mumbled bashfully.

"Didn't you tell her when you'd come?"

"No, ma'am."

They let him go; but if they kept him in the store, he would have to go later and let them have their dinner at noon. That was one reason why they wanted help. He was back in good time. "Well, didn't take *you* long to eat your dinner!" Floyd said. But maybe it wasn't a good thing to act surprised at his promptness. It would wear off soon enough, if they could infer anything from their experiences with Marcelle Johnston, who had pretended to work for them for three weeks in the Winter.

At intervals during the afternoon, Floyd and Lois reported to each other. "We're going to have an awful time teaching him to make a decent sundae. He doesn't catch on any too fast, but he seems to be willing to do whatever you tell him." Whether they wanted to keep him or no, it was evident that he meant to stay. He wanted the job. His surly little freckled face scarcely relaxed into a smile even when there was a dog fight outside and Miss Angie Robinson's little poodle sent that big hound of Ole Swanson's off yelping. He went at whatever he was told to do with dogged earnestness, although he didn't see things for himself. He said "Yes, ma'am" with sober respect; but he would ask: "What's the price of this here kind of tobacco, Lois?" and say to customers: "No, Floyd ain't in just now, he went over to the depot." As the afternoon wore along, his freckled face grew flushed. "Does it seem like a long day, Gerald?" Lois asked him once. He admitted: "Kind of. Not so very."

Late in the afternoon, the picnic trucks came rattling into town with all the children disheveled and shouting. A few moments afterwards, a group of girls came bursting into the store. Their bright-colored Summer dresses were wrinkled, their bobs were wildly rumpled, their tired eyes were shining.

"Oh, gee, but we're thirsty! We're just dying! Oh, look at Gerald Rayburn! Are you working in here, Gerald?"

"Yes, didn't you know he was?" his young sister Juanita asked. "We want six bottles of pop, Gerald," she ordered airily.

"Have you got any money?"

"Yes, I have!"

"Where'd you get it then?" he demanded suspiciously.

"None of your business, Mr. Smarty! I guess it's not yours, is it?"

A bright pink flared up in Juanita's cheeks. Her eyes sparkled angrily. She was a pretty child, with red hair, like Gerald's, blazing out in a fuzzy aureole around her freckled face. She flounced down into one of the white chairs. "We want a table, don't we, kids? We don't want to sit at the fountain, like the boys." When Gerald brought the six cold red bottles carefully toppling on the tray, she lifted her little chin and disdained to look at him.

"You needn't think because I'm working here, you can come in and order what you want," he told her.

"Shut up!" she whispered furiously.

Her eyes were brighter still with tears. Mamma had given her the nickel for helping with the ironing yesterday afternoon instead of going off with the girls. She had given it to her for ironing Julie Bronson's pink chemise, with all the lace, so beautifully. It was none of Gerald's business what she did with it! She said to the other girls, with flashing eyes and quivering lips:

"He thinks he's so smart now just because he's starting in to work and Betty and I aren't. You'd just think he *owned* us to hear the way he talks. I don't care. I guess he isn't the only one who does anything. I guess I do lots of things. I'd like to see Gerald Rayburn ever wash the dishes!"

She stuck two straws into her bottle of strawberry pop and sucked it all up defiantly. Maybe she ought to have saved her nickel, but Gerald had no right trying to boss her in front of all the girls.

He told her, when she was leaving the store:

"You needn't go running around now, you can go home and help mamma."

"You keep still!" She threw her nickel down with a ring on the white counter of the soda fountain. "I guess you aren't my boss *yet!*"

"That's all right, I know what I'm talking about."

"That's right, Gerald," old Hod Brumskill shouted, with humorous approval. "You make the womenfolks mind you. Ain't that so, boys?"

"You tell 'em it's so!"

They laughed loudly; and then, clustered together with their arms on the glass counter, that had a sign in red letters "Do not lean!", they tore open their packages of bitter-scented tobacco and began to talk in lowered voices about the Rayburn family: how it had been "left," how it got along, about the tragic death of Frank Rayburn, still disputing over the minutiae of that event which they had never yet been able to settle, although nearly a year had passed since the thing happened. "Well, I never could understand how a fella like that, that was used to climbin' all over everywhere, come to fall off that ladder like that—." "Why, he just kinda stepped backward-like—I s'pose he forgot maybe where he was at—." "Some says the ladder broke and let him down." "Naw, the ladder didn't *break*." "Well, was it true he'd been out drinkin' the night before? That's how I heard it." "Naw, he hadn't been out drinkin' the night *before*." "Well, I can't figger out—." "Why, he just kinda stepped backwards—." It was terrible, they all agreed with solemn faces, to think that poor little woman should have been left with those three children, although there was dispute again about how much they had been left *with*. Some said they "had something," some said they "had nothing." She was a nice woman. Yes, and she was a good-looking woman, too . . . And then they drew closer together, and one of them said something about "Art Fox," and their voices broke into a laugh and a snicker.

Gerald was washing glasses at the soda-fountain. His freckled face flushed a dull red, and when they snickered he looked over at them furiously. He had a notion of what they were saying. When they passed him, leaving the store, they praised him loudly and self-consciously.

"Well, Gerald, you're all right, ain't you? Takin' right a-hold!"

"You bet he's all right."

"Well, Gerald's the man now, ain't that so, Gerald! He's the one."

"That's right."

The six o'clock whistle blew.

Gerald looked about hesitatingly for Floyd. Finally he went out to the back room of the store to find him.

"Shall I go now? The whistle blew."

"Yes, sure, you go along now, Gerald. I wasn't paying any attention."

Floyd was busy over some boxes on the floor. Gerald hesitated. His face was red. He wanted to ask if he had "done all right." But he was ashamed. Finally he blurted:

"Do you want I should come back tomorrow morning?"

Floyd was still busy over the boxes. Gerald waited.

"Yes, you come back in the morning, Gerald," Floyd answered cheerfully.

IV

Gerald got out of the store as fast as he could. How bright the street seemed outside, and how fresh the air was! He felt as if he had been smelling camphor and perfumes all his life. He had a job! It seemed to him that every one must know. He wanted people to ask him what he had been doing, it made him feel proud and important; although when Mr. Baird, the minister, who had been in the store earlier in the day, greeted him with: "Well, is the day's work over, young man?" he was suddenly too bashful to do more than grunt an answer. He walked soberly down the main street, and broke into a run as he cut across the corner.

His feet burned. It was hard to stand all day like that, although he had told Lois he didn't mind it. He grew hot all over when he thought of the mistakes he had made. But the ache that had seemed lodged in his chest somewhere, ever since the day when his father was buried and all the relatives had told him: "Well, you'll have to look after your mamma now, Gerald, won't you?"—when his mother cried and clung to him that night—that ache was strangely eased. He was earning money. He could take care of his mother. It humiliated him that his mother should have to be doing the washing for other people, although it was only some of their neighbors; but she wouldn't have to do it always. He had not heard more than a few words of what those men in the drug-store were saying. But at the thought—the very suspicion of it—his mind felt hot and sore. If they'd been saying anything about his mother, they'd be sorry for it. He'd—he didn't know just what—but anyway, they'd better look out!

The new little semi-bungalow house looked bleak and desolate. It had been that way ever since his father died. No new flowers had been planted this Spring, the clothes-line hadn't been fixed, the garage for the car they had been going to get this Summer stood unpainted just as his father had left it last Fall. But they would have things again. The relatives needn't say anything; he guessed he could take care of his own mother without their telling him. He loved her, but it was none of their business to know it.

She was standing in the doorway. Gerald evaded her kiss, ducked away from her and went tramping out to the kitchen. He was afraid she was going to make a fuss.

"I gotta wash my hands," he told her importantly.

She followed him and stood looking at him, pitiful and proud.

"Why don't you go up to the bathroom, sweetheart?"

"I druther wash down here."

It was what his father had done when he came home from work.

"Are you ready for supper?" she pleaded.

"You bet."

She touched his face, he couldn't avoid that. But he got into the dining-room as fast as he could and sat down with satisfaction. There were all the things that he liked—hot biscuits, and jelly, and strawberries. He demanded coffee, and his mother gave it to him. Betty's little mouth puck-ered up and her eyes were round with amazement.

"You don't let *us* have coffee," she said.

"Well, brother's been working. He has to have it."

The two little girls chattered eagerly about the school picnic. Gerald stuck to the business of eating. He had never been so hungry; hot biscuits had never tasted so good. He replied briefly to his mother's fond questions about what he had been doing all day.

"Were Floyd and his wife good to you? Did they show you what to do?"

"Yeah, they were all right."

"Did you know how to wait on people?"

"Sure."

"Didn't it seem terribly long to you?"

"Naw."

"Well, you want to eat a good supper."

It was over now, and he didn't want to talk about it. He wished she'd let him alone.

The one cooky left on the plate was given to Gerald. Betty followed her mother into the kitchen, weeping and complaining. She was the baby, and the extra pieces of everything were for her.

"I don't see why you gave it to Gerald, mamma. You didn't even make him give me half."

"Well, darling, listen—when men have been working they get hungrier than women and little girls do, and then we have to let them have what they want to eat. We don't get so hungry."

"*I* was hungry!"

"Were you, pet?" Her mother laughed, half commiseratingly. "Then you eat this strawberry mamma puts into your little mouth."

"I don't want a strawberry. I had enough strawberries. And I was working," Betty insisted. "I put on all the knives and forks. I *was* working, mamma."

"Were you? Well, you were helping. You're a nice little helper."

"Before I'd make a fuss about an old cooky!" Jaunita said scornfully.

She flashed a quick indignant glance at Gerald, remembering how he had talked to her in the drug-store. Let him have everything in the house to eat if he wanted it, and if mamma wanted to give it to him. But there was an obscure justice that silenced her even while it made her resentful. Well, she wouldn't be here all her life. She'd get married some day—and then she'd do as she pleased.

Gerald went out and sat on the steps of the porch. This was the time of day when his father always used to come out here and look at the paper. Gerald was ashamed of having eaten the cooky. He thought it belonged to him, but let that baby Betty have it! He would after this. He didn't know when he had had such a good supper. He watched Bobby Parker's yard across the street so that he could shout across at Bobby the instant he came outdoors. Maybe they could go over and see those turtles Bobby's uncle had in his back-yard. It would be fun to see if they could really be taught tricks. He could hear the girls complaining about the dishes. "It's your turn tonight." "It isn't!" Gee whizz, if they couldn't even do a little thing like washing dishes!

V

The evening came on cool and bright. Gerald stayed on the porch steps, although Bobby didn't appear in the yard. What he had really meant to do was to ask Bobby about the picnic, and try to find out, without saying it in so many words, whether any other boy had hung around Arlene Fedderson. He didn't care, anyway. He had thought about it in the store all the time, but it didn't matter so much now. His mother was the one he had to look after. Again he felt a fine, tired glow of satisfaction. He had put in a good day's work, all right.

Then he blushed. He remembered those men at the drugstore. Here was that old Art Fox coming up the walk with a pailful of strawberries! Well, if he thought he was coming here with those berries, he could just go away again.

"H'lo, Gerald," Art Fox called out cheerfully. He was a good-natured man, a widower, with a red sunburned face and grayish hair and mustache. He lived about a block away from the Rayburns, in a good-sized house. Gerald had always thought he was a nice man, because he never said any more than " 'Lo, boys!" when the boys ran across his lawn playing run-sheep-run.

"H'lo," Gerald answered briefly.

"Your ma around anywhere?"

"I don't know."

Art Fox halted. "Oh, well. . . . She ain't gone out anywhere, has she?"

"I guess she has."

What did it matter whether that was true or not? Art Fox had no business coming here. He felt a sense of pain and outrage.

"That's too bad. I thought I'd drop around and see if you folks couldn't use a few strawberries. I got a bunch of 'em ripe—too many for an old fellow to eat by himself," he added with a mild attempt at jocularity. "Didn't know as you folks had any."

"We got some."

"That so? Well, I guess you can use a few more, can't you?"

"No, we got all we want."

"That so? Well, if you got all you need . . ." Art Fox

stood there awkwardly for a moment. "Well, I guess I'll have to try to dump these on somebody else."

Gerald was silent.

"Your ma be home pretty soon, will she?"

"No, she ain't here."

"That so? Well . . . good-by, then."

Gerald said nothing. He could feel his heart thumping. He looked away. Art Fox was going down the walk with the strawberries newly washed and freshly red in the bright tin pail. Just as he turned the corner, Mrs. Rayburn came to the door.

"I thought I heard somebody. Have they gone? Was anybody here, Gerald?"

"Art Fox." Gerald did not turn around.

"Oh!" His mother seemed a little flustered. "What did he want? Has he gone away?" she asked.

"He brought some of his strawberries."

"Why, Gerald, why didn't you call me?"

" 'Cause I told him we didn't want 'em. We got some of our own."

"Why, *Gerald*—"

"Well, we don't want him around here," Gerald said roughly.

He stared straight ahead at a little bird hopping about on the lawn, fighting down the childish tears that made his throat ache and his eyes burn. That sense of pain and outrage swelled in his heart. He thought of the unfinished garage standing bare and desolate in the back-yard—his father's old coat still hanging in the kitchen entry. If his mother couldn't take care of herself, he'd do it for her. He was the man of the house now. Art Fox could stay at home where he belonged. This was *their* home. She was *his* mother. Above that ache of unmanly tears he felt a hard

exultance. They wouldn't laugh any more in the drug-
store. They wouldn't talk about her.

She looked flushed and disconcerted. She stood in the
doorway looking at Gerald. The back of his red head was
like his father's. So was the set of his sturdy shoulders.
She looked at them with an unwilling respect that turned
slowly to resentment. All these last few weeks, a secret
girlish pleasure had been growing up in her heart most
surprisingly out of the blackness of her grief and loneliness. She knew that she was admired. She had thought it
hidden from every one. At times she had laughed and
called herself a fool; and at times her eyes were dreamy
and a warmth settled softly about her. Now it was shamed
and trampled. . . .

She started to say something to Gerald. But she
stopped, as she had always stopped with Frank. She felt
her anger melting helplessly away from her. He was so
proud of working for her. He was so proud of his strength.
He was only a little boy, after all—her little boy, sitting
small and pitiful and unapproachable in the twilight.

She turned, her face suddenly quivering, went back into
the hot darkness of the empty house, and sat down there
alone.

MANUEL KOMROFF

EACH STORY A NEW PROBLEM

It is not easy for a writer to sit down and tell what the creative process is. It would even be a difficult task for psychologists and I believe only one, a German, of course, ever tackled the problem. I have heard many men describe what they thought were their processes but most of it was romance . . . something that they wanted to believe about themselves. William James in "Varieties of Religious Experience" tells something about it and even quotes letters from people like Tolstoy. But I know very little about how the trick is done. That is, I know something about the outside forms but what really happens inside would be beyond my depth.

First of all, I could tell you that I am lazy. I am terribly lazy. And therefore I refuse to write anything unless it is very clear in my mind. I hate the labor of correcting and rewriting because I must do all my writing in long hand with a pen and ink. Of course I can write letters on the machine but not fiction. The reason for this is because of the ear. I hear the words before I write them and my choice of words is first for meaning and then for sound. Many words mean quite the same thing but few words sound alike. The choice is made for the interplay of vowel sound. I think this one of the great secrets of fine writing. The O and U in English are the deep and male or minor sounds . . . read any passage in the Bible. The I and E are the light and airy and major key sounds. Read Shelley's "To a Skylark." But then I could go on and talk a long time about this. But the point I want to make is that I am lazy and the interplay of sound is important and this beat that I hear when I write is all mashed up when I try to do it on the machine . . . for a two-syllable word might on the machine have five or six clicks. Bertrand Russell told me that he likes to do all his rubbing out in his head and not write anything until it is all clear. He uses pen and ink and I have seen many pages of his manuscripts in which not more than a word on the whole page was changed . . . and Russell is a fine stylist.

On the other hand, Lafcadio Hearn was also a fine stylist

and he wrote and rewrote as many as seven and eight times for each page. However, I must say that I am not extra successful in being lazy for many of my stories were rewritten several times. Only about half were written once without any changes to speak of. "The Little Master of the Sky," which, I guess, has been more reprinted than any that I have done, was done in one day . . . I only had to stop in the middle to eat some lunch. Then reading it over I made several minor changes though not involving more than half a dozen words. But then I must add that the scheme of the story had been in my mind for three and a half or four years and the only reason I wrote it was because I was bored; my brother had gone away for the day and there was nobody to talk to. "The Christian Bite," which was in one of the O'Brien books, was also done in one day. My story called "How Does It Feel To Be Free" was done over a greater space of time. The story was almost all written when I discovered that if I were to say that it is sometimes too late to be free it would be preaching and not fiction . . . yet the story depended upon this. About a year later I hit upon the device of the iron wires in the bottle and it was an easy matter to insert this symbol into the fabric of the story. This meant rewriting which is a job that I do not like.

And so, you see, each story was done differently. Each requires its own method and some are done easily and others are never done. Now you remind me of half a dozen or more stories that I have begun and for one reason or another have never completed. The main reason is either the story was not clear in my mind from start to finish or because the heat has cooled off and I see now, without writing another word, that the story is no good.

Each story has its own problem and must be solved in its own way. Sometimes the story depends upon plot and the characters must be carefully drawn, sometimes the main idea is in the character or characters and they must be strung on a thread like colored beads. Sometimes the story is built on an idea and both the characters and plot must be invented and, lastly, sometimes it is on a theme (which is not an idea but the expression of a human emotion) and not only the people and the plot must be constructed, but idea or fantasy must be inserted.

Now if I weren't too lazy I could write you several pages on each of these types of stories but that would be going into the technical considerations of the story form. I would, however, like to say a word about direction. There are stories that have a circular movement in which the end returns to the beginning, and there are stories that shoot right off into space . . . in between these there are any number of forms—spiral, zig-zag, etc., etc.,—but in all cases the effect depends upon accumulation. This should be easy, natural, gradual and cool like the falling of snow. It should be constant and continuous . . . and like the falling of snow after a while a terrific weight will be felt. At no time should the effect be like standing before a show-window and have the porter come out to lower the awning and dump a load of snow over you. It is true that the shock would be most arresting but the effect is cheap and not artistic. O. Henry suffers from this shock method but I claim that his best stories do not go in for it.

How do I get an idea for a story? This I do not know how to answer. For each idea came to me in a different way. Sometimes a piece of paper on the floor or a strange noise or anything at all may set a long chain of story-making ideas into motion. The finished product is sometimes only remotely related to the thing that first began the process. The flower never resembles its seed but the seed must contain a good deal of the essence of the flower; but, alas, we are none of us clever enough to know what it is or how it will turn out before it is planted. The essence of a story does not come from a piece of paper on the floor or the strange sound . . . it comes from the writer himself . . . it comes from his personality or his experience, from his mental or emotional life or from the weather of his soul; it is something very inward, so far inward that I have no probe that could reach it . . . and even if I had I do not think that the emotional bile would stand very much stirring up.

There is nothing that I know that I should not be glad to tell you and there are many things that I do not know that I also could tell you about, but the main thing is that I am lazy and I get little or no pleasure in writing long essays.

HOW DOES IT FEEL TO BE FREE?[1]

AFTER the usual breakfast he was taken downstairs, given a bath, a fresh suit of civil clothes and brought to the office. Here he was presented with several documents and a five dollar bill. The warden got up from his desk. "I see by your papers, Joe, that you have been here twelve years. Well, you have been a good prisoner; good-by and good luck to you." They shook hands.

He was led through the yard to the gate. The moment had come. He stepped through. Again they shook hands before the gate was closed behind him and locked. . . . Locking him free.

He carried his hat in his hand as he started along the road and down the hill. He was confronted by a fresh bracing breeze and a most bewildering sense of vastness; a vastness bathed in light. His eyes blinked and his steps were short and hesitating.

On the top of the high gray wall a guard, rifle in hand, walked in the same direction. "Good-by, Joe," he shouted. "How does it feel to be free?"

How does it feel to be free? . . . To be confined, bottled-up, held in check, restricted, controlled—and suddenly turned loose upon a dizzy world!

A gray mist rolls in like a wave. Imagine yourself completely enveloped as though your life had been becalmed by a fog. A fog through which it is difficult to see. Only overhead can you see a tiny circular opening through which the bright sky shines like a sparkling jewel. Soon you discover that the mist has hardened about you. The

[1] First printed in *Atlantic Monthly*, September, 1925. From *The Grace of Lambs*, Boni and Liveright, 1925. Reprinted by permission of the author and of the publisher.

fog has encased you completely, except for that far-away opening overhead. You examine the walls and find that they are composed of long narrow ribbons of gray celluloid hung from what appears to be a small hoop in the sky. No, you have more space than that. Your walls are round, but you have ten feet from side to side . . . and every side is alike. From the sky to the ground your life is encased in a celluloid tube made of cold gray ribbons and you are unable to see what is outside of yourself.

But when you examine the walls closer you find that the strips are made entirely of little squares and each square has a queer design. You had not noticed them at first, but everywhere you look and as far as you can see, you find the little squares. Then on examining them closer you discover that each square is a separate little picture in which you yourself appear! Each square a frozen moment of your life. Each picture a tiny recollection dimmed and made gray by that rapid piling-up—that multiplication called past.

Frozen memories in miniature . . . as though the ribbons were discarded cinematographic records—records of your discarded past—complete and shameless.

There are different scenes of long ago; some are comforting and some are horrid. At some you tarry, but others you are happy not to see at all. Those high up are hard to see, though some seem clear and fairly distinct. You make vague guesses at what they are and some you are sure you recognize. It is like a game. The forgotten past hangs over you as high as you can see and a circle of light comes through from the sky.

The whole thing is quite natural and at first you see nothing very strange about the affair; a little odd, perhaps, or maybe like a dream, but it does not seem very startling until suddenly you discover that the sequence is wrong. Why should it be wrong? Why do the scenes not follow one another as they happened? Why is this thing all helter-skelter? You try to select and arrange but the task is enormous. Here and there and everywhere are pictures that you have not included and some that you would like to . . . If you could only cut them away with a pen-knife. . . . Yes, cut little toy windows so you could see clearly outside. The outside world. The real world that at present you can see only by looking through your own experiences, and see dimmed by the shadows of past images. But you have no knife that could sever. . . . And it would not help.

Oh, how tired you are of it all! How dreary, how op-pressing, how monotonous! Days are gray and nights are gray. You are tired of yourself, . . . the constant repeti-tion of yourself. If you could only run away. But the cyl-inder is light, airy and nimble. It rotates as you run. You are imprisoned in this strange thing called life—life dreary and gray—surrounded by cameos and smudges of black.

The sequence is wrong. You try to escape. The walls are pliable and with pressure could yield. You wedge a hand through, and another; you work a foot through, making still another opening, but at no time can you man-age to get your body through. Then, too, where would you go? You give it up and in time you are resigned and engage in that restful play of thinking back and of look-ing out at the real world through the lightly tinted squares.

You see the world. . . . The real world that is made of kisses and snow. Of fire, milk, dreams, straw, water, tobacco and children. You watch the real world that is

built solidly of things that do not last; built firmly of vital
sparks that cannot endure.

Every now and then you discover a new square or two
added to your walls. Something that happened only yesterday; but what was in its place before, you are unable
to tell, try hard as you may. In a year many different
pictures have presented themselves. In three years a fair
number are new, in six, three-quarters are added pictures,
but in twelve hardly any of the old remain and these seem
greatly dimmed. A comforting dimness. Time makes all
things restful.

In the outside world you can see children playing. They
are playing with matches, lighting old brooms and paper
and running across the fields with trailing flames and
shooting sparks. They had never done this before.

You watch closely. They are putting fire to the whole
business! Suddenly a flash—a puff of smoke—a blaze of
light and there you stand on a hill confronted by real
colors and a free bracing breeze. In the distance the
frightened children are running and you hear one whimper, "I did not know it could burn."

Everything is sky and land. You are surrounded by a
vastness bathed in light. You blink at the glamour of it
all, as with hesitating steps you wander down the road to
. . . The station is a mile away. Here a train comes from
somewhere and can take you to—exactly where you do not
know but it can take you there. You must go!

That is how it feels to be free.

At the station Joe changed his five dollar bill to buy a
ticket and a plug of chewing tobacco. The train carried
him home; to the city of his former life.

The streets are paved with stone. . . . Square next to

square with hardly a crack between. Cruelly mortised by men for the benefit and convenience of their fellow men. Long lines cemented together so that mud and dirt are not tracked about—tracked into the little pigeon-holes called home.

Joe reached home all right. His wife had been dead a number of years and his children had all grown up and married. Old memories were quite dim. He hardly knew them and they certainly did not recognize him; but it was all very pleasant.

In the evening they all had supper together, that is, after the babies had been put to bed in one room. The table was dressed as in a movie, the room was bright with lights and everything was merry.

A steaming duck was brought on and the oldest stood up, removed his coat and rolled up his cuffs before carving. "Now, dad, I am going to cut for you this here leg, first and second joint," and pointing the knife at him, "also a good big chunk of the breast. . . . Mollie, dish the gravy."

They spoke about the comic strips in the illustrated newspapers, about recent screen dramas, about dance-records for the phonograph, about everything that amused them. The checkered past was carefully avoided. They were all quite intelligent and they said they understood.

Joe had a nice home. He could stay about the house and just "rest up." The children had seen all kinds of re-unions in the movies and would do their best to make him happy. They gave him a room to himself, a warm pair of carpet slippers, a pipe with a yellow stem and fancy gold band, a pair of cotton flannel pajamas, razor blades and everything that a male mortal needs for comfort.

But Joe spent a most uncomfortable night. The large meal did not agree with him and kept him awake. The rushing light of morn came blaring into the room. He looked about. Small photographs hung on the walls. There were scenes of Niagara Falls, Yellowstone Park and of big trees in California. Little gray squares dotted the walls—views that Joe had never experienced.

It was all very natural that Joe should be a bit uncomfortable at first. The children said they understood and that it would take a little while for him to really feel at home.

Joe proceeded to make himself comfortable. He tried the carpet slippers but found them loose, soft and uncomfortable. The pipe was a nice thing, too, though he did not really enjoy smoking. The pictures he removed from the walls into which he drove nails to hang his coat and pajamas. He greatly distrusted the closet where it was dark and where mice perhaps were free to wander.

He amused himself by collecting old bits of wire that he found on old picture frames and in the basement of the apartment house. It gave him great pleasure to send the wire down the neck of a bottle and watch the odd twists and coils it would make in the bottle . . . as though it were life itself going through its many painful convulsions. He kept the bottle on the open fire-escape in front of his window.

As soon as Joe found that the friendliness of his children was really genuine he proceeded to make himself really comfortable. He brought up some thin boards to slip under the mattress of the cot. This made it much firmer. He nailed up the closet door and painted the rods of the fire-escape black under the pretext that its former color showed the dirt too much. At night he had several times been bothered by a notion that there might be rats about and that his cot was too low. This he soon fixed by bringing up some old wood from the basement and raising the cot so that it resembled an upper berth in a cabin. He was careful to eat very little meat and kept closely to a diet of soup and hot cereal. Day by day he was feeling more comfortable. Now only one thing more needed his attention. The room was too large! Too large for one person. This he remedied by rigging a pole across the room and hanging down a heavy curtain dividing the space in half. It also divided the window. Now all seemed cozy.

By this time the bottle on the window was packed tight with bits of wire. He carried it down to the basement and broke it over an ash can. The heavy wad of iron wire was freed from its container. It was nothing but a rusty solid mass the same shape as the bottle that now scattered in fragments.

He turned it in his hand and examined it closely. Was it an experiment that had failed? Did he imagine that the rough springy wires would jump back to their former state once freed? No. It was a rusty solid mass, brown as a cough mixture and shaped like a bottle. If he had a label he could paste it on and mark it, "Free!"

He brought it back to his room and carefully put it in its place on the window. Then he climbed up on his cot.

Outside it rains, and outside it snows and then the sun sings forth and dries up the long lines of pavements made of stone cunningly mortised. From his cot he can see a tiny bit of sky—a small bright opening far away. Now and then a figure walks across a neighboring room and reminds him of the man on the high wall who held a rifle in his hand and shouted, "How does it feel to be free?" From his cot he can see glimpses of the outside world. The real world that is made of kisses and snow. But between him and the great outside is the window ledge upon which stands that rusty, packed-together wad of wire—shaped like a bottle.

RICHARD CONNELL

STORY, PART OF THE AUTHOR

About my own experience in writing short stories—I'm afraid I can't make the process very clear in a letter, or even in a book. It isn't clear to me. I don't mean by that that I believe in "pure inspiration" or some equally strange external force. Writing a story is a conscious mental process, but an extremely complicated one.

A hardened short-story writer, like myself, writing twenty or so stories a year, schools himself to see life as a series of short stories—an unrelated series. First, he has his own experiences to draw on—comic, sad, gay, happy, unhappy, interesting, dull. Then he observes what other people do and what happens to them. Of course he can only interpret the experiences of others in the light of his own experiences—his characters can only feel what he himself has felt. Even the most synthetic and machine-made story is a slice of the writer's soul. He chose the subject and treated it in that way because the story was a part of him. All of which seems rather abstract.

Life is made up of an unaccountable number of dramatic atoms—some, of course, more dramatic than others. The task of the short-story writer is to select a number of these atoms and arrange them in an effective sequence, with a beginning, a middle and an end. As he has not the scope of a novelist, he must select with care, choosing the atoms (or scenes) which are interesting and essential. His story must move, it must get somewhere. So he must select the atoms vital to its advancement. Now to be less abstract.

I'll take my story "A Friend of Napoleon" which appears in my book *Apes and Angels* and won a second O. Henry prize some years ago. I'll try to trace its genesis.

In 1913 I was a reporter on a New York newspaper. I was not writing short stories. I was sent to cover the sale of the old Eden Musée, and the auction of its wax works. In the basement I came across a woe-begone little man in a faded uniform. I talked with him and he told me that he had been an attendant in the wax works for twenty years, and the wax figures were the only friends he had and that he was heartbroken because now he would have to part from them. The wish to love something—even a wax figure—is a common human trait—and one I understood well. His loneliness, too, was something I understood because I was lonely. I remembered that little man.

The seed of the story was planted in my mind. I had a situation and a character and an emotional understanding of them. I had my beginning. To get a middle and an end—in short a complete *story*—requires the exercise of a conscious technic. That is why the study of short-story forms and training in using them are so important.

I thought, now and then, of my little man in the museum, but it was not until six years later that I actually wrote the story. I don't mean to say I was trying all that time to find a plot in which he would fit. He was simply stored in my mind, ripening. In Paris, after the war, I went to the Musée Grevin, a little wax works, and saw there an excellent statue of Napoleon. Also I saw a little old Frenchman dusting it reverently. The setting made an instant appeal to me, and I decided to write my story and to make it a simple story of the loyalty (or love) of a simple mind for his only friend—the wax figure of Napoleon. Of course I was completely aware of the inherent pathos of the situation. I do not think that short-story writers very often achieve *accidental* emotional effects. At the same time, while the story must hold pathos, it could not be treated as a stark tragedy. It was a small tragi-comedy and the manner of telling had to fit the mood. It would serve no point to have my old man cut his throat in despair.

I planned out the course my story must follow. I must first establish the love of the old man for the wax Napoleon, then have him lose Napoleon; then have him make some sacrifice to gain back his wax friend. In this form the story seemed to me to be rather thin, to lack *body*. So I cast about for other characters to serve as a support for the main thread of my story —and introduced the young lovers, for their love would form a sort of sub-plot, and would serve as a background for his love for Napoleon. In a short story, as in chess, it is well to have a number of pieces to move about to support your king. The device of having the old man not know who Napoleon really was, was an after-thought. It seemed to me that a touch of irony would keep the story from being over sentimental. The court room scene was one I had actually witnessed in a French court. I had all my elements now—and I worked out the story in fairly complete detail in my mind—even to the wording. The actual writing of it took a week. When I have a story planned in my head, I work on it three or four hours a day, and stop the instant I feel my interest flagging. A second week was spent in a careful revision. The story was first published in the *Saturday Evening Post*.

I hope this brief description of the development of one story may be of some small help to your classes. The process in my other stories is very much the same, I suppose. To avoid procrastination and the temptation to be too lazy, I usually set myself a quota of stories to be finished within a year—twenty, anyhow. This works for me. It might not for others. Some writers do only four or five. I do my stories as they mature. I think one major fault in young writers is that they rush into a story before they have really thought it through, before they have examined all the possible angles, and have a really firm grip on the story. The commonest thing I hear editors say is "So-and-so has *wasted* a good story." A story writer is constantly on the alert for stories. His first question when he meets a new person is, "What is his story?" "What is her story?" While it is true that every human being has at least one, and probably a dozen stories, it does not follow that they are good ones. So the writer must learn to discard ruthlessly ideas which examination and thought show him are ordinary or not very interesting.

A FRIEND OF NAPOLEON [1]

ALL Paris held no happier man than Papa Chibou. He loved his work—that was why. Other men might say —did say, in fact—that for no amount of money would they take his job; no, not for ten thousand francs for a

[1] From *The Saturday Evening Post*, June 30, 1923. Reprinted by permission of the author.

single night. It would turn their hair white and give them permanent goose flesh, they averred. On such men Papa Chibou smiled with pity. What stomach had such zestless ones for adventure? What did they know of romance? Every night of his life Papa Chibou walked with adventure and held the hand of romance.

Every night he conversed intimately with Napoleon; with Marat and his fellow revolutionists; with Carpentier and Caesar; with Victor Hugo and Lloyd George; with Foch and with Bigarre, the Apache murderer whose unfortunate penchant for making ladies into curry led him to the guillotine; with Louis XVI and with Madame Lablanche, who poisoned eleven husbands and was working to make it an even dozen when the police deterred her; with Marie Antoinette and with sundry early Christian martyrs who lived in sweet resignation in electric-lighted catacombs under the sidewalk of the Boulevard des Capucines in the very heart of Paris. They were all his friends and he had a word and a joke for each of them, as on his nightly rounds he washed their faces and dusted out their ears, for Papa Chibou was night watchman at the Musée Pratoucy—"The World in Wax. Admission, one franc. Children and soldiers, half price. Nervous ladies enter the Chamber of Horrors at their own risk. One is prayed not to touch the wax figures or to permit dogs to circulate in the establishment."

He had been at the Musée Pratoucy so long that he looked like a wax figure himself. Visitors not infrequently mistook him for one and poked him with inquisitive fingers or canes. He did not undeceive them; he did not budge. Spartanlike he stood stiff under the pokes; he was rather proud of being taken for a citizen of the world of wax, which was, indeed, a much more real world to him than the world of flesh and blood. He had cheeks like the small red wax pippins used in table decorations, round eyes, slightly poppy, and smooth white hair, like a wig. He was a diminutive man and, with his horseshoe mustache of surprising luxuriance, looked like a gnome going to a fancy-dress ball as a small walrus. Children who saw him flitting about the dim passages that led to the catacombs were sure he was a brownie.

His title "Papa" was a purely honorary one, given him because he had worked some twenty-five years at the museum. He was unwed, and slept at the museum in a niche of a room just off the Roman arena where papier-mâché lions and tigers breakfasted on assorted martyrs. At night, as he dusted off the lions and tigers, he rebuked them sternly for their lack of delicacy.

"Ah," he would say, cuffing the ear of the largest lion, which was earnestly trying to devour a grandfather and an infant simultaneously, "sort of a pig that you are! I am ashamed of you, eater of babies. You will go to hell for this, Monsieur Lion, you may depend upon it. Monsieur Satan will poach you like an egg, I promise you. Ah, you bad one, you species of a camel, you Apache, you profiteer—"

Then Papa Chibou would bend over and very tenderly address the elderly martyr who was lying beneath the lion's paws and exhibiting signs of distress and say, "Patience, my brave one. It does not take long to be eaten, and then, consider: The good Lord will take you up to heaven, and there, if you wish, you yourself can eat a lion every day. You are a man of holiness, Phillibert. You will be Saint Phillibert, beyond doubt, and then won't you laugh at lions!"

Phillibert was the name Papa Chibou had given to the

venerable martyr; he had bestowed names on all of them. Having consoled Phillibert, he would softly dust the fat wax infant whom the lion was in the act of bolting.

"Courage, my poor little Jacob," Papa Chibou would say. "It is not every baby that can be eaten by a lion; and in such a good cause too. Don't cry, little Jacob. And remember: When you get inside Monsieur Lion, kick and kick and kick! That will give him a great sickness of the stomach. Won't that be fun, little Jacob?"

So he went about his work, chatting with them all, for he was fond of them all, even of Bigarre the Apache and the other grisly inmates of the Chamber of Horrors. He did chide the criminals for their regrettable proclivities in the past and warn them that he would tolerate no such conduct in his museum. It was not his museum of course. Its owner was Monsieur Pratoucy, a long-necked, melancholy marabou of a man who sat at the ticket window and took in the francs. But, though the legal title to the place might be vested in Monsieur Pratoucy, at night Papa Chibou was the undisputed monarch of his little wax kingdom. When the last patron had left and the doors were closed Papa Chibou began to pay calls on his subjects; across the silent halls he called greetings to them:

"Ah, Bigarre, you old rascal, how goes the world? And you, Madame Marie Antoinette; did you enjoy a good day? Good evening, Monsieur Caesar; aren't you chilly in that costume of yours? Ah, Monsieur Charlemagne, I trust your health continues to be of the best."

His closest friend of them all was Napoleon. The others he liked; to Napoleon he was devoted. It was a friendship cemented by the years, for Napoleon had been in the museum as long as Papa Chibou. Other figures might come and go at the behest of a fickle public, but Napoleon held his place, albeit he had been relegated to a dim corner.

He was not much of a Napoleon. He was smaller even than the original Napoleon, and one of his ears had come in contact with a steam radiator and as a result it was gnarled into a lump the size of a hickory nut; it was a perfect example of that phenomenon of the prize ring, the cauliflower ear. He was supposed to be at St. Helena and he stood on a papier-mâché rock, gazing out wistfully over a nonexistent sea. One hand was thrust into the bosom of his long-tailed coat, the other hung at his side. Skin-tight breeches, once white but white no longer, fitted snugly over his plump bump of waxen abdomen. A Napoleonic hat, frayed by years of conscientious brushing by Papa Chibou, was perched above a pensive waxen brow.

Papa Chibou had been attracted to Napoleon from the first. There was something so forlorn about him. Papa Chibou had been forlorn, too, in his first days at the museum. He had come from Bouloire, in the south of France, to seek his fortune as a grower of asparagus in Paris. He was a simple man of scant schooling and he had fancied that there were asparagus beds along the Paris boulevards. There were none. So necessity and chance brought him to the Museum Pratoucy to earn his bread and wine, and romance and his friendship for Napoleon kept him there.

The first day Papa Chibou worked at the museum Monsieur Pratoucy took him round to tell him about the figures.

"This," said the proprietor, "is Toulon, the strangler. This is Mademoiselle Merle, who shot the Russian duke. This is Charlotte Corday, who stabbed Marat in the bath-tub; that gory gentleman is Marat." Then they had come to Napoleon. Monsieur Pratoucy was passing him by.

"And who is this sad-looking gentleman?" asked Papa Chibou.

"Name of a name! Do you not know?"

"But no, monsieur."

"But that is Napoleon himself."

That night, his first in the museum, Papa Chibou went round and said to Napoleon, "Monsieur, I do not know with what crimes you are charged, but I, for one, refuse to think you are guilty of them."

So began their friendship. Thereafter he dusted Napoleon with especial care and made him his confidant. One night in his twenty-fifth year at the museum Papa Chibou said to Napoleon, "You observed those two lovers who were in here tonight, did you not, my good Napoleon? They thought it was too dark in this corner for us to see, didn't they? But we saw him take her hand and whisper to her. Did she blush? You were near enough to see. She is pretty, isn't she, with her bright dark eyes? She is not a French girl; she is an American; one can tell that by the way she doesn't roll her r's. The young man, he is French; and a fine young fellow he is, or I'm no judge. He is so slender and erect, and he has courage, for he wears the war cross; you noticed that, didn't you? He is very much in love, that is sure. This is not the first time I have seen them. They have met here before, and they are wise, for is this not a spot most romantic for the meetings of lovers?"

Papa Chibou flicked a speck of dust from Napoleon's good ear.

"Ah," he exclaimed, "it must be a thing most delicious to be young and in love! Were you ever in love, Napoleon? No? Ah, what a pity! I know, for I, too, have had no luck in love. Ladies prefer the big, strong men, don't they? Well, we must help these two young people, Napoleon. We must see that they have the joy we missed. So do not let them know you are watching them if they come here tomorrow night. I will pretend I do not see."

Each night after the museum had closed, Papa Chibou gossiped with Napoleon about the progress of the love affair between the American girl with the bright dark eyes and the slender, erect young Frenchman.

"All is not going well," Papa Chibou reported one night, shaking his head. "There are obstacles to their happiness. He has little money, for he is just beginning his career. I heard him tell her so tonight. And she has an aunt who has other plans for her. What a pity if fate should part them! But you know how unfair fate can be, don't you, Napoleon? If only we had some money we might be able to help him, but I, myself, have no money, and I suppose you, too, were poor, since you look so sad. But attend; tomorrow is a day most important for them. He has asked her if she will marry him, and she has said that she will tell him tomorrow night at nine in this very place. I heard them arrange it all. If she does not come it will mean no. I think we shall see two very happy ones here tomorrow night, eh, Napoleon?"

The next night, when the last patron had gone and Papa Chibou had locked the outer door, he came to Napoleon, and tears were in his eyes.

"You saw, my friend?" broke out Papa Chibou. "You observed? You saw his face and how pale it grew? You saw his eyes and how they held a thousand agonies? He waited until I had to tell him three times that the museum was closing. I felt like an executioner, I assure you; and he looked up at me as only a man condemned can look.

He went out with heavy feet; he was no longer erect. For she did not come, Napoleon; that girl with the bright dark eyes did not come. Our little comedy of love has become a tragedy, monsieur. She has refused him, that poor, that unhappy young man."

On the following night at closing time Papa Chibou came hurrying to Napoleon; he was a-quiver with excitement.

"She was here!" he cried. "Did you see her? She was here and she kept watching and watching; but, of course, he did not come. I could tell from his stricken face last night that he had no hope. At last I dared to speak to her. I said to her, 'Mademoiselle, a thousand pardons for the very great liberty I am taking, but it is my duty to tell you—he was here last night and he waited till closing time. He was all of a paleness, mademoiselle, and he chewed his fingers in his despair. He loves you, mademoiselle; a cow could see that. He is devoted to you; and he is a fine young fellow, you can take an old man's word for it. Do not break his heart, mademoiselle.' She grasped my sleeve. 'You know him, then?' she asked. 'You know where I can find him?' 'Alas, no,' I said. 'I have only seen him here with you.' 'Poor boy!' she kept saying. 'Poor boy! Oh, what shall I do? I am in dire trouble. I love him, monsieur.' 'But you did not come,' I said. 'I could not,' she replied, and she was weeping. 'I live with an aunt; a rich tiger she is, monsieur, and she wants me to marry a count, a fat leering fellow who smells of attar of roses and garlic. My aunt locked me in my room. And now I have lost the one I love, for he will think I have refused him, and he is so proud he will never ask me again.' 'But surely you could let him know?' I suggested. 'But I do not know where he lives,' she said. 'And in a few days my aunt is taking me off to Rome, where the count is, and oh, dear, oh, dear, oh, dear—' And she wept on my shoulder. Napoleon, that poor little American girl with the bright dark eyes."

Papa Chibou began to brush the Napoleonic hat.

"I tried to comfort her," he said. "I told her that the young man would surely find her, that he would come back and haunt the spot where they had been happy, but I was telling her what I did not believe. 'He may come tonight,' I said, 'or tomorrow.' She waited until it was time to close the museum. You saw her face as she left; did it not touch you in the heart?"

Papa Chibou was downcast when he approached Napoleon the next night.

"She waited again till closing time," he said, "but he did not come. It made me suffer to see her as the hours went by and her hope ebbed away. At last she had to leave, and at the door she said to me, 'If you see him here again, please give him this.' She handed me this card, Napoleon. See, it says, 'I am at the Villa Rosina, Rome. I love you. Nina.' Ah, the poor, poor young man. We must keep a sharp watch for him, you and I."

Papa Chibou and Napoleon did watch at the Musée Pratoucy night after night. One, two, three, four, five nights they watched for him. A week, a month, more months passed, and he did not come. There came instead one day news of so terrible a nature that it left Papa Chibou ill and trembling. The Musée Pratoucy was going to have to close its doors.

"It is no use," said Monsieur Pratoucy, when he dealt this blow to Papa Chibou. "I cannot go on. Already I owe much, and my creditors are clamoring. People will no longer pay a franc to see a few old dummies when they can see an army of red Indians, Arabs, brigands and dukes in the moving pictures. Monday the Musée Pratoucy closes its doors for ever."

"But, Monsieur Pratoucy," exclaimed Papa Chibou, aghast, "what about the people here? What will become of Marie Antoinette, and the martyrs, and Napoleon?"

"Oh," said the proprietor, "I'll be able to realize a little on them, perhaps. On Tuesday they will be sold at auction. Some one may buy them to melt up."

"To melt up, monsieur?" Papa Chibou faltered.

"But certainly. What else are they good for?"

"But surely monsieur will want to keep them; a few of them anyhow?"

"Keep them? Aunt of the devil, but that is a droll idea! Why should any one want to keep shabby old wax dummies?"

"I thought," murmured Papa Chibou, "that you might keep just one—Napoleon, for example—as a remembrance—"

"Uncle of Satan, but you have odd notions! To keep a souvenir of one's bankruptcy!"

Papa Chibou went away to his little hole in the wall. He sat on his cot and fingered his mustache for an hour; the news had left him dizzy, had made a cold vacuum under his belt buckle. From under his cot, at last, he took a wooden box, unlocked three separate locks, and extracted a sock. From the sock he took his fortune, his hoard of big copper ten-centime pieces, tips he had saved for years. He counted them over five times most carefully; but no matter how he counted them he could not make the total come to more than two hundred and twenty-one francs.

That night he did not tell Napoleon the news. He did not tell any of them. Indeed he acted even more cheerful than usual as he went from one figure to another. He complimented Madame Lablanche, the lady of the poisoned spouses, on how well she was looking. He even had a kindly word to say to the lion that was eating the two martyrs.

"After all, Monsieur Lion," he said, "I suppose it is as proper for you to eat martyrs as it is for me to eat bananas. Probably bananas do not enjoy being eaten any more than martyrs do. In the past I have said harsh things to you, Monsieur Lion; I am sorry I said them, now. After all, it is hardly your fault that you eat people. You were born with an appetite for martyrs, just as I was born poor." And he gently tweaked the lion's papier-mâché ear.

When he came to Napoleon, Papa Chibou brushed him with unusual care and thoroughness. With a moistened cloth he polished the imperial nose, and he took pains to be gentle with the cauliflower ear. He told Napoleon the latest joke he had heard at the cabmen's café where he ate his breakfast of onion soup, and, as the joke was mildly improper, nudged Napoleon in the ribs, and winked at him.

"We are men of the world, eh, old friend?" said Papa Chibou. "We are philosophers, is that not so?" Then he added, "We take what life sends us, and sometimes it sends hardnesses."

He wanted to talk more with Napoleon, but somehow he couldn't; abruptly, in the midst of a joke, Papa Chibou broke off and hurried down into the depths of the Chamber of Horrors and stood there for a very long time staring at an unfortunate native of Siam being trodden on by an elephant.

It was not until the morning of the auction sale that Papa Chibou told Napoleon. Then, while the crowd was gathering, he slipped up to Napoleon in his corner and laid his hand on Napoleon's arm.

"One of the hardnesses of life has come to us, old friend," he said. "They are going to try to take you away. But, courage! Papa Chibou does not desert his friends. Listen!" And Papa Chibou patted his pocket, which gave forth a jingling sound.

The bidding began. Close to the auctioneer's desk stood a man, a wizened, rodent-eyed man with a diamond ring and dirty fingers. Papa Chibou's heart went down like an express elevator when he saw him, for he knew that the rodent-eyed man was Mogen, the junk king of Paris. The auctioneer in a voice slightly encumbered by adenoids, began to sell the various items in a hurried, perfunctory manner.

"Item 3 is Julius Caesar, toga and sandals thrown in. How much am I offered? One hundred and fifty francs? Dirt cheap for a Roman emperor, that is. Who'll make it two hundred? Thank you, Monsieur Mogen. The noblest Roman of them all is going at two hundred francs. Are you all through at two hundred? Going, going, gone! Julius Caesar is sold to Monsieur Mogen."

Papa Chibou patted Caesar's back sympathetically.

"You are worth more, my good Julius," he said in a whisper. "Good-by."

He was encouraged. If a comparatively new Caesar brought only two hundred, surely an old Napoleon would bring no more.

The sale progressed rapidly. Monsieur Mogen bought the entire Chamber of Horrors. He bought Marie Antoinette, and the martyrs and lions. Papa Chibou, standing near Napoleon, withstood the strain of waiting by chewing his mustache.

The sale was very nearly over and Monsieur Mogen had bought every item, when, with a yawn, the auctioneer droned: "Now, ladies and gentlemen, we come to Item 573, a collection of odds and ends, mostly damaged goods, to be sold in one lot. The lot includes one stuffed owl that seems to have moulted a bit; one Spanish shawl, torn; the head of an Apache who has been guillotined, body missing; a small wax camel, no humps; and an old wax figure of Napoleon, with one ear damaged. What am I offered for the lot?"

Papa Chibou's heart stood still. He laid a reassuring hand on Napoleon's shoulder.

"The fool," he whispered in Napoleon's good ear, "to put you in the same class as a camel, no humps, and an owl. But never mind. It is lucky for us, perhaps."

"How much for this assortment?" asked the auctioneer.

"One hundred francs," said Mogen, the junk king.

"One hundred and fifty," said Papa Chibou, trying to be calm. He had never spent so vast a sum all at once in his life.

Mogen fingered the material in Napoleon's coat.

"Two hundred," said the junk king.

"Are you all through at two hundred?" queried the auctioneer.

"Two hundred and twenty-one," called Papa Chibou. His voice was a husky squeak.

Mogen from his rodent eyes glared at Papa Chibou with annoyance and contempt. He raised his dirtiest finger —the one with the diamond ring on it—toward the auctioneer.

"Monsieur Mogen bids two hundred and twenty-five," droned the auctioneer. "Do I hear two hundred and fifty?"

Papa Chibou hated the world. The auctioneer cast a look in his direction.

"Two hundred and twenty-five is bid," he repeated. "Are you all through at two hundred and twenty-five? Going, going—sold to Monsieur Mogen for two hundred and twenty-five francs."

Stunned, Papa Chibou heard Mogen say casually, "I'll send round my carts for this stuff in the morning."

This stuff!

Dully and with an aching breast Papa Chibou went to his room down by the Roman arena. He packed his few clothes into a box. Last of all he slowly took from his cap the brass badge he had worn for so many years; it bore the words "Chief Watchman." He had been proud of that title, even if it was slightly inaccurate; he had been not only the chief but the only watchman. Now he was nothing. It was hours before he summoned up the energy to take his box round to the room he had rented high up under the roof of a tenement in a near-by alley. He knew he should start to look for another job at once, but he could not force himself to do so that day. Instead, he stole back to the deserted museum and sat down on a bench by the side of Napoleon. Silently he sat there all night; but he did not sleep; he was thinking, and the thought that kept pecking at his brain was to him a shocking one. At last, as day began to edge its pale way through the dusty windows of the museum, Papa Chibou stood up with the air of a man who has been through a mental struggle and has made up his mind.

"Napoleon," he said, "we have been friends for a quarter of a century and now we are to be separated because a stranger had four francs more than I had. That may be lawful, my old friend, but it is not justice. You and I, we are not going to be parted."

Paris was not yet awake when Papa Chibou stole with infinite caution into the narrow street beside the museum. Along this street toward the tenement where he had taken a room crept Papa Chibou. Sometimes he had to pause for breath, for in his arms he was carrying Napoleon.

Two policemen came to arrest Papa Chibou that very afternoon. Mogen had missed Napoleon, and he was a shrewd man. There was not the slightest doubt of Papa Chibou's guilt. There stood Napoleon in the corner of his room, gazing pensively out over the housetops. The police bundled the overwhelmed and confused Papa Chibou into the police patrol, and with him, as damning evidence, Napoleon.

In his cell in the city prison Papa Chibou sat with his spirit caved in. To him jails and judges and justice were terrible and mysterious affairs. He wondered if he would be guillotined; perhaps not, since his long life had been one of blameless conduct; but the least he could expect, he reasoned, was a long sentence to hard labor on Devil's Island, and guillotining had certain advantages over that. Perhaps it would be better to be guillotined, he told himself, now that Napoleon was sure to be melted up.

The keeper who brought him his meal of stew was a pessimist of jocular tendencies.

"A pretty pickle," said the keeper; "and at your age too. You must be a very wicked old man to go about stealing dummies. What will be safe now? One may expect to find the Eiffel Tower missing any morning. Dummy stealing! What a career! We have had a man in here who stole a trolley car, and one who made off with the anchor of a steamship, and even one who pilfered a hippopotamus from a zoo, but never one who stole a dummy—and an old one-eared dummy, at that! It is an affair extraordinary!"

"And what did they do to the gentleman who stole the hippopotamus?" inquired Papa Chibou tremulously.

The keeper scratched his head to indicate thought.

"I think," he said, "that they boiled him alive. Either that or they transported him for life to Morocco; I don't recall exactly."

Papa Chibou's brow grew damp.

"It was a trial most comical, I can assure you," went on the keeper. "The judges were Messieurs Bertouf, Goblin, and Perouse—very amusing fellows, all three of them. They had fun with the prisoner; how I laughed. Judge Bertouf said, in sentencing him, 'We must be severe with you, pilferer of hippopotamuses. We must make of you an example. This business of hippopotamus pilfering is getting all too common in Paris.' They are witty fellows, those judges."

Papa Chibou grew a shade paler.

"The Terrible Trio?" he asked.

"The Terrible Trio," replied the keeper cheerfully.

"Will they be my judges?" asked Papa Chibou.

"Most assuredly," promised the keeper, and strolled away humming happily and rattling his big keys.

Papa Chibou knew then that there was no hope for him. Even into the Musée Pratoucy the reputation of those three judges had penetrated, and it was a sinister reputation indeed. They were three ancient, grim men who had fairly earned their title, The Terrible Trio, by the severity of their sentences; evildoers blanched at their names, and this was a matter of pride to them.

Shortly the keeper came back; he was grinning.

"You have the devil's own luck, old-timer," he said to Papa Chibou. "First you have to be tried by The Terrible Trio, and then you get assigned to you as lawyer none other than Monsieur Georges Dufayel."

"And this Monsieur Dufayel, is he then not a good lawyer?" questioned Papa Chibou miserably.

The keeper snickered.

"He has not won a case for months," he answered, as if it were the most amusing thing imaginable. "It is really better than a circus to hear him muddling up his clients' affairs in court. His mind is not on the case at all. Heaven knows where it is. When he rises to plead before the judges he has no fire, no passion. He mumbles and stutters. It is a saying about the courts that one is as good as convicted who has the ill luck to draw Monsieur Georges Dufayel as his advocate. Still, if one is too poor to pay for a lawyer, one must take what he can get. That's philosophy, eh, old-timer?"

Papa Chibou groaned.

"Oh, wait till tomorrow," said the keeper gayly. "Then you'll have a real reason to groan."

"But surely I can see this Monsieur Dufayel."

"Oh, what's the use? You stole the dummy, didn't you? It will be there in court to appear against you. How entertaining! Witness for the prosecution: Monsieur Napoleon. You are plainly as guilty as Cain, old-timer, and the judges will boil your cabbage for you very quickly and neatly, I can promise you that. Well, see you tomorrow. Sleep well."

Papa Chibou did not sleep well. He did not sleep at all, in fact, and when they marched him into the inclosure where sat the other nondescript offenders against the law he was shaken and utterly wretched. He was overawed by

the great court room and the thick atmosphere of seri-
ousness that hung over it.

He did pluck up enough courage to ask a guard,
"Where is my lawyer, Monsieur Dufayel?"

"Oh, he's late, as usual," replied the guard. And then,
for he was a waggish fellow, he added, "If you're lucky
he won't come at all."

Papa Chibou sank down on the prisoners' bench and
raised his eyes to the tribunal opposite. His very marrow
was chilled by the sight of The Terrible Trio. The chief
judge, Bertouf, was a vast puff of a man, who swelled
out of his judicial chair like a poisonous fungus. His
black robe was familiar with spilled brandy, and his dirty
judicial bib was askew. His face was bibulous and brutal,
and he had the wattles of a turkey gobbler. Judge Goblin,
on his right, looked to have mummified; he was at least a
hundred years old and had wrinkled parchment skin and
red-rimmed eyes that glittered like the eyes of a cobra.
Judge Perouse was one vast jungle of tangled grizzled
whisker, from the midst of which projected a cockatoo's
beak of a nose; he looked at Papa Chibou and licked his
lips with a long pink tongue. Papa Chibou all but fainted;
he felt no bigger than a pea, and less important; as for
his judges, they seemed enormous monsters.

The first case was called, a young swaggering fellow
who had stolen an orange from a pushcart.

"Ah, Monsieur Thief," rumbled Judge Bertouf with a
scowl, "you are jaunty now. Will you be so jaunty a year
from today when you are released from prison? I rather
think not. Next case."

Papa Chibou's heart pumped with difficulty. A year for
an orange—and he had stolen a man! His eyes roved
round the room and he saw two guards carrying in some-

thing which they stood before the judges. It was Napoleon.

A guard tapped Papa Chibou on the shoulder. "You're next," he said.

"But my lawyer, Monsieur Dufayel—" began Papa Chibou.

"You're in hard luck," said the guard, "for here he comes."

Papa Chibou in a daze found himself in the prisoner's dock. He saw coming toward him a pale young man. Papa Chibou recognized him at once. It was the slender, erect young man of the museum. He was not very erect now; he was listless. He did not recognize Papa Chibou; he barely glanced at him.

"You stole something," said the young lawyer, and his voice was toneless. "The stolen goods were found in your room. I think we might better plead guilty and get it over with."

"Yes, monsieur," said Papa Chibou, for he had let go all his hold on hope. "But attend a moment. I have something—a message for you."

Papa Chibou fumbled through his pockets and at last found the card of the American girl with the bright dark eyes. He handed it to Georges Dufayel.

"She left it with me to give to you," said Papa Chibou. "I was chief watchman at the Musée Pratoucy, you know. She came there night after night, to wait for you."

The young man gripped the sides of the card with both hands; his face, his eyes, everything about him seemed suddenly charged with new life.

"Ten thousand million devils!" he cried. "And I doubted her! I owe you much, monsieur. I owe you everything." He wrung Papa Chibou's hand.

Judge Bertouf gave an impatient judicial grunt.

"We are ready to hear your case, Advocate Dufayel," said the judge, "if you have one."

The court attendants sniggered.

"A little moment, monsieur the judge," said the lawyer. He turned to Papa Chibou. "Quick," he shot out, "tell me about the crime you are charged with. What did you steal?"

"Him," replied Papa Chibou, pointing.

"That dummy of Napoleon?"

Papa Chibou nodded.

"But why?"

Papa Chibou shrugged his shoulders.

"Monsieur could not understand."

"But you must tell me!" said the lawyer urgently. "I must make a plea for you. These savages will be severe enough, in any event; but I may be able to do something. Quick; why did you steal this Napoleon?"

"I was his friend," said Papa Chibou. "The museum failed. They were going to sell Napoleon for junk, Monsieur Dufayel. He was my friend. I could not desert him."

The eyes of the young advocate had caught fire; they were lit with a flash. He brought his fist down on the table.

"Enough!" he cried.

Then he rose in his place and addressed the court. His voice was low, vibrant and passionate; the judges, in spite of themselves, leaned forward to listen to him.

"May it please the honorable judges of this court of France," he began, "my client is guilty. Yes, I repeat in a voice of thunder, for all France to hear, for the enemies of France to hear, for the whole wide world to hear, he is guilty. He did steal this figure of Napoleon, the lawful property of another. I do not deny it. This old man, Jerome Chibou, is guilty, and I for one am proud of his guilt."

Judge Bertouf grunted.

"If your client is guilty, Advocate Dufayel," he said, "that settles it. Despite your pride in his guilt, which is a peculiar notion, I confess, I am going to sentence him to—"

"But wait, your honor!" Dufayel's voice was compelling. "You must, you shall hear me! Before you pass sentence on this old man, let me ask you a question."

"Well?"

"Are you a Frenchman, Judge Bertouf?"

"But certainly."

"And you love France?"

"Monsieur has not the effrontery to suggest otherwise?"

"No. I was sure of it. That is why you will listen to me."

"I listen."

"I repeat then: Jerome Chibou is guilty. In the law's eyes he is a criminal. But in the eyes of France and those who love her his guilt is a glorious guilt; his guilt is more honorable than innocence itself."

The three judges looked at one another blankly; Papa Chibou regarded his lawyer with wide eyes; Georges Dufayel spoke on.

"These are times of turmoil and change in our country, messieurs the judges. Proud traditions which were once the birthright of every Frenchman have been allowed to decay. Enemies beset us within and without. Youth grows careless of that honor which is the soul of a nation. Youth forgets the priceless heritages of the ages, the great names that once brought glory to France in the past, when Frenchmen were Frenchmen. There are some in France who may have forgotten the respect due a nation's great"—here Advocate Dufayel looked very hard at the judges—"but there are a few patriots left who have not forgotten. And there sits one of them.

"This poor old man has deep within him a glowing devotion to France. You may say that he is a simple, unlettered peasant. You may say that he is a thief. But I say, and true Frenchmen will say with me, that he is a patriot, messieurs the judges. He loves Napoleon. He loves him for what he did for France. He loves him because in Napoleon burned that spirit which has made France great. There was a time, messieurs the judges, when your fathers and mine dared share that love for a great leader. Need I remind you of the career of Napoleon? I know I need not. Need I tell you of his victories? I know I need not."

Nevertheless, Advocate Dufayel did tell them of the career of Napoleon. With a wealth of detail and many gestures he traced the rise of Napoleon; he lingered over his battles; for an hour and ten minutes he spoke eloquently of Napoleon and his part in the history of France.

"You may have forgotten," he concluded, "and others may have forgotten, but this old man sitting here a prisoner—he did not forget. When mercenary scoundrels wanted to throw on the junk heap this effigy of one of France's greatest sons, who was it that saved him? Was it you, messieurs the judges? Was it I? Alas, no. It was a poor old man who loved Napoleon more than he loved himself. Consider, messieurs the judges; they were going to throw on the junk heap Napoleon—France's Napoleon—our Napoleon. Who would save him? Then up rose this man, this Jerome Chibou, whom you would brand as a thief, and he cried aloud for France and for the whole world to hear, 'Stop! Desecraters of Napoleon, stop! There still lives one Frenchman who loves the memories of his native land; there is still one patriot left. I, I, Jerome Chibou, will save Napoleon!' And he did save him, messieurs the judges."

Advocate Dufayel mopped his brow, and leveling an accusing finger at The Terrible Trio he said, "You may send Jerome Chibou to jail. But when you do, remember this: You are sending to jail the spirit of France. You may find Jerome Chibou guilty. But when you do, remember this: You are condemning a man for love of country, for love of France. Wherever true hearts beat in French bosoms, messieurs the judges, there will the crime of Jerome Chibou be understood, and there will the name of Jerome Chibou be honored. Put him in prison, messieurs the judges. Load his poor feeble old body with chains. And a nation will tear down the prison walls, break his chains, and pay homage to the man who loved Napoleon and France so much that he was willing to sacrifice himself on the altar of patriotism."

Advocate Dufayel sat down; Papa Chibou raised his eyes to the judges' bench. Judge Perouse was ostentatiously blowing his beak of a nose. Judge Goblin, who wore a Sedan ribbon in his buttonhole, was sniffling into his inkwell. And Chief Judge Bertouf was openly blubbering.

"Jerome Chibou, stand up." It was Chief Judge Bertouf who spoke, and his voice was thick with emotion.

Papa Chibou, quaking, stood up. A hand like a hand of pink bananas was thrust down at him.

"Jerome Chibou," said Chief Judge Bertouf, "I find you guilty. Your crime is patriotism in the first degree.

I sentence you to freedom. Let me have the honor of shaking the hand of a true Frenchman."

"And I," said Judge Goblin, thrusting out a hand as dry as autumn leaves.

"And I also," said Judge Perouse, reaching out a hairy hand.

"And, furthermore," said Chief Judge Bertouf, "you shall continue to protect the Napoleon you saved. I subscribe a hundred francs to buy him for you."

"And I," said Judge Goblin.

"And I also," said Judge Perouse.

As they left the court room, Advocate Dufayel, Papa Chibou and Napoleon, Papa Chibou turned to his lawyer.

"I can never repay monsieur," he began.

"Nonsense!" said the lawyer.

"And would Monsieur Dufayel mind telling me again the last name of Napoleon?"

"Why, Bonaparte, of course. Surely you knew—"

"Alas, no, Monsieur Dufayel. I am a man the most ignorant. I did not know that my friend had done such great things."

"You didn't? Then what in the name of heaven did you think Napoleon was?"

"A sort of murderer," said Papa Chibou humbly.

Out beyond the walls of Paris in a garden stands the villa of Georges Dufayel, who has become, every one says, the most eloquent and successful young lawyer in the Paris courts. He lives there with his wife, who has bright dark eyes. To get to his house one must pass a tiny gatehouse, where lives a small old man with a prodigious walrus mustache. Visitors who peer into the gatehouse as they pass sometimes get a shock, for standing in one corner of its only room they see another small man, in uniform and a big hat. He never moves, but stands there by the window all day, one hand in the bosom of his coat, the other at his side, while his eyes look out over the garden. He is waiting for Papa Chibou to come home after his work among the asparagus beds to tell him the jokes and the news of the day.

STRUTHERS BURT

IDEAS, NOT SLICES OF LIFE

I don't know that I can be of very much help to you and perhaps what I have to say will be of positive evil to your students, for the more I write the less interested I find myself in either the story for its own sake or for the sake of its art. I am not even very much interested in it as a transcription of actuality.

By nature, I suppose, I am a poet, not really a prose writer at all, and, as you know, by nature a poet is in reality always a propagandist. This at first blush seems a paradox, but it isn't. The poet is always putting forward some passionate belief, whether it be the belief in beauty, or whatever it is. When he confines himself to his own medium this is not so clear because poetry by its nature is concise and elliptical. When the poet gets to writing prose, however, his cloven hoof is more apparent.

Therefore, more and more, I am interested in the idea back of a story and more and more I find that my stories originate in an idea. This of course, has its obvious dangers and the writer must guard, first, against dullness, secondly, against too direct preaching, thirdly, against using his characters merely as automatons to express his beliefs. But if he is fairly successful in doing all these things, in other words, if he does not allow his point of view to run away with him, then, at least, so it seems to me, he is in the line of the only sort of great literature that has ever been written.

I know that this idea is by no means the popular one today amongst the intelligentsia, but to me it seems the only valid one. Mere slices of life without any arrangement mean nothing. I can see them better for myself by simply going out and looking for them. It seems to me only very young people or people very much circumscribed could find them vitally important or informing.

Following this line of reasoning, the bigger the writer's audience the more he satisfies the impulses that are in him. There is not much use preaching progress in *The Forum* or revolution in *The Independent,* because not only are the readers

251

of both limited, but the former are almost always progressive and the latter fairly revolutionary anyway. But if you can preach beauty and some degree of intelligence and rebellion against evil to, let us say, the average reader of "the big flats" then you have done something. This naturally has its limitations. "The big flats" have their editorial policies, but you can circumvent them if you know how.

It seems to me less and less important that your hero and heroine should marry at the end of your story, thus imparting what is known as a "happy ending," if, during your story, you have convinced a reader or two that all is not well with marriage as it is now generally practiced.

This is a crude instance, and "the big flats" in reality no longer require happy endings. They do require, however, the catharsis, and I am not at all sure that philosophically they are not right. For a little while the complete cynicism of *The American Mercury* does good, after that it inevitably results in a reaction not altogether healthy.

In short, I come back more and more to Carlyle's dictum and rest my case entirely on that. If a man has something to say he'll find a way to say it.

I do not know that it is particularly worth while going into the genesis of any one of my stories, but a simple instance is a story called "Beauty and the Blantons," published in *McCall's*, a couple of years ago, and included in my collection of short stories called *They Could Not Sleep* and published by Scribner's.

I saw the magnolia gardens at Charleston and could not get them out of my head. I wondered what had impelled the man who had planted them. The inner idea, that is. And then I saw them against the background of the country, of the United States, so utterly at variance in many ways. Finally I wrote the story as a story of three generations, from the early eighteen-hundreds until today. The idea was the idea of this thirst for beauty struggling through the limitations of various personalities—personalities limited by heredity, varying circumstances and historical happenings and movements. In the background always was the country itself, changing as were my characters.

BEAUTY AND THE BLANTONS [1]

THE gardens were started by the Reverend Jeremiah Blanton—the first Blanton—somewhere in the middle '40s, four years after he had married for his second wife the rich Miss Almuce of Boston, who brought him a large fortune, a suppressed disposition, nothing of a figure, and complete liberty.

The last was fortunate, for without a change of climate the Reverend Jeremiah would have speedily joined numerous former members of his congregation in the bleak graveyard, laid out with a determination that death should be just as ugly as life, upon a treeless, rocky hillside of Gadsboro, Massachusetts. The Reverend Jeremiah had developed that frequent accompaniment of a Christian life, a pair of weak lungs. Simultaneously with this development, a cousin, a heretofore disregarded Blanton, died a childless old bachelor, leaving behind him a large plantation on the Cape Fear River in southern North Carolina. As he died intestate, Jeremiah Blanton, as the next of kin, inherited the estate: three hundred slaves, an immense old red brick house with white columns, many acres.

For a month or two after receiving word of this additional windfall, the Reverend Jeremiah had endured an unbroken spiritual gasp. Outwardly he was unchanged, but inwardly he was in a state of turmoil resembling that of a staring fish caught in a whirlpool. He wasn't in the least sure what was happening. In his more depressed moments he suspected that the whole thing was an assault on the part of the devil, determined to break down the recti-

[1] From *They Could Not Sleep*, copyright, 1928, by Charles Scribner's Sons. Reprinted by permission of the author and of the publishers.

tude of a leader of theological endeavor. In a way, it was bad enough that Dorcas was so rich—there was, when you came to think of it, a taint of the flesh and other abominations about such solid wealth—but then her wealth was honest wealth, sanctified by the most conservative of banking methods, and it had been his intention to use it for the benefit of the community at large and the furtherance of the gospel amongst the heathen of Africa in particular. But this second windfall displayed a different character; was blandishing, soft, cajoling, appealed richly to the imagination. Besides, there were the slaves. Slavery was an abomination before the Lord. He took his doubts to his wife.

She raised her pale gray eyes, bordered by heavy dark lashes, and regarded him thoughtfully.

"I have been thinking about it a great deal, too," she said, "and I have arrived at the conclusion that it is your duty to undertake whatever burden the Lord has seen fit to place upon your shoulders." Her meager voice was quite emotionless.

"Duty?" He had not thought of it in that light before.

"Yes, undoubtedly. If He had not desired you to be a Southern planter, Jeremiah, this inheritance would never have come to you. Possibly it is a test. If you cannot live as godly a life there as you can here, then it is a sign that there is a weakness somewhere. You are favored beyond most men; you are tested beyond most."

"But I do not believe in bondage, and they tell me these plantations cannot be worked in any other way."

"That is but a further test. You have always taken an extreme interest in the soul of the black man, and now is your opportunity to work with him personally—my opportunity, too. You can found a church and introduce the true light—for I have no doubt that at present they are no better than infidels—and if, after a certain time, you still find the institution of slavery unchristian, you can set them free. At all events, I see in this a special call." She returned to her sewing with the quiet, demure closing of her lips with which she was used to conclude the rare expression of her opinions. She was a young woman; not over twenty-five; and there was a tradition that in her extreme youth she had had a tempestuous, unhappy love affair.

But the Reverend Jeremiah was not convinced; he was not convinced until three weeks later when his friend Doctor Frothingham told him the reasons for his lassitude and the perpetual cough that had recently afflicted him.

"If you stay here," said Doctor Frothingham bluntly, "you'll die."

"It is the Lord's will," replied Jeremiah meekly, already won over in his mind, but enjoying as usual, with gelid obstinacy, the prospects of an argument.

"The Lord's sheer nonsense!" retorted Doctor Frothingham. "Don't talk that way to me about the Lord. The Lord is a much more sensible man than you clergymen try to make him out. He gives us physical afflictions, like any other afflictions, in an effort to make real people out of mighty poor material. You get out of here. Didn't a cousin of yours die a little while ago and leave you a plantation in North Carolina? Well, you go there and live."

It was, of course, a direct revelation. Paul of Tarsus was not more clearly designated. There was some especial object; some future task Providence had in mind. Even Jeremiah's disputatious soul could no longer refuse to see the thing in any other way.

He arranged his affairs in Gadsboro, settled a large sum of money upon the church, which made its pulpit for all time a sinecure and a refuge for worthless young clergymen, and departed with his wife, his library, and his opinions for the Cape Fear River. The name and the circumstances attendant upon his going caused him to feel that in many ways he was a new Christian setting out for a new Celestial City. Only Christian had left his wife behind him and that, much as the Reverend Jeremiah mentally approved of the action, was more than a nineteenth-century New England Puritan could do. Women —lawfully mated—had their uses, as the same Paul of Tarsus had indicated.

At this time the Reverend Jeremiah was a man of forty-five; lank, clean-shaven, over-lapping lipped, with a long narrow head and expressionless light eyes; the head and eyes slightly reminiscent of a proud, uncertain horse. His black hair was beginning to thin out on top, and he moved very briskly, with long strides, so that his black clothes flapped about him as he walked. He was the second son of a sea-captain and he had fled inland and to the bosom of the church because he had found the sea disturbing and boisterously tempting, and because, in the person of his father, he had seen how little compatible such a passion was with the calm indifference a converted man should show.

It must have been a curious sight, that August day of 1843, when the high leather-springed traveling-coach, covered with the mud and dust of half a county, turned in at the white gate-posts of "Holy Oak"—that was the name of the dead cousin's place—and rolled slowly up the half-mile avenue, overhung with gnarled gray trees festooned with drooping moss. On either side was the bare brilliance of the rice-fields, but the avenue was haunted by a perpetual golden gloom, sun-moted and iridescent. Two small colored boys ran on ahead, their eyes wide with excitement, and in front of the great brick house, and overflowing into the gardens that swept up from behind in a half-moon of breast-high hedges, were gathered a couple of hundred house-servants and field-hands, Mr. Martin, the general manager and chief overseer, at their head. Mr. Martin was dressed in white linen; a tall, slim, wiry, alert man, with black turned-down mustaches; inclined to be a trifle insolent, but very competent.

He took off his wide soft hat, which he wore at a rakish angle, and mopped his forehead with a silk handkerchief. "Here they come," he said unenthusiastically.

The coach swung around the circle before the house and stopped. McNab, the ancient butler, who despite his dark face wore an incongruous Highland name due to the Gaelic settlement of the country to the west, stepped forward and opened the door. There was a sigh of expectation. Jeremiah, lankier, grimmer, more tight-lipped than usual, travel-stained and slightly moist, descended blinking into the sunlight, and behind him appeared the slim, dove-gray figure of his wife.

"Welcome, Mr. Blanton!" said Martin gallantly. "You will find everything quite ready for your occupancy, Mrs. Blanton . . . allow me, ma'am." He came forward in welcome.

"You—are?" said Jeremiah.

"Martin, sir; your manager."

"Oh, yes. Well, Mr.—er, Maxim, have Mrs. Blanton shown to her room. . . . She is fatigued by the long journey."

"Martin, sir." The overseer remained bland.

"Mr. Martin." Jeremiah's manner was determinedly formal.

Jeremiah's rigid face and attitude of disapproval did not relax. He surveyed the assembled slaves without interest, and then following his wife and Martin, went up the long flight of brick steps that led to the terrace, and from there, up the shallow wooden steps to the great pillared porch of the house. His black figure lost itself in the shadows. The door opened and closed. He was inside his house. . . . It was three years later that the idea of the gardens came to him.

These three years had been in many ways years of disappointment to Jeremiah. He had found himself spiritually and physically at a loss. Physically he had not enough to do to satisfy the long hard muscles bequeathed him by pioneering ancestors, and spiritually his well-laid plans had gone astray. Martin was a most efficient manager; under his direction the plantation continued to prosper and the rotation of spring, summer, autumn, and winter passed with an automatic precision that resembled more the glittering infallibilities of machinery than the incertitudes of nature. Jeremiah pocketed his increasing profits and grew, if anything, sterner. In his bleak soul he was afraid of Martin. The man's skill and knowledge and hardy audacity abashed him. There was, when you came down to it, nothing to do except to ride around and inspect fields and assume an appearance of overlordship that was but a husk of the reality. And spiritually, the negroes had not taken kindly to the bare, white little chapel Jeremiah had built and in which at first he preached every Sunday. Jeremiah's ideas of religious worship were not suited to their colorful souls. Of course he could have enforced attendance, but debating this in his mind, he decided that such coercion would be placing a further emphasis upon the fact of a slavery which still troubled him greatly. He began to confine his theological efforts to ministering to the material comforts of the people dependent upon him, a task in which his wife Dorcas had long been active. Eventually they both began to attend, rather shamefacedly, the small Episcopalian parish church four miles distant. It was either this or else giving up church-going entirely, and Jeremiah consoled himself by the fact that the parish church was such a small church, and the services so simple, and the pews so uncomfortable, that a man felt almost as if he were worshiping in an edifice where the truth of religion was not so clouded.

He and Dorcas saw few people. "Holy Oak" was a lonely and self-contained place. There were few neighbors and these few were widely scattered, and Jeremiah and Dorcas were aware that courteous as these neighbors were, and would be to a Blanton and his wife, they none the less regarded these newcomers as creatures of an outlandish derivation. The neighbors went to Charleston or Richmond for their gayety, but Jeremiah and Dorcas once a year returned to Boston, where, for a month or two, they refreshed themselves in the bracing moral atmosphere of New England and, as far as Jeremiah was concerned, caught fresh colds.

It was on one of these trips that stopping off with a cousin, a Mr. Braithwhite, in Baltimore, Jeremiah had a glimpse of the heaven he was subsequently to create.

Mr. Braithwhite was a rose-fancier and an importer of exotic plants, and his most recent importations were some glossy self-reliant bushes which he spoke of as azaleas. He had brought them over from England. "And yet," he had added, "they grow wild all over our mountains. They are not so different, after all, from our Rhododendron ponticum or Rhododendron catawbiense, except that they have been greatly beloved and cared for and crossed with their cousins of China and Japan and India. It shows what love and kindliness and attention will do, doesn't it?"

He sighed. He was a little, plump, rosy-faced man; a great traveler; and he endured Jeremiah, as he endured every one else, because he was too kindly not to endure him. He had a way, however, of looking quickly up at Dorcas with a puzzled, sidelong intentness.

"Stop off again on your way South in the spring," he continued, "and I'll show them to you in bloom. I am not quite sure that this is the best climate for them. There are several gentlemen from Charleston greatly interested. Perhaps they would do well with you also."

Jeremiah decided to stop. For a long time the garden at "Holy Oak" had been bothering him; he did not know why, for gardens had never bothered him in Gadsboro, but this particular garden did. It was too much like an empty treasure-chest; like one of those empty treasure-chests he had known in his father's home. The background was there; long hedge-bordered walks, stretches of green turf, a little lake of somber wine-colored water, great groves of live-oak from which the gray Spanish moss drooped like the ashes of wistaria; but the spirit was lacking; cohesiveness; any infusion of purpose. Jeremiah had told himself that this was due—and his homesickness as an adjunct of it—to a lack of variegated color, of simple brilliant flowers, of homely, sweet-smelling herbs, such as he had known in the brief summers of Gadsboro; and there were moments when he longed painfully for gray small rocks thrusting themselves up through the medley of July.

Rather furtively he had planted some sweet-william and phlox and pansies and marigolds, but when these bloomed he had been disappointed. The sweet-william and phlox and pansies and marigolds seemed, somehow, out of place; the garden remained as it had been—haunted, postulant and supplicatory. Jeremiah was annoyed; he was afraid the climate of the South was beginning to have upon him its enervating effect.

Reveneered with New Englandism, black except where the dust had collected in the wrinkles of his coat and trousers, he appeared before Mr. Braithwhite two months later. It was a warm day.

Mr. Braithwhite's gardens slept in perfume and color; there was a great going to and fro of bees. Jeremiah and his cousin turned a corner.

Jeremiah stopped, his long upper lip, with the little beads of perspiration upon it, trembling.

Before him was a cloud of flame; a dawn-rose annunciation of beauty; something that hung between the blue of the sky and the green of the grass like the opalescent wings of a ship setting sail at sunrise.

"Are those the azaleas?" Jeremiah asked finally in a small voice.

"Yes," said Mr. Braithwhite.

Jeremiah did not speak again for a long moment.

"They are like the Rose of Sharon!" he said softly. He continued to twist together his harsh shiny-knuckled hands.

After a while he asked: "Do you think there is anything wrong—er—Nathaniel, in a clergyman devoting himself to a garden? That is—er—a retired clergyman?"

Mr. Braithwhite's lively eyes showed signs of laughter, and then suddenly grew sad. "Far from it, my dear Jere-

miah," he said gravely. "I can think of no more holy or
fitting task. 'For I am come into my garden, my sister,
my spouse, I have gathered my myrrh with my spice; I
have eaten my honey-comb with my honey; I have drunk
my wine with my milk: eat, O friends; drink, yea, drink
abundantly, O beloved.' I will send you some bushes," he
concluded in a matter-of-fact voice.

Jeremiah flushed. "Oh, no, thank you!" he said hastily.
"There is no reason for that. I will procure them myself."

It occurred to Mr. Braithwhite that the figure of Jason
and his Golden Fleece, or perhaps better, the figure of
Sir Perceval and The Grail, showed itself in many and
strange reincarnations.

And Jeremiah did collect his own plants; he collected
them all over the world wherever they were to be found.
Dorcas, whenever she was able to do so, went with him.
The cities and countries through which they passed seemed
to have made little impression upon them except for the
purposes of Jeremiah's voyages. They remembered nothing of London, only a tulip-garden or two in Holland;
and the fact that there was an opera in Paris escaped
them entirely, nor would they have gone to see it even if
their religious scruples had permitted. They drifted about
Europe in the tumultuous years following 1848 without
the vaguest perception that they were witnessing history.
In India they passed near the Taj Mahal and never knew
it was there. But they met some missionaries. Meanwhile,
Jeremiah's assortium grew: expanded like a trumpet-vine
covering the brown and green restraint of a tree. There
were pink azaleas the color of little clouds in the morning;
there were azaleas the color of a stormy sunset; there were
azaleas red as the blood of sacrifice; azaleas of the curious
almost fawn rose of a young girl's lips (when natural);

and white azaleas whose blanched perfection seemed to withdraw into itself scornfully at the prismatic flamboyancy of gayer relatives.

The gardens of "Holy Oak" were possessed with brilliant petals that reflected themselves in the quiet waters of the lake and lost themselves like the thin outer edge of flame beneath the festooned ashes of the live-oaks.

Jeremiah was always home in April when the azaleas bloomed, and Dorcas, with the thoughtfulness of a true partner and wife, somehow always managed to give birth to her children at about the same time. Her coöperation was frequent. In the fifteen years between 1843 and 1858 she gave birth to seven children, five of whom died. The cemetery at "Holy Oak," situated on a small island between two sluggish canals and overhung with trees whose moss, under the circumstances, seemed appropriately funereal, received almost as many additions in proportion as did Jeremiah's gardens. It was a rich soil growing richer. But enough children survived to carry on the purposes of this recital and the purposes of that strange intention which resolves that children should be born at all.

Dorcas became thinner and more silent; Jeremiah also became thinner, but strangely enough, in his latter years, developed a new garrulousness. He attended numerous meetings of horticulturists and was famous for his wealth, his eccentricities, and the impassioned speeches, interlarded with scriptural quotations, in which he indulged at any moment, appropriate or otherwise. He was called "Blanton of Holy Oak," and the title that ten years before would have seemed to him a godless affectation, now did not displease him. Good fortune had clothed him with a sort of gangling self-assurance. He could not abide contradiction except from Martin, and this he seldom provoked, because in Martin's presence he seldom ventured an opinion. He had even ceased worrying about slavery. Like Aristotle, he had come to the conclusion that great civilizations are built upon the enforced labor of inferior men.

Only once in all these years had his world needed questioning, and then only for a short time, and then, because of an incident so abnormal, so startling, so beside anything he had ever heard or experienced, that subsequently he was able to dismiss it from his mind as a man would the misty grotesques of fever.

This is what had happened. Jeremiah had gone out of his house one moonlit night in April—this was ten years after his coming to "Holy Oak," seven years after he had started his garden. He had kissed Dorcas and sent her up to her room. But as for himself, he was not yet ready for bed, for he wanted to walk and see his azaleas by night; wanted to smell the drowsy perfume that was like dusk itself.

The gardens shimmered in the yellow light; the masses of flowering bushes—still small individually; by no means the wilderness of bloom they were to become in later generations—seemed caught by some expectancy of the hour, some moment before the moment when a secret tale, mysterious but translucent, is related; under the live-oak trees the ground was spread with a magic tapestry. Jeremiah walked slowly, his hands clasped behind his back, turning his head from side to side; a quaint somber figure, like a detached and migratory shadow. A mocking-bird broke suddenly into song. At the end of half an hour, Jeremiah retraced his steps and entered the house and went soberly up to his room.

He opened the door quietly lest he disturb his wife, and

then, with a hollow feeling, as if all but his bones had dropped away from him, he stepped back against the door so that he was once more in the shadow. He was not sure that he was not seeing a ghost. His hand bit into the glass knob until its hard edges cut him.

The room was filled with a soft radiance that made the opposite walls look diaphanous and unenclosing. Along the wide, open windows the white muslin curtains hung motionless. The only solidity was the black bulk of the great four-poster bed. A recurrent breath of perfume, vague and hesitant, compounded of moonlight and azaleas and wild plum and honeysuckle, rose and fell. The mocking-bird sang. And at the heart of this witchery of light and shadow and inhalation, danced a silver figure slowly, its arms outspread. About its shoulders dusky hair hung like a cloud.

Jeremiah Blanton pressed closer to the door; the blood slowly suffusing his horror-stricken eyes and beginning to sing in his temples. . . . This was his wife; this was the woman to whom he had been married eleven years; the mother of his four children, three of them dead; a woman of thirty-five; a godly woman; and she was dancing naked in the moonlight!

At first he did not know what to do. The dark fears of forefathers not so remote chilled his heart. For all he knew, this might be sorcery; an overtaken nightmare; a changeling with whom all unsuspecting he had shared his life. Perhaps if he stepped forward the silver column, which was his wife, would sink in ashes at his feet, or even worse, take wings into the night, leaving behind a question forever unanswered and a screaming terror of the mind. Then Jeremiah's better sense prevailed and his lips tightened. This figure was not alarming, it was merely outrageous. (As a matter of fact, it was only pathetically slim and childlike.) Jeremiah's mind did not form the following words, yet he experienced a sense of astonishment that Dorcas, seen this way, was still so young and urgent and wind-blown. Wind-blown was not his adjective; neither was urgent—he had never used such adjectives in his life; but he had an impression of wildness and youth. He had another sensation as well, an even more disturbing one; a sudden quick rippling of the heart. Possibly in the remote past some of his seafaring ancestors had loved women who had danced before them this way in the dusks of tropic twilights.

Jeremiah stifled his heart—in fact, he refused to understand it; he stepped forward, an avenging fury.

"Dorcas!" he said in a terrible voice.

She paused, and he thought he could hear the startled beating of her pulses. She seemed to shrink into herself, as if the necromantic metamorphosis he had dreaded was about to take place, and then, without a word, without even an exclamation, in utter silence, she went over to the bed and picking up her nightgown, thick and long and buttoned to the throat, slipped it on.

"Get down and pray," said Jeremiah icily; "and ask God to forgive you. I will see you later!"

He found his way blindly back to the garden. Where the tracery of the live-oaks was thickest he knelt down.

"O God," he murmured, "O King of All, who knows the hearts of thy servants, and their comings in and goings out, interpret for me this shame and blackness. . . . But do not blame her, O God—do not blame her too much, for she is a woman and weak. Yea, the fault is mine. I have fallen away too much from the straight and narrow path; I have eaten of the flesh-pots; I have erred too much in

the ways of softness and the world. In the beauty of tem-
poral things I have forgotten the beauty of the life ever-
lasting. Help me, O God; help me and let me find again
the way!"

Into the silence that fell after he had ceased, the presence of the garden seemed to step once more; shining, absorbed, passionate. Jeremiah got to his feet and blinked
back at the radiance. Then a slow thought came to him.
. . . The trouble with Dorcas, he reflected, was that she
was not sufficiently occupied. She had had no children for
considerably over two years. She should have more children. It would be his Christian duty to see to that. In his
selfish pursuit of his azaleas he had neglected her spiritual
guidance. Women without children were incalculable. He
would go up and speak to her about it at once. . . . And
never again was the subject of her madness mentioned between them.

This was in 1853, and in 1859, when he was sixty years
old, the Reverend Jeremiah Blanton died; and a year
later his wife, Dorcas, as if there was very little left in
life to hold further her curiosity, followed his example.

It was fortunate that Jeremiah died when he did, for
within two years his heart would have been torn in a manner more terrible than any he had ever imagined. His
fundamental instincts would have found themselves at war
with his recently acquired habits of thought, and probably he would have fallen into the unenviable position of
those Southern landholders who, brought up north of the
Mason and Dixon line, were unable either to desert their
states or their nation. As it was, he departed this life fully
convinced that the talk of secession was merely the idle
chatter of the hot-headed politicians of a neighboring
state. Possibly it was also fortunate that he did not live

to see Jeremiah II, now a youth of sixteen, drinking iced whiskey with Mr. Martin on the back porch of a summer evening. Mr. Martin was by now a gray, distinguished, bitter-tongued man of fifty-two, with no morals whatsoever outside of business hours.

With Jeremiah II we have little to do, nor with Dorcas II, his sister, who married ten years later, and moved to Savannah, and died angrily of the fever. Jeremiah II had the misfortune to belong to a war generation, a fact which makes a man historically important but individually uninteresting. It is the generation following a war that rewards study. Second lieutenants are magnificent but too epochal; too much made and ruined by events too great for them. They cease to become men and become symbols; and try as they may, in the nuances of their souls, they remain symbols always, never quite getting over what they imagine they have got over.

Jeremiah II had no such doubts as would have troubled his father. At the first signs of hostility he joined a cavalry regiment and four years later was discharged a captain. He was a black-haired white-faced man, completely semitropical. When he returned to "Holy Oak," although he was only twenty-four, he was an old man; his digestion ruined, his left arm practically useless, his veins full of rheumatism. He seldom spoke except in expletives. The bland Mr. Martin, a full colonel, had been killed at the battle of Cold Harbor.

Jeremiah married a girl from Virginia and spent most of his time out on the terrace denouncing a fate which, in political matters, had behaved so scurvily. In reality he was better off than the majority of his neighbors, since enough of the Almuce fortune had been left in Northern enterprises to insure against complete ruin. The only important fact of Jeremiah II's life, outside of his having been a soldier, was that he had a son, Jeremy, born in '69, five years before Jeremiah II's death at the age of thirty.

In the third generation the name Jeremiah had been softened to its French derivative. Outwardly the last trace of New England had disappeared.

Mrs. Blanton, used to misfortune and released from the paralyzing influence of her husband, expanded amazingly. She tightened her lips and set herself to the task of bringing up the young Jeremy and running, upon an inadequate income, a large estate. She even found time, and money, pinched together from little surpluses left from other expenditures, to prevent the gardens from returning to a jungle. They were no longer stately, or tended, or obviously a luxury, but they began to have a certain new wild beauty of their own, as if the azaleas were stretching their limbs like dryads broken loose from captivity. The young Jerry lost himself under the pink bloom in the spring. The soft, girlish, tired voice of his mother called him. He remembered that.

But he was a difficult person to bring up; morally, not physically. Physically he grew straight and tall and black-haired like his father; with his father's white face and brilliant eyes and thin features; but morally from an early age he began to exhibit the uncomfortable obstinacy derived from his grandfather and the occasional exciting, but alarming, rages of his grandfather's son. Mrs. Blanton adored him, and feared him, and brooded over him as a mother, especially a mother who has been beautiful and knows something of what men are, will. She need not, however, have feared for his future along certain lines. Under the pallor of the South was the dourest kind of determination when aroused. The dour blood of seafaring men who had ridden out storms and taken slaves, and, when trade was slack, had even sailed perilously close to piracy, and the dour blood of zealots who had enjoyed nothing so much as fighting the devil, particularly when the devil seemed to have an initial advantage. There had been a Blanton famous for his detection and persecution of Molly Brindlekirk, of Haverstraw, Mass., who, without doubt, and while she was bedridden, had at the age of seventy taken to riding a broom and milking the neighbors' cows.

Jeremy developed three senses: a sense of anger—at men who had taken away what was his and didn't care that they had; a sense of selective devotion; the concentration, that is, upon the few people and things he really cared for—his mother and "Holy Oak"; and a sense of indifference to the world at large. The man who has a clear sense of anything is armed as a rule above his neighbors, but the man who has several senses, well defined, is completely embattled; is dangerous to interfere with— has eyes that are far-sighted and not easily confused. Behind such eyes lies the fundamental secret of success; the ability, that is, to endure any amount of present punishment in order to gain a distant end. Men are failures not because they are stupid but because they are not sufficiently impassioned. The really cold man is never successful, for although the successful man may seem cold, somewhere there is a hidden pressure. Only the nonobservant think the Puritan frigid; the Puritan is made of the same stuff as his enemy the convinced drunkard; both are passionate seekers lacking perspective.

Nothing could have kept Jeremy away from New York. As soon as he could think he was impatient to go there, and when he got there, it is doubtful if any man

ever spent sixteen years in such a great city and remained so little intrinsically affected. New York neither
stirred Jeremy's pulses nor compelled his affection. He
made many friends and cared not two straws whether he
ever saw them again or not; and he was careful not to
make any intimate friends except those who would be useful to him in his career. When necessary, he sacrificed a
friend if it were possible to do so without creating an
impression of disloyalty. His looks and his charming man-
ners gained him a reputation for cordiality he did not deserve. In reality his mind sat far off, like an eagle watching a valley, and when the time came it plummeted with
deadly accuracy. Jeremy was not ethical; but then, few
men of the '90s and early 1900s were. The kindly ex-
teriors of today, the small smiling moral speeches, cover,
as a rule, in men over fifty very rapacious young fellows
of three decades ago. Those alive today who were alive
thirty years ago, and who think that the present age has
retrogressed spiritually, have a quaint conception of
locomotion.

And the sardonic point of the jest was that Jeremy deceived those who most thought they were deceiving him;
deceived them by his drawling voice, his courtesy, his
dreamy appearance, and the tradition that the South was
easy-going and shiftless. These qualities and this tradition made for a lowering of guards. Afterward, the in-
jured man was a trifle hazy as to what had hit him; was
inclined to lick the punishing hands like a lion whose
keeper has beaten him.

Jeremy's secret life was as carefully premeditated as
his public life. At times it was necessary for him to get
drunk—life became unendurably lonely, unsatisfactory,
and taut—and when this necessity grew unbearable he

went out and got drunk with white-faced intentness and efficiency. But he never got drunk where anybody could tell about it afterward; and when he was drinking he never did anything else but drink. He was always quite sober when he made love to certain shallow young women and nearly frightened them out of their wits.

During these periods of incandescence his concentration upon the goal of his present life relaxed and the memory of "Holy Oak" surged back into his mind. It was like the opening of the windows of a closed house in spring. Jeremy would see again the flame-colored apotheosis of the garden; the old brick house; the figure of his mother; the little shadowy island between the canals where, below the garlanded live-oaks, the graves of his family thrust up like eternally unanswered question-marks. And he would say to himself: "O God, how is this possible? How is it possible that the finest things in a man's life are mixed up with the worst? Why is it a man understands so much when he's drunk? How is it possible that a man's heart can melt so to his mother and harden to this sort of business? Why can't we see the world as a whole, so that we would no more hurt ourselves or those we do not know well than we would hurt those we love? We are all the same; all equally to be hated or loved. The mother of to-day is only the girl of yesterday; the man you fight is only the little boy of awhile back." Then he would take another drink.

Quite drunk, Jeremy would go home to his boarding-house apartment and, tilting a chair against the wall, would stare at nothing and wrestle with these problems.

The next morning he would wake up very pale and determined and a trifle ill, and go about his business as if nothing had happened. He forced himself to forget entirely, and his shakiness only added to his zest for work by giving him something more to overcome.

Occasionally his mother visited New York and at rare intervals he managed to run down to "Holy Oak" for a week or two. He would have liked to have had his mother live with him, but he knew she would never leave her wardenship, and he did not ask her.

Meanwhile, he was prospering greatly. At thirty, he was well-to-do; at thirty-one, by a stroke of fortune and a not too great scrupulousness as to where he stood when it fell, he became an exceedingly rich man. He allowed himself some privileges. The first of these was to marry a blond, quiet, gray-eyed girl with whom he had been in love for five years. Her name was Cecily Sloan and she belonged to a family of social pretensions and little money. Jeremy and she made a remarkable-looking couple; he dark and straight, and she slim and upright and appealing, something about her like a silver-beech tree at noon.

A year or so after his marriage, Jeremy said to her in his soft, caressing voice: "Honey, you wouldn't mind very much if you left all this and went back with me to that place of mine, would you? You see, I've got to go, because"—he finished rather obscurely—"my going there is the reason for my coming to New York."

She smiled, and then, as if she was listening to something very young and ingenuous, touched his hair with a little pinching touch.

"You know less about women," she said soothingly, "than any other man on earth. . . . And that's saying a good deal. Men are queer. They'll never get over worrying about where to live on account of their wives, when it would be so much easier and cheaper just to keep on loving them. The only time a woman cares where she lives is when she's stopped caring for a man, and the only time she stops caring for a man, if she ever has really cared, is when he stops caring for her. You invented caves, we didn't—we're wild and itinerant."

Which was fairly advanced for a quiet, gray-eyed girl of that period.

But if Jeremy knew nothing about women, he had begun to learn something about life. That something he had learned the previous winter. Up until then he had believed that life was exactly what a man—especially a man like himself—wished it to be. Afterward, for all time, he realized there are certain outer barriers before which the human will, no matter how adamant, falls back baffled and amazed; that intention and eagerness and determination have their limits. He learned all this because, one day, sitting in his office, a telegram was handed to him. He opened the envelope carelessly, and then let it fall to the floor while he stared out of the window.

Across the roofs of the near-by office-buildings, serrated here and there by the long shafts of the earlier skyscrapers, he could see, beneath a soft February sky, the sparkling ribbon of the river, on it a steamer putting out to sea. Suddenly he could no longer see the roofs or the sky or the steamer.

He got to his feet and began to walk up and down. His heart was a crumbling fire inside of him. "O God!" he said to himself. "O God!" and he picked up a book and hurled it from him. The desires of mankind seemed to him pitifully feeble. . . .

He went down to "Holy Oak" that afternoon. His mother was buried two days later. A breathless, wintry, gray day when the hanging moss had an appearance of watching rigidity. Jeremy wished it was April with the azaleas out. . . .

It was two years after this that Jeremy found himself able to leave New York.

Jeremy was very gay; he hadn't been so gay for years. All the way South, the car-wheels seemed to be saying to him: "You're done! You're done! You're done! You've just begun! begun! begun!" He perplexed Cecily by his youth and unexpectedness and mischief.

He watched constantly her rapt face as she stared out of the window. He thought to himself: "It's all behind you, my son, that damned city! All behind you! No more of it for you, except when you go up there with Cecily and buy it for her."

He had arranged his affairs so that the date of their arrival should fall in April. The train came to the little station that served "Holy Oak," and he saw Melchior, his colored man, waiting with a team. His heart almost choked him. This was what he had been waiting for; this was the end of his journey. He handed Cecily to the platform.

At the end of a mile drive, the carriage turned through the white gate-posts and rolled slowly up the long avenue between the live-oak trees, as, sixty years before, the coach of Jeremiah I and Dorcas had rolled. The live-oaks looked as trim and well-tended as their shaggy age would permit —for three years Jeremy had kept a large force of men restoring them, and pruning and grading. At the end of the avenue, above the terrace, the old ruddy house, facing the sinking sun, was like a giant wine-cup held up in welcome.

"Oh, Jerry!" said Cecily breathlessly.

"We'll go up and dress and bathe," he retorted indifferently. "And then you come down and I'll show you the gardens."

She shook her head smilingly. "But I want to see the house first."

"No, you come down. The azaleas will be in bloom. There're some nice Cherokee roses, too."

He was cunningly unconcerned. He chuckled inwardly at his success in deceiving her into thinking that the azaleas were nothing very extraordinary after all; a few bushes planted by his grandfather. He enjoyed her implicit faith in his deception.

He went up-stairs and plunged into the cool soft water of the bath that had been run for him, and changed into a soft shirt and old flannels and a shooting-jacket. The house was full of warm shadows and silvery reflections. When he was through he went down to the terrace and waited for Cecily. He was as impatient as a small boy watching the outcome of a cherished trick.

The sun sank lower; he was afraid Cecily wouldn't be in time to catch the full color; and then he saw her coming toward him, slender and white and golden-haired, the light shining into her gray eyes.

"Come along!" he begged, and took her by the hand and hurried her along the narrow walk where the breast-high hedges of Jeremiah I's time had grown into two walls of concealing greenness. Beyond was a sunken garden where a white mass of the roses he had mentioned spread a delicate carpet.

She wanted to stop here, entranced, but he led her on.

At the end of the sunken garden, beyond a sun-dial of wood carved into the semblance of a Grecian column, was another massive hedge overtopping the view beyond, and in its exact center an opening had been cut, flanked high on either side by privet trained to represent proud and alert guinea-fowl. Jeremy and Cecily skirted the garden, and turned the corner of a bed of roses, and paused in the opening. Five stone steps, lichen-covered, led down to the little wine-colored lake, and across the lake, beneath the spreading plantations of the live-oak, the evening radiance of the azaleas burned.

The moment, the lapse of time since the buds had first opened, the blend of sky and air and shadow, seemed to have struck together into a note so perfect that you knew when its echoes died away not for a long while would such beauty be realized again. Beneath the gray pallor of the Spanish moss blossomed leaping flames that had been caught at their crest by a magic wand and held immovable; a sea of rose conflagration; the heart of the passion in nature you see when the sun sinks in the Occidental ocean. And yet it was a beauty of itself, and, like all true beauty, only to be defined in its own terms; moreover, it was the beauty of a growing thing; transient, changing in a myriad small ways, even as you looked and were unaware of the change. In the wine-colored lake the reflections floated, a mist of rose.

Cecily paused with parted lips, the color rising into her cheeks and then receding, her hand going up to her breast. "You devil!" she said softly to Jeremy. "You wicked, wicked devil!" She turned her smiling face away; her voice was uncertain. "It almost makes you want to cry, doesn't it?" she said.

Jeremy laughed quietly . . . he had found at last complete happiness, permanent and assured. . . . At least, he thought he had. So have many other men.

"Holy Oak" changed as the years passed. Jeremy and Cecily no longer had to go to New York, or Charleston,

or Europe to see people, because people came to see them.
Some of the surrounding places were bought by rich
Northerners, and with the emergence of the motor-car the
world became incredibly foreshortened. Jeremy could get
into his big car and if the weather was good, in two days,
or three, be almost anywhere he wanted to be. In an instant life grew more magic and at the same time possessed
of infinitely more capacity for boredom. Jeremy had always had men and their wives down for the shooting, but
now "Holy Oaks" began to expand into something like
its pre-Revolutionary gayety; and from the growing re-
sorts of Aiken and Camden and Pinehurst friends came to
see "the dear Blantons" and "their marvelous place." The
gardens enjoyed an increasing fame! a fame almost equal
to their neighbors to the south. Strangers made them an
object of pilgrimage. Also there was the young Dorothy,
who in a few years from now—seven, eight . . . would
be wanting house-parties herself.

Long before, Jeremy had made a compromise with himself and his wife, and the devil. It was an old, childish
sort of compromise. You assumed that a thing which
existed did not exist; that something which took place
did not take place; that four or five times a year you
counted out entirely a week or so of excellent, solid,
twenty-four-hour-a-day days. You erased them, that is,
as you would a blur of chalk from a blackboard. Or rather,
in reality, the other way around, for the blur was black
and the board was white. The year came to have only three
hundred and thirty, or three hundred and thirty-seven
days, instead of three hundred and sixty-five.

When Jeremy had first found this old calenture of desire coming upon him he had been contemptuous; he had
refused to believe in it; he had put it down to physical

causes; the relaxation of too much good fortune; not enough exercise. He was a full-grown man, completely master of himself. These uneasy longings were a chimera. Life poured itself into a mold of his own making; it had always been so; always would be so. Never but once had he found anything so intractile that he could not bend it, as it were, between his long sinewy fingers, and that once had been his mother's death. Since then he had obliterated death from his consciousness, limiting his horizon as a fighting-man limits his class. He wanted to forget the conception of defeat. Now here was defeat staring him in the face in a much more subtle guise than ever before. Those nights in New York had been different. He had deliberately planned them; deliberately set out upon them; deliberately left them behind. They had not conquered him; instead, he had used and conquered them. Jeremy did not know that black blood, as said before, is black blood no matter how expressed.

The first time he had gone to Charleston he had made himself the excuse that he wished to consult the library there in connection with a pamphlet he was writing. For a day or so he had kept himself to his task. The weather was very hot; the houses along the Battery slept in a gray haze. The third night, Jeremy had fled along the narrow walled streets like a shadow pursued by shadows. . . .

When he came back to "Holy Oak" he was very much ashamed of himself. Something inside of him had been damaged; not broken, but weakened—a pride, a self-assurance; and he was never to get it back again. It seemed impossible to him that he and Cecily and this other self of his could all exist together in the same house. But they did; and they continued to exist. He never told Cecily, but she knew. Never by word or sign, however, did she show her knowledge except that when his restless spells came upon him her tenderness and solicitude redoubled. Only once was this pretense broken through and that was on a moonlight night when Jeremy had suddenly put his head down on his wife's knees and sobbed. She had said nothing; neither had he. They both wanted to speak, but somehow couldn't. They had been pretending things too long. And as for Jeremy, he dared not break with the burden of his words the wall of protection he felt—quite mistakenly—he had built up between Cecily and that part of him he would not have her know.

The room where this happened was the same room in which Dorcas sixty years before had danced; the moonlight was there; the translucence; the smell of azaleas and wild plum and honeysuckle; even a mocking-bird. But this time it was a Jeremiah who tasted humiliation and not a Dorcas.

Sometimes Jeremy thought he had won this wearying conflict. There were long periods when he was tranquil and absorbed and during which he caught back most of his old self-confidence, and on the whole his personality improved. Relieved of competition, he enlarged; became singularly lovable and gentle and humorous, saving his fierceness for the occasional stranger who crossed him.

Eventually the War came and he bundled off to Washington with his usual precipitant dreaminess, and by means of his position and wide acquaintanceship got himself made a captain in the Quartermaster Corps. Later he was sent to France, where he did something marvelous with garbage, and was decorated, and promoted to a colonelcy, and sent home full of honors and sardonicism. Occasionally the thought of the azaleas had disturbed him.

But Cecily had attended to the azaleas. She was as

capable as his mother and had considerably more to be capable with.

For a few months after Jeremy's return his path proved to be a singularly peaceful one. The break in ordinary routine the war had made, possibly its discipline, had given him apparently a new retention upon himself, a new hold. He began to hope that the sinister strength which so often had beaten him to his knees was beginning to weaken. And then once again, as if to show him that living is largely an oscillation between the conquest of self and defeat by circumstances, he received a telegram. He was in Washington at the time.

He hurried back to "Holy Oak." As he knelt by her bed, Cecily stroked his hair. "Dear Jerry!" she said. "Dear, lovely Jerry. And so beautiful, too; no one knows you the way I do, do they? Dear, lovely, beautiful Jerry. I'm glad I married you and your azaleas. Poor Jerry! Funny Jerry! . . ."

Jeremy decided that life was a matter of building sand castles in the face of a threatening sea. You built your castle, you elaborated it, you made turrets and tunnels and banqueting-halls, and then a wave came and washed it away. Sometimes, if the wave was a very large one, it took you with it and for a while buffeted you in the surf; blinded you; drowned you; until, as if weary with its roughness, it cast you back half dead upon the shore. Whereupon, you got weakly to your feet and built another castle. But you weren't quite so strong as you had been the first time nor quite so enthusiastic. Every one did this, except a few narrow-faced people who, looking about them timorously, went inland and camped upon the farther dunes, safe but uninterested.

Why did you do this? Why in this world did you build

things you knew would be washed away? Was it only because you wished to keep your mind off the constant
menace of the sea and pretend that between it and yourself you were constructing actually a defense?

Dorothy was growing up. Jeremy directed his attentions upon her. Dorothy was seventeen; with bobbed blond
hair and a ravishing, slim figure that looked like a boy's
figure that had suddenly decided to become more gracious.
Dorothy also had the bluest of blue eyes under long lashes
and an assortment of words, gathered at boarding-school,
which made Jeremy wonder how the young of his own
generation had expressed themselves as well as they had.
He was a little afraid of Dorothy; afraid lest some day
she would find him too sentimental and descriptive. Her
conversation was pointed, acute, and Doric; her point of
view direct and sparse. She knew all about life except what
life really is.

Jeremy took Dorothy abroad and stayed there two
years. He was startled, amused, and made a trifle angry
to find that full-grown Englishmen and Italians actually
wanted to marry Dorothy, some of them men of great
position who should have had more serious minds. Jeremy
was a very good-looking man himself at this period; lean,
graceful, sunburned, with iron-gray hair and a black
mustache. Numerous ladies whose ages were as dispropor-
tionate to his as their countrymen's were to Dorothy's cast
languishing eyes upon him, but in vain. Upon his return
from Europe he turned Dorothy over to his mother-in-
law and allowed that excitable lady to give all the dinners
and dances and various other parties for which her starved
soul had been longing. In the spring he took Dorothy
down to "Holy Oak" again.

He had not dared go there before; but he found, once

there, what all mature people find sooner or later, or should find, and that is that a place once greatly beloved may be sad but is never unbearable, since all spirits who have once loved it continue to inhabit it. He became almost happy again. The house was never empty. A blond caravan that got about the country by means of high-powered cars followed Dorothy. The members of it appeared unexpectedly, were very polite to Jeremy—some of them irritatingly polite—wooed the object of their quest with an odd, passionate indifference, and then went away again. The object was equally indifferent. There were also some very nice neighbor boys, who looked just like the other boys and had the same high-powered cars. There was one especially—William Humphrey. Jeremy thought he detected an even more passionate indifference in Dorothy's manner toward William, and took this as a good sign. Dorothy was nineteen.

He was sitting in his library one night reading. The month was April and the azaleas were in full bloom and the windows of the great book-lined room were open. He heard a motor on the drive outside—that would be William. Dorothy had said that he was coming. He heard Dorothy's fresh young voice uttering words of greeting, followed by a silence, followed by something very earnest and low-toned from William; and then Dorothy's voice once more, but this time with a new, excited contralto note in it.

"Here? Just now? Oh, Billy, don't be so absurd! You really mean it? Me? Come out into the garden and we'll talk it over."

Jeremy got to his feet and began to pace up and down. "He's proposing to her, the young pup! Proposing from the front seat of a car! Probably leaning back from the wheel while she's standing up! Well—different times—"

The door of the car opened and shut; William's feet made a creaking sound upon the gravel as he descended to the drive; voices and steps died away.

Jeremy continued to pace the room. Presently the footsteps and the voices returned and crossed the porch and entered the house. They were in the hall just beyond the door.

"Come out into that garden again," said the boy's voice eagerly, "after you've got your coat."

Dorothy's laugh was clear; a small tinkling, slightly metallic bell. "Garden? No more of that garden tonight, my child. It makes you sloppy and hard to control. You take me out in your car and go fast. When we're married we'll live in New York, and see these gardens about once a year and then at high noon. Brr! They're creepy. They remind me of lockets with hair in them. When you've lived with azaleas as much as I have, William, you'll think less of them."

The voices went back to the closet under the stairs, repassed, went outside. There was the sound of the starting of the engine, a rasp of controls, a departing murmur of wheels.

Jeremy had not moved from the spot where he had paused. His head was sunk forward on his chest; his drooping figure had lost its alertness. . . . So this was the final defeat! The final sardonic laughter! His little girl! The symbol of eighty years! Of the lives of six people! And she thought these things!

He turned and walked unseeingly to a window at the back of the room from whose level, above the sunken garden and the hedge beyond, the heart of the real garden was visible. There they were, the azaleas, dreaming under the moon.

Jeremy leaned for a long while upon the sill before his tired brain began to form connected visions. What was this thing? This beauty? This incredible hurt and alleviation? This loveliness that surrounded you and beckoned you and yet could not be made part of you? This thing you smelled, touched, saw, drank in, and yet could not lay hold of? Permanent, encompassing, close; more real than flesh that passed, or laughter that was silenced, or tears that were dried, and yet never completely incorporated? The moving spirit of every man's life; the thing that impelled him; however distorted and base his conception of it might be. What was it? Why did men seek it, when they knew they could only touch the outer hem of its garments?

The moonlight over the azaleas seemed to grow deeper, fuller, more complete.

What was this beauty you never knew until you had almost lost it; you could not feel until you had felt agony and ugliness?

Jeremy, forced back to the inner citadel of his thoughts, saw for the first time clearly what all this had meant to his own race—the repressed lost passions of his grandfather, that grim old man; the broken desires of his father; the quiet radiance of his mother; his own tortured, bitter pursuit. And Cecily! He stretched out his arms.

"My little love!" he said to himself. "My little love!"

They were all there—out in the azaleas. Not as individuals, but more than individuals; greater than individuals; the essence of them; their ultimate yearnings for loveliness. Caught up and made eternal. As his yearnings some day would be. Yes, and Dorothy's too. She and all her pathetic, self-steeled little generation; driven back into themselves, frightened before they were men and women by a horror which, not being able to interpret, they were attempting to forget. But they would learn some day . . . learn about this mystery you never knew until you had almost lost it; could not feel until you had felt agony and ugliness first; could not touch until most of your youth and half your own beauty were gone. . . . Why, the thing was an epitome of his whole country; this beauty, this garden, which was one of its expressions. His scarred, beautiful, blinded, struggling country. The tragic repression of the first decades; the broken passions of the middle period; the half-tender, half-brutal savagery of his own time striving to build securely in a changing world; the hardness of this new generation—hard lest their hearts be touched too greatly.

But it was there eternally, this beauty. It was strong; it did not die; it could not die. It was a sign that there was eternity. Beauty did not die—no, nor love, which was part of it.

He raised his head.

ZONA GALE

LETTING THE STORY DEVELOP

In my own experience a story sometimes comes out of a title and sometimes from a theme, and sometimes from a characterization. For me the best result always comes when I begin to write with no more than one of these pegs on which to hang a story, and when I let the development come as I write. I never make an outline before beginning to write, or at all. I do not often know how a story is "coming out," and repeatedly when a story is printed I have had the experience of being unable to tell, as I reread it, how the action progressed. This refers to definite progress of the action—not of course to theme—or final event.

I think this is the best that I can do; and this of course is of no use at all.

As to rewriting, sometimes I do not rewrite at all, sometimes I merely make inserts. But if I rewrite I do as I always did when I was beginning my work, that is, I make it a practice to rewrite from the beginning.

IN THE LOBBY [1]

"THIS whole love thing isn't enough," said Bruce. "I tell you, it isn't enough."

He stared down the lobby and saw himself on a winter afternoon, fourteen years before, in the street with his two children, and he helpless, so to say, to stem them. When Lois ran ahead, he had quickened his loping step, stooped, and dabbed at her shoulder, apparently unaware that she was unaware of him. He had whirled and threatened, "Come, now!" when little Larry fell behind. One passing could have detected that finding himself alone with these two, Bruce lost his own finished creaturehood, died, rose as their attendant, and existed as an amateur.

[1] From *Yellow Gentians and Blue,* by Zona Gale, copyright, 1927, by D. Appleton and Company. Reprinted by permission of the author and of the publishers.

One, passing, spoke to her chauffeur and drew to the curb—a dovelike woman, already in a ripening youth, who looked on the children with the look which was intended for Bruce. She said:

"You've not forgotten tonight?"

He had. But remembering, he vowed his remembrance. And Miss Anna Wild, with her brooding way of attention to the children, to him, drove on, with his negative, unconcerned eyes tormenting her, like a positive.

He had gone up one step to his habitable white house, and worked the children into the passage. The passage was right, paneled, discreetly mirrored; the nurse maid was right, by her voice, her eyelids, her quiet, a genius at servitude. When Larry bellowed, "See you tonight, Father," and Lois hit Larry in the head to gain the balustrade side of the stair, this maid hadn't a rebuke; she had: "Only fancy what's for tea." All three vanished.

Bruce had gone into the room where his tea table stood. This room also was right, it rested him as could the cherishing brightness of something happy to think about. But there had been nothing happy to think about, and the very charm of the room had beaten at him like a desire. The whole house had charm; the children, too. But Fanny wasn't there any more, and he was only thirty-six years old.

Overcome by this climax, he had stood staring at his tea table. In a little while Mrs. Beryl would come in and pour. Her cousin would come too, and probably Cory. Cory would hate that hour, and so would he himself. The women would perhaps hate it; only, he thought, they wouldn't know that they did, having known hatred of so much for so long that pretense had now taken its place, unconsidered. But Fanny had loved the tea hour. Had she? Certainly she had. Little thing, in her delicate clothes, living for his love and without another idea—no, no, he didn't mean that; but she *had* loved him. To have lost her after five years of love was ludicrous. He had faced a wall of amazement over which two years had not let him look. From the panels her portrait regarded him, remote, amused. How could she be amused when she was dead, and when he was left here without her and adventureless? He had gone close to the portrait, had remembered her kisses, had her in his arms. He said over her name, "Fanny, Fanny, Fanny." Its reality was a giddiness.

Mrs. Beryl had come into the room, followed by her cousin and Cory. And as he looked into the eyes of the cousin, Lucy Beryl, Bruce had seen that here was a woman whom also he could love.

He had been stupefied, then seized with an excitement beyond anything that he had ever known. Love for Fanny had been the fruit of propinquity. This was the fruit of something else. As strong as his excitement throbbed his sickening sense of guilt. To love some one who was not Fanny? It was even more improbable than had been Fanny's death.

Tea went on. Mrs. Beryl poured, and he had noticed that she powdered her hair so that it should boast of the youth of her face. Her opals had winked like the eyes of a fox. Having no conversation, she had learned emphasis, and the last word of every sentence escaped her with its vowel trained like a seal. He liked her, laughed at her, looked at Lucy Beryl and trembled. She was as smooth and clear and perfumed as transparent soap. And her little sentences spread from her like lather.

"Can't we have the children in?" Cory had demanded

shortly. "Jolly little beggars." Bruce could have embraced old Cory. Bruce wanted to show his children to Lucy Beryl. His children. She did not second the suggestion, and he liked her indifference. Mrs. Beryl said: "Oh, Brucie, do let us! Do-o!" For "o" was such a becoming vowel.

Lois and Larry had come in, and for conduct they dealt in the unbelievabilities, the naïve, the saucy, the devilish, all composed, too, with their courtesy. So far as they had been taught, they were irreproachable; their irregularities lay in their improvisations. But there was one improvisation for which Bruce had forgiven his Lois.

"Daddy," she said, "are you sad like you look? Larry and I betted. I betted. . . ."

Mrs. Beryl's look enveloped Bruce, appealed to Lucy, and lit on Cory, who crunched a nut.

"They are motherless, the darlings," she explained to Lucy, who blushed. A pretty moment. Mrs. Beryl could not keep her hands off it.

"Go and ask Miss Lucy if she won't tell you a story sometime, lo-vies," she said.

"Know any?" Larry demanded, wheeling on Miss Lucy. "I mean any that are any good?"

"I'm afraid not," said Lucy Beryl. "People always have to tell stories to me."

"Aren't you growned-up?" demanded Lois.

"No," she said, and her eyes danced on Bruce. "Is anybody?" she asked him.

"I hope not," he said gently. He had been enchanted.

"I don't understand children very well, I'm afraid," she said, and Mrs. Beryl looked as if she knew, but was afraid Bruce wouldn't know, that Lucy, from confusion, was lying; but Bruce was thinking merely that this angel was above pretending to swallow his children alive for his sake. Still, when they kissed her as they went away, she did without fervor kiss them rather at large and on the ear; he noticed that. But by then the hour had become, he could recall, a swinging censer whose smoke coursed curling through his veins. When they took their leave, he had gone up to his room and entered it a stranger.

The room was small and sweet and colored. The covers, the linen, the draperies, were of Fanny's choosing. She had liked blue. He stood in the doorway that night and wondered how the room would look in rose.

He had dined alone, and had the children down. He looked at them with anxiety. Lois was six, Larry was five. Soon there would be for them school, college. Somebody must help them, he was not doing enough. At dessert he had leaned to them and admonished them: "You two must be good—you must be good." When Lois returned languidly, "Wha' for, Daddy?" he felt terror. Already was he too late?

He barely remembered his engagement with Miss Anna Wild, and to keep it, late in the evening, dragged himself from his dream. He telephoned her first to ask if he might still come, heard the patience and sweetness of her voice, was rested by it. He thought with pleasure—the pleasure of the man literally caught away from himself, as we say, that he would tell her, this old friend, what had happened to him. Perhaps then he could believe that it had happened, for Anna Wild had known Fanny. And now the name of Fanny was no longer a giddiness, but instead seemed to steady him, or, it might be, rather to take him aback. He had resolutely repeated the name Fanny as he walked under the stars.

He remembered that the night had come in a whirl of

wind and the cold. Streams of air tore through the darkness, their thin spray switching and stinging, and from inner coverts broke and regathered a thin roar as from some ambiguous beast too old and worn to care to roar. From the core of the cold blew an odor of clean, far plains, tended by the sweep of snow and the killing quality of frost, an odor like the odor of frozen furrows, the pang of spring. Nor was the spring far distant, for already this turmoil was behaving like music, with a recurrent quiet. At such intervals, cloudy spring stars looked on and then withdrew, as if to attend on brighter immediacies. All this came back to him as pungently present as remembered perfume.

Before Anna Wild he had sat down in his tremendous preoccupation. Usually he talked to her about himself. Come to think of it, even though he had been trying to talk of Lucy Beryl, Anna could not have observed the slightest difference. For he had been telling how Lucy Beryl affected *him*. Such had been his conception of talking about Lucy. He had described her by relating how much he needed her, and had said, "My children, they are motherless." Anna had been a receiving station for his analysis of his own case. He had hardly seen her plain, dark face, her careful hair. She was an imperishable-looking lady, and he had always loved the perishables. "I wanted to tell you about Lucy Beryl," he had said lamely. "It is so overwhelming a thing to feel that I could ever again think of any woman save Fanny." She did not say: "You are not thinking of any other woman. You are thinking of yourself." She said merely: "Dear old Brucie!" and he had thought what a brick Anna was. "I don't know how to get along without you," had been his way of expressing his admiration; and she had said dryly that she would still be there, that it wasn't *she* who had changed, and had asked after the children. When she did this the look in her face made him pause. He could see that look now. It was a look such as a traveler wears who faces a memento of home. "Why don't you adopt a child or two, Anna?" he had asked, and she had questioned: "Yours?" But he had said no, that *he* needed them. What sort of mother would Lucy Beryl make, did she think? (If he had been as crude in society as he was on that hearth, he now thought grimly, he would have been voted back to pre-cave days before man noticed that a woman was peering about for a shelter other than the sky.)

But he had continued to look at Anna. He had seen her tenderness. He had seen it turn from the thought of the children to the thought of him. Afar off he saw, as a man sees a town where he does not intend to tarry. He was dazzled, as by a glitter of sparks which fell from the sky and did not burn him. Good old Anna!

When shortly he had opened his house on the sound for a week-end, and had down Mrs. Beryl and Lucy and Cory, he invited Anna, in the spirit of unto the least this was the least that he could do.

On the first afternoon at tea Lois and Larry were brought in by their admirable English nurse and handed about like curios. It was as if he himself had been saying, "I picked these up with Fanny." They had behaved as the angels behave, had submitted to being touched by strange hands, had looked small and helpless and evanescent, dancing on the ledge overhanging the abyss of the past, the future, heredity, hazard, and diet. The firelight played upon all the people, made them quick with false motion, rich with red and orange, drunken with warmth, and

magical with difference. He remembered that Larry had
played with a little cloth flower, had showed it to Cory,
whom he adored, had whispered to his father to ask if he
might give it to Cory, had found a box and bestowed on
Cory the flower in an excess of dignity and denial of self,
and then had burst into tears for the sake of the lost
flower. Cory had said, "Oh, I say, old chap, take it back!"
Lucy Beryl had cried, "Oh, give him back his flower!"
and she had looked beautiful and flushed and indignant
as she had folded Larry in her arms. Bruce recalled his
enchantment at her bright head bowed above his boy's
head. Then he had heard Anna Wild saying:

"Bruce, don't you think it's important not to let him
have back that flower? It's really rather crucial for him,
isn't it?"

"You're right," Bruce had said, and cried: "Son, you've
given away the flower, you know. That's all. . . ."

He saw Lucy Beryl charmingly pout, he saw the quiet
power in the face of Anna Wild. And on no more than
that cloth flower in his son's hand, it had come to him as
by words written in fire on the air that Lucy was no more
a mother for his children than a cup of tea, but that Anna
Wild was one of those women who mother the very apples
on the trees. Mrs. Beryl, who discerned that her niece was
failing, said under her voice that Lucy was far too sympathetic; but he saw through Mrs. Beryl as if he had tasted
the blood of a covey of dragons.

His eyes being opened and his ears unsealed, he lived
through those three days of the house party like a creature
without a cuticle, raw to every contact. He watched his
new love with his children, saw her spoil them, puzzle them,
tease them, lie to them, all adorably and damnably. Knowing little of his children's nervous systems, he learned

much by watching the sportive bombardments of that beloved, in her play with Lois and Larry. When he came on
her, at dusk, wrapped in a sheet and telling them a ghost
story, her sweet voice undulating in silvery wails, he stood
stricken. This sheet she threw from her face, stood meshed
in it, breathless and sparkling, a child, still shuddering,
circled by each arm. He throbbed at her presence and
winced at her performance, after an ancient manner in
men. On a pretext he carried the children off, and that
night he sat by their beds long after they slept. With
social values, with modern values of the individual's
motions of duty toward society, Bruce was not much concerned; but the immemorial need of the parent to foster
the offspring was in his blood like passion. It was in that
hour that he read his own course.

On the station platform, the morning that his house
party returned to town, Bruce, as one who has died and
is henceforth divorced from earth, watched all those pos-
tures, those half looks, those abstractions of Lucy Beryl,
and knew that he was seeing them for the last time. By
the station door Mrs. Beryl asked him to dine with them
on Lucy's last evening, and he accepted, knowing quite
well what was hoped of him, knowing too, that he would
send some excuse to that dinner and knife a dream, for
him already dead or dying. It required days for the dream
to die—days spent down in the country alone.

In six months he asked Anna Wild to be his wife. That
was what he asked her, but what he meant was merely,
"Will you be their mother?" And she knew.

Sitting now with Cory in the lobby of that Florida
hotel, he was thinking of his wife. She had been to him
such a wife as few men have, he thought, and to his children such a mother as they had not known even in Fanny.

But he had never loved her; he had loved Lucy Beryl. And now, after these fourteen years, with Lois married and Larry gone round the world, here he was, at fifty, married to a woman whom he did not love and never had loved. She had done an admirable job, but he was bored by her. And a quarter century of her stared him in the face.

He tried to think that he was in no worse case than millions of men, but he admitted that he was, because with her he never had known romance. All of romance that he had seen in his life was still his five years with Fanny. It was impossible that he should die in such poverty of experience. He felt richly justified in looking for something else, or so he told himself at that moment. He felt richly justified in his present occupation of looking for Lucy Beryl.

He had deliberately suggested to Anna that they come to Miami, and he had chosen the hotel where he knew that Lucy Beryl lived. He had invited Cory to go, too—Cory who had looked on for fourteen years and, if he had made deductions, had always kept still about them.

This first night in the hotel dining room Bruce had watched the door unceasingly. Anna, plump and content and completely imperishable, looked on, saying nothing, and if she divined, she did not reveal anything at all. She had now the family-off-my-hands look of fifty. Through dinner Bruce had seen her plump throat, the wide parting of her hair, her hand cut by his wedding ring. He thought of Lucy Beryl. If he had married her, his children might now both be in jail. Or would they? They had his blood, and Fanny's. Why hadn't he thought of that in time? And now after dinner, with Cory there in the lobby, this thought recurred to him passionately as his eyes followed Anna, who was looking at the lobby art. He saw that round head, that profile tilted estimatingly before a Victorian waterfall at sunset.

Fourteen years, a quarter of a century to carry.

The elevator door clicked and slid and clicked again. From its threshold stepped a woman in corn color, her light hair bulking about her ears. She was large, snugly fitted above the thick, straight waist, slow, very aware. One might discern at once how, forty-five years earlier, her baby pictures had looked.

"There she is," said Cory.

Bruce stared. Unmistakably, there she was. Lucy Beryl Sanderson, he remembered. And on her track came a drawn man, with a mothy look, but not from choice. There she was, his Lucy Beryl, and here was her husband.

With no thought of Cory or of his Anna, Bruce got to his feet and followed not far from the drawn man's side. This man Bruce barely saw. His own eyes were on Lucy, her indolent turn of the head, her ripe shoulders, as smooth as soap. The air of her came back to him, and he breathed it.

The three passed Anna, intent on her Victorian waterfall, her round head tilted appraisingly, now this way and now that. And as they passed her, the drawn man brushed roughly by Bruce, who turned and regarded him, and was stupefied to discern that this man was staring hungrily at Anna, at Anna, who looked so like a dove.

In that instant Bruce could feel himself in the drawn man's shoes, could feel those fourteen years of proximity to this great flaxen Lucy, and those twenty-five years of her to carry. And yoked to Lucy, even as was this drawn man, he saw himself passing Anna, as a stranger in some lobby, and turning to look approvingly at her dovelike presence.

The words which Bruce was framing for Lucy died. He wavered, looked once more at the retreating flax on Lucy's head, once more at her soaplike shoulders. For one moment he breathed her air. Then he wheeled, came back, and sat down by Cory.

"This whole love thing," said Bruce, loudly, "isn't enough. I tell you, it isn't enough."

"Why, no," said Cory. "Of course not."

CHARLES CALDWELL DOBIE

THE STORY GROWS

It is very hard for me to put a finger on my method in writing a short story. But one thing is certain, I never have a plan in mind and I rarely know until the last page how it is all to end. Of course, it is fatal to indulge in generalities, and I can think of one or two stories that give me the key to their endings early. "Laughter" and "The Open Window" must surely have ended with the victims' deaths almost from the first page. Yet the methods whereby the hunchback accomplished the murders were a day-by-day development as I pounded my Corona.

"Slow Poison," which appeared in the July *Harper's,* 1927, was suggested by the knowledge of a woman who had disinherited a son to leave her money to a strange man. I remember saying at the time: "But how did the beneficiary explain the matter to his wife!" Almost at once I saw that it would make a good story. This likewise expanded merely from day to day as I sat at my desk.

"Wild Geese," which won one of the Harper prizes, was suggested by the incident of a woman friend who foolishly squandered her household allowance on a ship model only to sell it in the end for a tremendous sum to a British collector who wanted it for his collection. If you know the story you will see how far removed it is from this meager suggestion.

The stories like "The Elder Brother" and "The Fallen Leaf" were suggested by a character—Josef Vitek, who is the teller and hero of these stories and four others. He was a real character, a Bohemian baker, whom I fell in with one day on a walk through San Francisco's large park to the ocean. These stories seem to write themselves.

"The Leech" was a combination of suggestions. The usual defaulter who steals to keep things going financially, an untimely rain that came once in September and ruined a prune crop that would have made every planter rich, and the desire for *Harper's Magazine* to have a story of rural California life.

"Our Dog" was written from an incident which happened to me and which was almost identical with the opening scene of the story. From that point it was pure imagination.

The Arrested Moment, which names my latest short-story volume, was suggested by a statement that Sargent had given up portraits because he painted always the diabolic thing that lurked beneath the surface of his subjects.

"The Cracked Tea-pot" was pure imagination and developed at the suggestion of a syndicate looking for stories of a thousand words. After I finished the sketch I decided I would be wasting the idea and so I developed it at greater length.

You see how unsatisfactory I am for your purpose. I can give you the germ only. Its development is in the lap of the gods. But my method is more or less subconscious. I suppose I've developed an unconscious technic. I write slowly and rarely revise. My first copy is my last with the change in a word or phrase here and there. Reassure any of your pupils who can't plan before they write. I fought this for years thinking it a lack. But it isn't a good plan for everybody. However, some people find it their salvation. But it is good to try and write to scenario until you get your stride.

Most of the stories I mention are in *The Arrested Moment.*

THE OPEN WINDOW [1]

"IT happened just as I have said," Fernet reiterated, tossing the wine-dregs from his glass.

The company at the table looked instinctively toward the kitchen. Berthe was bringing a fresh pot of coffee. They all followed Fernet's example, lifting their empty glasses for her to serve them in their turn.

The regular boarders of the Hôtel de France, after the fashion of folks who find their meal a duty to be promptly despatched, had departed, but the transients still lingered over their *café noir* and cognac in the hope that something exciting might materialize.

As the sound of Fernet's voice died away, a man who had been sitting in an extreme corner of the room scraped

[1] From *Harper's Magazine,* August, 1918. Reprinted by permission of the author.

back his chair and rose. Fernet looked up. The man was a
hunchback, and, instead of paying for his meal and leaving, he crossed over and said to Fernet, in the most perfect French imaginable:

"I see, my young fellow, that you are discussing something of interest with your friends here. Would it be im-
pertinent for me to inquire into the subject?"

Fernet drew out a chair for the newcomer, who seated
himself.

"By no means. We were discussing a murder and suicide. The murdered man was an Italian fisherman who
lodged at the Hôtel des Alpes Maritimes, the suicide was
a musician named Suvaroff."

"Ah," said the hunchback, cracking his fingers. "Why
a murder and suicide? Why not two murders?"

"Because," returned Fernet, pompously, "it was abundantly proved to the contrary. This man Suvaroff suffered
from neuralgia; the Italian fisherman was given to playing the accordion at all hours of the night. Suvaroff
was, in addition, a musician—a high-strung person. The
Italian's playing was abominable—even his landlady says
as much. In short, Suvaroff deliberately killed this simple-
minded peasant because of his music. Then, in a fit of
remorse, he killed himself. I leave it to any one here to
dispute the fact. Besides, I was on the coroner's jury. I
should know what I am talking about."

"Oh, without doubt," agreed the hunchback, smiling
amiably. "But, as I remember, the knives in both cases
were plunged hilt-deep into the backs of the victims. One
does not usually commit suicide in this fashion."

Fernet coldly eyed the curiously handsome face of his
antagonist. "It seems you know more about this thing
than a coroner's jury," he sneered.

"It seems I do—granting that such an important item was left out of the evidence."

"Then, my good sir, will you be good enough to tell me who *did* kill Suvaroff, since you do not admit that he died by his own hand?"

The hunchback cracked his fingers again. "That is simple enough. Suvaroff was killed by the same person who stabbed the Italian."

"And who might that be, pray?"

The hunchback rose with a malignant smile. "Ah, if I told you that you would know as much as I do, my friend."

And with that he walked calmly over to the proprietor, put down thirty-five cents for his meal upon the counter, and without another word left the room.

A silence fell upon the group. Everybody stared straight ahead, avoiding the eye of his neighbor. It was as if something too terrifying to be remarked had passed them.

Finally, a thick-set man at Fernet's right, with a purple wart on his cheek, said, uneasily, "Come, I must be going."

The others rose; only Fernet remained seated.

"What," said another, "haven't you finished?"

"Yes," returned Fernet, gloomily, "but I am in no hurry."

He sat there for an hour, alone, holding his head between his hands. Berthe cleared off the soiled plates, wiped the oilcloth-covered tables, began noisily to lay the pewter knives and forks for the morning meal. At this Fernet stirred himself and, looking up at her, said:

"Tell me who was the hunchback who came and sat with us? Does he live here—in San Francisco?"

"His name is Flavio Minetti," she replied, setting the

lid back upon an uncovered sugar-bowl. "Beyond that I know nothing. But they tell me that he is quite mad."

"Ah, that accounts for many things," said Fernet, smiling with recovered assurance. "I must say he is strangely fascinating."

Berthe looked at him sharply and shrugged. "For my part, he makes me shiver every time I see him come in the door. When I serve him my hand shakes. And he continually cracks his fingers and says to me: 'Come, Berthe, what can I do to make you smile? Would you laugh if I were to dance for you? I would give half my life only to see you laughing. Why are you so sad?' . . . No, I wish he would never come again."

"Nevertheless, I should like to see him once more."

"He comes always on Thursdays for chicken."

"Thanks," said Fernet, as he put on his hat.

Fernet walked directly to his lodgings that night. He had a room in an old-fashioned house on the east side of Telegraph Hill. The room was shabby enough, but it caught glimpses of the bay and there was a gnarled pepper-tree that came almost to its windows and gave Fernet a sense of eternal, though grotesque, spring. Even his landlord was unusual—a professional beggar who sat upon the curb, with a ridiculous French poodle for company, and sold red and green pencils.

This landlord was sitting out by the front gate as Fernet entered.

"Ah, Pollitto," said Fernet, halting before the old man and snapping his fingers at the poodle who lay crouched before his master, "I see you are enjoying this fine warm night."

"You are wrong," replied the beggar. "I am merely sitting here hoping that some one will come along and rent my front room."

"Then it is vacant?"

"Naturally," replied the old man, with disagreeable brevity, and Fernet walked quickly up to his room.

"Why do I live in such a place?" he asked himself, surveying the four bare walls. "Everything about it is abominable, and that beggar, Pollitto, is a scoundrel. I shall move next week."

He crossed over to the window and flung it open. The pepper-tree lay before him, crouching in the moonlight. He thought at once of Flavio Minetti.

"He is like this pepper-tree," he said, aloud, "beautiful even in his deformity. No, I would not trade this pepper-tree for a dozen of the straightest trees in the world." He stepped back from the window, and, lighting a lamp, set it upon a tottering walnut table. "Ah, André Fernet," he mused, chidingly, "you are always snared by what is unusual. You should pray to God that such folly does not lead you to disaster."

He went to the window and looked out again. The pepper-tree seemed to be bending close to the ground, as if seeking to hide something. Presently the wind parted its branches and the moonlight fell at its feet like a silver moth before a blackened candle.

André Fernet shivered and sighed. "Yes," he repeated, again and again, "they are alike. They both are at once beautiful and hideous and they have strange secrets. . . . Well, I shall go on Thursday again, and maybe I shall see him. Who knows, if I am discreet he may tell me who killed this ridiculous musician Suvaroff."

And with that he suddenly blew out the light.

On the next Thursday night, when Fernet entered the dining-room of the Hôtel de France his glance rested immediately upon Flavio Minetti. To his surprise the hunchback rose, drawing a chair out as he did so, and beckoning Fernet to be seated next him. For a moment Fernet hesitated. Berthe was just bringing on the soup.

"What! Are you afraid?" she said, mockingly, as she passed.

This decided Fernet. He went and sat beside Minetti without further ado.

"Ah, I was expecting you!" cried the hunchback, genially, as he passed the radishes.

"Expecting *me?*" returned Fernet. His voice trembled, though he tried to speak boldly.

"Yes. Women are not the only inquisitive animals in the world. What will you have—some wine?"

Fernet allowed Minetti to fill his glass.

Other boarders began to drift in. Minetti turned his back upon Fernet, speaking to a new-comer at his left. He did not say another word all evening.

Fernet ate and drank in silence. "What did I come for and why am I staying?" he kept asking himself. "This man is mocking me. First of all, he greets me as if I were his boon companion, and next he insults me openly and before everybody in the room. Even Berthe has noticed it and is smiling. As a matter of fact, he knows no more than I do about Suvaroff's death."

But he continued to sit beside the hunchback all through the meal, and as fruit was put on the table he touched Minetti on the arm and said, "Will you join me in a *café royal?*"

"Not here . . . a little later. I can show you a place where they really know how to make them. And, besides, there are tables for just two. It is much more private."

Fernet's heart bounded and sank almost in one leap. "Let us go now, then," he said, eagerly.

"As you wish," replied Minetti.

Fernet paid for two dinners, and they reached for their hats.

"Where are you going?" asked Berthe, as she opened the door.

Fernet shrugged. "I am in his hands," he answered, sweeping his arm toward Minetti.

"You mean you will be," muttered the hunchback, in an undertone.

Fernet heard him distinctly.

"Perhaps I had better leave him while there is yet time!" flashed through his mind. But the next instant he thought, contemptuously: "What harm can he do me? Why, his wrist is no bigger than a pullet's wing. Bah! You are a fool, André Fernet!"

They stepped out into the street. A languorous note was in the air; the usual cool wind from the sea had not risen. A waning moon silvered the roof-tops, making a pretense of hiding its face in the thin line of smoke above Telegraph Hill.

The hunchback led the way, trotting along in a fashion almost Oriental. At the end of the second block he turned abruptly into a wine-shop; Fernet followed. They found seats in a far corner, away from the billiard-tables. A waiter came forward. They gave their orders.

"Be sure," said Minetti to the waiter, "that we have plenty of anisette and cognac in the coffee."

The man flicked a towel rather contemptuously and made no answer.

"Now," Minetti continued, turning a mocking face toward Fernet, "what can I do for you, my friend?"

Fernet was filled with confusion. "I . . . you . . ." he stammered. "Really, there is nothing. Believe me——"

"Nonsense," interrupted Minetti. "You wish to know who killed Suvaroff. But I warn you, my friend, it is a dreadful thing to share such a secret."

He looked at Fernet intently. The younger man shuddered. "Nevertheless, I should like to know," Fernet said, distinctly.

"Well, then, since you are so determined—it was I who killed him."

Fernet stared, looked again at the hunchback's puny wrists, and began to laugh. "*You!* Do you take me for a fool?" And as he said this he threw back his head and laughed until even the billiard-players stopped their game and looked around at him.

"What are you laughing at?" asked the hunchback, narrowing his eyes.

Fernet stopped. He felt a sudden chill as if some one had opened a door. "I am laughing at you," he answered.

"I am sorry for that," said Minetti, dryly.

"Why?"

The hunchback leaned forward confidentially. "Because I kill every one who laughs at me. It—it is a little weakness I have."

The waiter came with two glasses of steaming coffee. He put them down on the table, together with a bottle of cognac and a bottle of anisette.

"Ah, that is good!" cried the hunchback, rubbing his hands together. "The proprietor is my friend. He is going to let us prepare our own poison!"

Fernet felt himself shivering. "Come," he thought,

"this will never do! The man is either mad or jesting." He reached for the anisette.

"Let me pour it for you," suggested Flavio Minetti. "Your hand is shaking so that you will spill half of it on the floor."

The hunchback's voice had a note of pity in it. Fernet relinquished his hold upon the bottle.

"Don't look so frightened," continued Minetti. "I shall not kill you here. The proprietor is a friend of mine, and, besides—"

"What nonsense!" cried Fernet, with a ghastly smile. "But I must confess, you did make my blood run cold for a minute."

Minetti stirred some cognac into his glass. "And, besides," he finished, coldly, "I give everybody a sporting chance. It adds to the game."

That night André Fernet was restless. He lay on his bed looking out at the blinking lights of the harbor. "I must stop drinking coffee," he muttered to himself.

Finally he fell asleep, and when he did he had a strange dream. It seemed that the pepper-tree outside his window suddenly began to move in the night breeze and its long green boughs became alive, twisting like the relentless tentacles of a devil-fish. Its long green boughs became alive, crawling along the ground, flinging themselves into the air, creeping in at André Fernet's open window. He lay upon the bed as he had done earlier in the evening, watching the harbor lights. Slowly the green boughs writhed over the faded carpet, scaled the bedpost and fell upon the bed. André Fernet waited, motionless. He felt the green tentacles close about his legs, clasp his hands, slide shudderingly across his throat. Yet he made no move to free himself. It was only when he felt a breath upon his cheek that he turned slightly, and instead of the tentacle-like boughs of the pepper-tree he fancied himself staring down at the hands of Flavio Minetti. . . . He awoke with a start. The sun was pouring in at the open window. He got up quickly. A noisy clatter issued from the passageway. Fernet opened his door. Two men were carrying a trunk up the stairs. Pollitto, the beggar, walked behind.

"Ah, I see you have rented your front room," said Fernet, stepping out.

"Yes," returned the other. "It was taken as early as six o'clock this morning—by a hunchback."

Fernet stopped breathing. "A hunchback? Was his name Flavio Minetti?"

"Yes. How did you know?"

Fernet tried to smile. "He is a friend of mine," he answered, as he walked back into his room. "Perhaps it would be better if I moved away," he thought. "I do not like this room. Heaven knows why I have stayed this long. Is this fellow Minetti really mad or merely making sport of me? I should not like to have him think that I am afraid of him. As for his story about Suvaroff, that is, of course, ridiculous. If I thought otherwise I should go at once to the . . . No, it is all a joke! I shall stay where I am. I shall not have it said that a little, mad, puny, twisted fellow frightened André Fernet out of his lodgings. Besides, it will be curious to watch his little game. What a beautiful morning it is, after all! And the pepper-tree— how it glistens in the sun! I should miss that pepper-tree if I moved away. But I must stop drinking *cafés royals.* They upset one. I do not know whether it is the coffee, or the cognac, or the anisette, or all three. Of course, that dream I had toward morning means nothing—but such dreams are unpleasant. I hate this place. But I shall not move now. No, I shall wait and see what happens."

Fernet did not see Minetti for some days. Indeed, he had dismissed the whole thing from his mind, when, one night, returning home early to get out of a drizzle, who should stop him on the stairway but the hunchback.

"Ah, so here you are!" called out Fernet, gayly, in spite of his rapidly beating heart. "I have been waiting for you to call on me ever since I heard that you were lodging under the same roof."

"I have been busy," replied the hunchback, laconically.

Fernet threw open his bedroom door and waved Minetti in.

"Busy?" he echoed, as he struck a light. "And what do you find that is so absorbing, pray?"

"You know my specialty," replied Minetti, flinging off his cap.

Fernet looked up sharply. A malignant look had crept into the hunchback's face.

"Oh, there is no doubt of it, he is quite mad!" said Fernet to himself. Then aloud: "Yes, I have been wanting to talk to you more about this. Take a seat and I shall make some coffee. For instance, do you always employ the knife in despatching your—"

"Scarcely," interrupted Minetti, quickly. "Slow poison has its fascinations. There is a very delicate joy in watching a gradual decline. It is like watching a green leaf fading before the breath of autumn. First a sickly pallor, then a yellowing, finally the sap dries completely, a sharp wind, a fluttering in the air, and it is all over. I have tried nearly every slow way—except mental murder. I fancy that, too, would be exquisite."

"Mental murder. . . . I do not understand."

Minetti stretched himself out and yawned. "Accomplishing the thing without any weapon save the mind."

Fernet picked up the coffee-pot and laughed. "Why, my dear fellow, it is too absurd! The thing cannot be done. You see I am laughing at you again, but no matter."

"No, as you say, it is no matter. You can die only once."

Fernet's laughter stopped instantly. He went on with his preparation for coffee. Minetti changed the subject.

It turned out that there was no sugar in the cracked bowl. Fernet was putting on his hat to go out for some, when the hunchback stopped him.

"Sugar will not be necessary," he said. And as he spoke he drew a vial from his vest pocket and laid it upon the table beside the cups. "You know what these are, of course."

"Saccharine pellets?" inquired Fernet as he threw aside his hat.

Minetti replied with a grunt. Fernet poured out the coffee, set a spoon in each saucer, laid three French rolls upon a blue plate. Then he sat down.

"Permit me!" said Minetti, reaching for the vial and rolling a tiny pellet into his palm.

Fernet held up his cup; the hunchback dropped the pellet into it. Then he corked the vial tightly and laid it aside.

"You forgot to serve yourself," said Fernet.

"So I did!" answered Minetti, nonchalantly. "Well, no matter. I very often drink my coffee so—without sweetening."

Fernet drew back suddenly. Could it be possible that . . . The hunchback was staring at him, an ironical smile was on his lips. Fernet shuddered.

"Drink your coffee!" Minetti commanded, sneeringly. "You are on the verge of a chill."

Fernet obeyed meekly. He felt for all the world like an animal caught in a trap. He tried to collect his thoughts. What had the hunchback been talking about?

"Slow poison!" muttered Fernet, inaudibly to himself.

"What is that you are saying?" demanded the other.

"You were speaking of slow poison. How do you go about it?"

"Oh, that is easy! For instance, once in London I lodged next door to my victim. We became capital friends. And he was always calling me in for a bite of something to eat. Nothing elaborate—a bun and a cup of tea, or coffee and cake. Very much as we are doing now. He died in six months. It is no trick, you know, to poison a man who eats and drinks with you—especially drinks!"

As he said this the hunchback reached for the coffee-pot and poured Fernet another cupful. Then he uncorked the vial again and dropped a pellet into the steaming liquid.

"I do not think that I wish any more," protested Fernet.

"Nonsense! You are still shivering like an old woman with the palsy. Hot coffee will do you good."

"No," said Fernet, desperately, "I never drink more than one cup at a sitting. It keeps me awake, and next morning my hand shakes and I am fit for nothing. I need a steady hand in my business."

"And what may that be, pray?"

"At present I am a draftsman. Some day, if I live long enough, I hope to be an architect."

"If you live long enough? You forget that you have laughed at *me*, my friend."

Fernet tried to appear indifferent. "What a droll fellow you are!" he cried, with sudden gayety, rubbing his hands together. And without thinking, he reached for his coffee-cup and downed the contents in almost one gulp. He laid the cup aside quickly. He could feel the sweat starting out upon his forehead.

"There, you see," said Minetti, "the coffee has done you good already. You are perspiring, and that is a good sign. A hot drink at the right moment works wonders."

The next morning Pollitto stopped Fernet as he swung out the front gate to his work.

"What is the matter with you?" exclaimed the beggar, in a surprised tone.

"Why . . . what?" demanded Fernet, in a trembling voice. "Do I look so . . . ? Pray, tell me, is there anything unusual about me?"

"Why, your face . . . Have you looked at yourself in the glass? Your skin is the color of stale pastry."

Fernet tried to laugh. "It is nothing. I have been drinking too much coffee lately. I must stop it."

It was a fine morning. The sun was shining and the air was brisk and full of little rippling breezes. The bay lay like a blue-green peacock ruffling its gilded feathers. The city had a genial, smiling countenance. But Fernet was out of humor with all this full-blown content. He had spent a wretched night—not sleepless, but full of disturbing dreams. Dreams about Minetti and his London neighbor and the empty sugar-bowl. All night he had dreamed about this empty sugar-bowl. It seemed that as soon as he had it filled Minetti would slyly empty it again. He tried stowing sugar away in his pockets, but when he put his hand in to draw out a lump a score or more of pellets spilled over the floor. Then he remembered saying:

"I shall call on Minetti's London neighbor. Maybe he will have some sugar."

He walked miles and miles, and finally beat upon a strange door. A man wrapped in a black coat up to his eyebrows opened to his knock.

"Are you Flavio Minetti's London neighbor?" he demanded, boldly.

The figure bowed. Fernet drew the cracked sugar-bowl from under his arm.

"Will you oblige me with a little sugar?" he asked, more politely.

The black-cloaked figure bowed and disappeared. Presently he came back. Fernet took the sugar-bowl from him. It struck him that the bowl felt very light. He looked down at his hands. The bowl had disappeared; only a glass vial lay in his palms. He removed the cork—a dozen or more tiny round pellets fell out. He glanced up quickly at Minetti's London neighbor; a dreadful smile glowed through the black cloak. Fernet gave a cry and hurled the vial in the face of his tormentor. Minetti's London neighbor let the black cloak fall, and André Fernet discovered that he was staring at himself. . . . He awakened soon after that and found that it was morning.

When he brushed his hair his hand had shaken so that the brush fell clattering to the floor. And he had spilled the cream for his morning coffee over the faded strip of carpet before the bureau. It had ended by his eating no breakfast at all. But he had drunk glass after glass of cold water.

After Pollitto's words he trembled more and more like

a man with the ague, and before every saloon-door mirror he halted and took a brief survey of his face. Pollitto was right—his skin was dead and full of unhealthy pallor. It was plain that he could not work in his present condition. His trembling fingers could scarcely hold a pencil, much less guide it through the precise demands of a drafting-board. He decided to go to the library and read. But the books on architecture which always enthralled him could not hold his shifting attention. Finally in despair he went up to the librarian and said:

"Have you any books on poison?"

The woman eyed him with a cold, incurious glance.

"Historical or medical?" she snapped out, as she went on stamping mysterious numbers in the pile of books before her.

"Both!"

She consulted a catalogue and made a list for him.

He sat all day devouring books which the librarian had recommended. He did not even go out for lunch. He read historical and romantic instances with a keen, morbid relish; but when it came to the medical books his heart quickened and he followed causes and effects breathlessly. By nightfall he had a relentless knowledge of every poison in the calendar. He knew what to expect from arsenic or strychnine or vitriol. He learned which poisons destroyed tissues, which acted as narcotics, which were irritants. He identified the hemlock, the horse-chestnut, the deadly toadstools. In short, he absorbed and retained everything on the subject. It seemed that the world teemed with poisons; one could be sure of nothing. Even beautiful flowers were not to be trusted.

He was so upset by all he had read that he could scarcely eat dinner. He went to an obscure *pension* in a

wretched basement, where he was sure he would be un-
known, and, after two or three mouthfuls of soup and a
spoonful of rice boiled with tomato, he rose, paid for his
meal, and went out to tramp up and down past the tawdry
shops of middle Kearny Street. He was trotting aimlessly
in the direction of Market Street when he felt a tug at his
coat-sleeve. He turned. Minetti was smiling genially up
at him.

"Come," said the hunchback, "what is your hurry?
Have you had coffee yet? I was thinking that—"

Fernet's heart sank at once. And yet he managed to say
boldly: "I have given up drinking coffee. You can see for
yourself what a wretched complexion I have. And today
I have scarcely eaten."

"Pooh!" cried Minetti. "A cup of coffee will do you
good."

Fernet began to draw away in futile terror. "No!" he
protested, with frightened vehemence. "No, I tell you! I
won't drink the stuff! It is useless for you to—"

Minetti began to laugh with scornful good humor.
"What has come over you?" he drawled, half-closing his
eyes. "Are you afraid?"

And as he said this Fernet glanced instinctively at the
puny wrists, no bigger than a pullet's wing, and replied,
boldly:

"Afraid? Of what? I told you last night I need a steady
hand in my business, and today I have not been able to
do any work."

Minetti's mirth softened into genial acquiescence.
"Well, maybe you are right. But I must say you are not
very companionable. Perhaps the coffee you have been
drinking has not been made properly. You should take
something. You do look badly. A glass of brandy? . . .

No? . . . Ah, I have it—coffee made in the Turkish fashion. Have you ever drunk that?"

"No," replied Fernet, helplessly, wondering all the time why he was foolish enough to tell the truth.

"Well, then," announced the hunchback, confidently, "we shall cross over to Third Street and have some Turkish coffee. I know a Greek café where they brew a cup that would tempt the Sultan himself. Have you ever seen it made? They use coffee pounded to a fine powder—a teaspoonful to a cup, and sugar in the same proportion. It is all put in together and brought to a boil. The result is indescribable! Really, you are in for a treat."

"If it is sweetened in the making," flashed through Fernet's mind, "at least we shall have no more of that pellet business."

"Yes—the result is quite indescribable," Minetti was repeating, "and positively no bad effects."

And as he said this he slipped his arm into Fernet's and guided him with gentle firmness toward the Greek café in question. Fernet felt suddenly helpless and incapable of offering the slightest objection.

A girl took their orders. She had a freckled nose and was frankly Irish. Naturally, she did not fit the picture, and Fernet could see that she was scornful of the whole business.

"Two coffees . . . medium," Minetti repeated, decisively. "And will you have a sweet with it? They sell taffy made of sesame seeds and honey. Or you can have Turkish delight or a pastry dusted with powdered sugar. Really they are all quite delicious."

Fernet merely shrugged. Minetti ordered Turkish delight. The girl wiped some moisture from the marble table-top and walked toward the coffee-shelf.

"So you were not able to work today?" Minetti began, affably. "How did you put in the time?"

"At the library, reading."

"Something droll? A French novel or—"

"Books on *poison!*" Fernet shot out with venomous triumph. "I know more than I did yesterday."

"How distressing!" purred Minetti. "Ignorance is more invulnerable than one fancies. Of course we are taught otherwise, but knowledge, you remember, was the beginning of all trouble. But you choose a fascinating subject. Some day when we get better acquainted I shall tell you all I know about it. Poison is such a subtle thing. It is everywhere—in the air we breathe, in the water we drink, in the food we eat. And it is at once swift and sluggish, painful and stupefying, obvious and incapable of analysis. It is like a beautiful woman, or a great joy, or love itself."

Fernet glanced up sharply. The hunchback had slid forward in his seat and his eyes glowed like two shaded pools catching greedily at the yellow sunlight of midday. Fernet shuddered and looked about the room. Groups of swarthy men were drinking coffee, or sipping faintly red draughts of cherry syrup and sweet soda. At a near-by table a group of six shuffled cards and marked their scores upon a slate. And, of course, there were those who played backgammon, rattling the dice and making exaggerated gestures as they spurred on their adversaries with genial taunts.

The girl came back carrying cups of thick steaming coffee and soft lemon-colored sweetmeats speared with two tiny silver forks. She set the tray down. Minetti reached for his coffee greedily, but Fernet sat back in his seat and allowed the waitress to place the second cup before him. As she did so the table shook suddenly and half of the hot liquid spilled over on the marble tabletop. Fernet jumped up to escape the scalding trickle; the girl gave an apologetic scream: Minetti laughed strangely.

"It is all my fault!" cried the hunchback. "What stupidity! Pray be seated. My young woman, will you give the gentleman this coffee of mine? And get me another."

"Pardon me," Fernet protested, "but I cannot think of such a thing!" And with that he attempted to pass the coffee in question back to Minetti. But the hunchback would have none of it. Fernet broke into a terrified sweat.

"He has dropped poison into it!" he thought, in sudden panic. "Otherwise why should he be so anxious to have me drink it? He kicked the table deliberately, too. And this cup of his—why was it not spilled also? No, he was prepared—it is all a trick!"

"Come, come, my friend," broke in Minetti, briskly, "drink your coffee while it is still hot! Do not wait for me. I shall be served presently. And try the sweetmeats; they are delicious."

"I am not hungry," replied Fernet, sullenly.

"No? Well, what of that? Sweetmeats and coffee are not matters of hunger. Really, you are more droll than you imagine!" Minetti burst into a terrifying laugh.

"He thinks I am afraid!" muttered Fernet.

And out of sheer bravado he lifted the cup to his lips. Minetti stopped laughing, but a wide smile replaced his diabolical mirth. The girl brought fresh coffee to the hunchback. He sipped it with frank enjoyment, but he did not once take his gaze from Fernet's pale face.

"Well," thought Fernet, "one cup of poison more or less will not kill me. . . . It is not as if he has made up his mind to finish me at once. He is counting on the ex-

quisite joys of a prolonged agony." And he remembered
Minetti's words: "It is like watching a green leaf fading
before the breath of autumn. First a sickly pallor, then a
yellowing, a sharp wind, a fluttering in the air. . . ." He
tossed off the coffee in one defiant gulp. "He thinks that
he has me in his power. But André Fernet is not quite a
fool. I shall go away tomorrow!"

They went home as soon as Minetti finished his coffee.
Fernet felt a sudden nausea; by the time he reached his
lodgings his steps were unsteady and his head reeled.
Minetti was kindness itself.

"Let me help you into bed," he insisted. "You must
have a congestion. Presently I shall heat some water and
give you a hot gin."

Fernet was too sick to protest. Minetti started the gas-
stove and filled the kettle and went into his room for gin.
Fernet dragged himself out of his clothes and crawled in
between the sheets. Minetti came back. Fernet lay with
his eyes half-closed, shivering. Finally the water boiled,
and the hunchback brought Fernet a huge tumbler of gin
and water with bits of lemon-peel and cloves floating in it.
It tasted so good that Fernet forgot his terror for the
moment. But when the tumbler was empty he felt helpless; he could scarcely lift his arms; so he lay flat upon his
back, staring up at the ceiling. He tried to recall scraps
of what he had been reading all afternoon. What was the
name of the poison that left one paralyzed? He could not
remember. He found his movements becoming more and
more difficult; he could scarcely turn in bed. Minetti
brewed another toddy. Fernet could not hold the glass.
He tried to push the tumbler away from his lips, but his
efforts were useless. Minetti hovered above him with a

bland, gentle smile, and Fernet felt the warm liquid trickling into his mouth and down his throat. In the midst of all this he lost consciousness. . . . Once or twice during the night Fernet had a wakeful interlude. Whenever he opened his eyes he saw Minetti sitting before the open window, gazing down at the twisted pepper-tree.

"Yes, they are both alike!" passed dimly through his mind. "They both are at once beautiful and hideous and they have strange secrets! It is no use, I must go away—tomorrow."

In the morning Minetti was standing by the bed. "I have sent for the doctor," he said. But his voice sounded far away.

The doctor came shortly after ten o'clock. He was a little wizened, dried-up old man with a profound air.

"He is a fraud!" thought Fernet. "He knows nothing!"

"Ah," said the doctor, putting a sly finger against his sharp nose, "our friend here has a nervous collapse. He should have a nurse!"

"A nurse!" exclaimed Minetti, with indignation. "And, pray, what do you call me? Do you not think that—"

"Well, we shall see! we shall see!" replied the doctor, rubbing his hands together. "But he will need all sorts of delicacies and—"

Minetti moistened his lips with sleek satisfaction. "You cannot name a dish that I am not able to prepare."

"How about a custard? Today he should eat something light."

"A custard is simplicity itself," answered the hunchback, and he cracked his fingers.

Minetti went out with the doctor, and came back shortly, carrying eggs and a bottle of vanilla extract and sugar. Fernet lay helpless, watching him bustling about. Finally the delicacy was made and set away in a pan of water to cool. At noon Minetti brought a blue bowl filled with custard to the bedside. It looked inviting, but Fernet shook his head.

"I am not hungry," he lied.

The hunchback set the bowl down on a chair so that Fernet gazed upon it all day. The hunchback did not leave the room. He sat before the open window, reading from a thick book. Toward nightfall Fernet said to him:

"What do you find so interesting?"

Minetti darted a sardonic glance at his patient. "A book on *poison*. I did not realize that I had grown so rusty on the subject. Why, I remember scarcely enough to poison a field-mouse!"

He rose and crossed over to the bedside. "Do you not feel ready for the custard?"

Fernet cast a longing eye upon the yellow contents of the blue bowl.

"No. To tell the truth, I never eat it."

Minetti shrugged.

"But I should like a glass of water."

The hunchback drew water from the faucet. Fernet watched him like a ferret.

"At least," thought Fernet, "he cannot drop poison in the water secretly. It is well that I can see every move he makes at such a time. I should not like to die of thirst."

A little later Minetti removed the bowl and threw out its contents. Fernet looked on with half-closed eyes.

"What better proof could I have?" he mused. "If the custard were harmless he would eat it himself. I must get away tomorrow."

But the next day he felt weaker than ever, and when

the doctor came Minetti said, in answer to questions:

"I made a delicious custard yesterday and he ate every bit. . . . An oyster stew? . . . with milk? I shall see that he has it at noon."

"God help me!" muttered Fernet. "Why does he lie like this? I must get the doctor's ear and tell him how things stand. I shall eat nothing—nothing! Thank Heaven I can drink water without fear."

At noon the oyster stew was ready. But Fernet would have none of it. "Oysters make me ill!" he said.

Minetti merely shrugged as he had done the previous day, and set the savory dish upon a chair before the bed. It exuded tantalizing odors, until Fernet thought he would go mad with longing. Toward evening Minetti threw out the stew. And as before, when the doctor called the hunchback said:

"He ate a quart of stew and there were plenty of oysters in it, I can tell you. Do you think that a chicken fried in olive-oil would be too hearty?"

Fernet groaned. "This is horrible—horrible!" he wept to himself. "I shall die like a starving rat with toasted cheese dangling just beyond reach. God help me to rouse myself! Surely the effects of the poison he has given me must soon wear off. . . . There he is, reading from that big book again. Perhaps he is contriving a way to put poison in my water even though I am able to watch him when he draws me a drink. . . . Poison—poison everywhere. It can even be administered with the prick of a needle. Why did I read about it? Chicken fried in olive-oil . . . what torture!"

The chicken fried in olive-oil was a triumph—Fernet knew all this by the wisps of appetizing fragrance which drifted from the sizzling pan. Minetti made a great stir over the preparations. The tender flesh had to be rubbed thoroughly with garlic and well dusted with salt and pepper. And a quarter of a bottle of yellow-green olive-oil was first placed in the pan. When everything was ready and the chicken cooked to a turn, Minetti carried it to Fernet with a great flourish. Fernet gritted his teeth and turned his face away. He did not have the courage to invent an excuse. Minetti laid it on the chair as usual. For two hours Fernet was tortured with the sight of this tempting morsel, but at the sound of the doctor's step upon the stair the hunchback whisked away the chicken.

"His appetite?" Minetti said, echoing the doctor's query. "Why, one could not wish for better! Only this morning he despatched a chicken as if it had been no more than a soft-boiled egg. As a matter of fact, he is always hungry."

"Well, well," beamed the doctor, "that is the best of signs, and it happens that way very often in nervous cases. You are a capital nurse, my good man, and by the end of the week, if you keep feeding him up in this fashion, he should be as hearty as a school-boy."

At that moment Minetti was called down-stairs by his landlord. Fernet struggled to lift himself; the doctor bent toward him.

"This hunchback," Fernet gasped, "he is trying to poison me. Already I have drunk four or five of his concoctions, and that is why I am in this condition . . . helpless. And he is lying when he says that I have eaten. I have touched nothing for three days."

The doctor laid the patient back upon the pillow.

"Poison you, my friend? And for what reason?"

"Because I laughed at him. In God's name, Doctor, see

that you keep a straight face in his presence or else—"

The doctor patted Fernet's hand and straightened the sliding bedclothes. By this time Minetti had come back. The doctor and the hunchback whispered together in a far corner. Minetti laughed and tapped his head. At the door Fernet heard the doctor say:

"Just keep up the good work and the idea will pass. It happens that way very often in nervous cases. I shall not look in again until the first of next week unless . . ."

Fernet groaned aloud.

"I must get away tomorrow. . . . I must get away tomorrow!" he kept on repeating.

By the end of the week the smell of food held no temptations for Fernet. Minetti stopped cooking. And when a glass of water was drawn from the faucet Fernet had difficulty in forcing his vision to answer the strain of a searching gaze.

"When my sight fails me," Fernet thought, dimly, "I shall either die of thirst or take the consequences."

When the doctor finally came again Fernet closed his eyes and pretended to be asleep.

"He seems thinner," remarked the doctor, as if he had made an important discovery.

"Well, to tell the truth," replied the hunchback, "he has lost his appetite. I have fed him milk and eggs, but—"

"There is nothing to do but be patient," said the doctor. "Medicine will do him no good. Just rest and food. Even a little starvation will not hurt him. People eat too much, anyway."

At this Fernet opened his eyes and broke into a laugh that startled even Minetti. The doctor looked offended.

"Well, he is in your hands," the old fraud said, pompously, to the hunchback. "Just keep up the good work—"

Fernet laughed again.

"He is hysterical," proclaimed the doctor, with an air of supreme wisdom. "It happens that way very often in nervous cases."

And he walked out with great solemnity.

"Ah, I have offended him!" thought Fernet. "Well, now they will finish me—*together!*"

There followed days of delicious weakness. Fernet lay for the most part wrapt in the bliss of silver-blue visions. It seemed as if years were passing. He built shining cities, received the homage of kings, surrendered himself to the joys of ripe-lipped beauties. There were lucid intervals shot through with the malignant presence of Minetti and the puttering visits of the doctor. But these were like waking moments between darkness and dawn, filled with the half-conscious joy of a sleeper secure in the knowledge of a prolonged respite. In such moments Fernet would stir feebly and think:

"I must get away tomorrow!"

And there would succeed almost instantly a languid ecstasy at the thought that tomorrow was something remote and intangible that would never come.

At times the hunchback seemed like nothing so much as a heartless jailer who, if he would, might open the door to some shining adventure. Gradually this idea became fixed and elaborated. Fernet's sight grew dimmer and dimmer until he followed the presence of Minetti by the sounds he made.

"He is jingling something," Fernet would repeat, weakly. "Ah, it must be his keys! He is searching for the

one that will set me free! . . . Now he is oiling the lock.
. . . He has shut the door again. I am to be held awhile
longer. . . . I am a caged bird and just beyond is the
pepper-tree. It must be glistening now in the sunlight.
Well, let him lock the door, for all the good it will do him.
Is not the window always open? When the time comes I
shall fly out the window and leave him here—alone. Then
we shall see who has the best of this bargain."

And all the silver-blue visions would steal over him
again, to be pierced briefly by the arrival of the wizened
doctor.

"It is he who keeps me here!" Fernet would say to himself. "If it were not for him I could fly away—forever.
Well, presently even he will lose his power."

One day a strange man stood at his bedside. Minetti was
there also, and the old fraud of a doctor. The strange man
drew back the covers and put his ear to Fernet's fluttering
heart and went through other tiresome matters. . . .
Finally he smoothed back the covers again, and as he did
so he shook his head. He spoke softly, but Fernet heard
him distinctly.

"It is too late. . . . You should have called me sooner.
He wishes to die. . . . There is nothing to be done."

"Yes, yes—it happens this way very often in nervous
cases."

"I have done my best. I have given him food and drink.
I have even starved him. But nothing seemed to do any
good."

"No," said the stranger; "it is his mind. He has made
up his mind that . . . You can do nothing with a man
when . . ."

Fernet closed his eyes.

"A man! They think I am a man. What stupidity!

Can they not see that I am a bird? . . . They have gone out. He is locking the door again . . . I can hear the keys jingle. . . . Well, let him lock the door if it gives him any pleasure. The window is open and tonight . . ."

The footsteps of the departing visitors died away. A chuckling sound came to André Fernet and the thump of ecstatic fists brought down upon a bare table-top. The voice of Flavio Minetti was quivering triumphantly like the hot whisper of a desert wind through the room:

"Without any weapon save the mind! Ha! ha! ha!"

Fernet turned his face toward the wall. "He is laughing at *me* now. Well, let him laugh while he may. . . . Is not the window open? Tomorrow I shall be free . . . and he? . . . No, *he* cannot fly—he has a broken wing. . . . The window is open, André Fernet!"

BEN AMES WILLIAMS

NOTE BOOK REGISTERS GROWTH

I ought to explain, in the first place, that any story which I write arises out of a routine which I have followed for years. I keep on my desk a note book, rather large size, each page of which contains the germ of a story. This germ may be an idea, a character, a dramatic situation, an incident, or a title.

Every day or so I run through this book, and give a few minutes' thought to each page. And if anything occurs to me which might contribute to the story that is taking shape on that page, I set it down. Usually this process of growth lasts for a long time. Some story ideas thus are carried over from one note book to the other, for a period of years, until they seem ready to be written.

Following this is a copy of the notes out of which the story called "Solitude" emerged. There are four titles at the head of this copy. The original one, and the germ idea from which the story sprang, was Cat and Mouse. That was not really intended as a title, but simply as a situation; a cat playing with a mouse. The other three titles were afterthoughts, and were set down probably on different days. As you see, the final title "Solitude" does not appear on this page at all.

Each paragraph on this page represents a note set down at a different time. And, as far as I can judge, from the time the original Cat and Mouse idea was set down in the work book until the time when I began to write the story was something over a year and a half.

As you will discover, if you read the story, it is epitomized in the next to the last paragraph on this page.

After the amount of thought here recorded, it was only necessary to attend to such details as choosing names for the characters, drawing a map of the locality where the incident occurred so as to have it clearly in mind, and going through the routine imaginative work necessary to fill in the details of personal appearance, antecedent material, and incident.

I suppose the notes of which I here send you a copy will seem rather empty to you, but you, of course, have had the experience of making a few brief notes of something in your mind, the notes representing to you as much as a volume would have meant to another man. I think, possibly, if you compare them with the finished story you may be able to get something out of it. In any case, I hope so.

NOTES ON "SOLITUDE"

A Matter of Perspective
The Fugitive
The Mouse
Cat and Mouse

A man struggling through the woods. Nature plays with him.
A man plodding stubbornly on—to a given destination.
Purpose in his movements.
Cold, no snow; cold has struck in and caught him unprepared.
Reaches a remote cabin; a man and woman there.

First a night in an abandoned barn and the horses. Then reaches cabin.

He is a fugitive. But he knew the cabin there and the man. His old buddy. Married now. Removed from him.

The man demands help; the buddy refuses as impossible; the girl was the fugitive's own girl once. Buddy puts him out; man marches on.

Girl overtakes him that night and will come where he goes.

In describing this man, view him as from a great distance; a mere speck; the vastness all about him. The world against him; he quite alone; and then the woman joins him and shuts out the world and fills his universe. Without her he feels the world upon him; with her he feels the world full of her.

His defiance of the world at last is followed by its surrender with the woman's coming.

SOLITUDE [1]

THE lonely reaches of the wilderness, motionless in the bonds of winter, extended to the utmost horizon. The black blur of the forests were mottled by snow which

[1] From *Collier's*, December 5, 1925. Reprinted by permission of the author.

clung to the great trees, and the even blackness of their masses was somewhat palliated by the fact that a blanket of snow lay on the ground beneath them, faintly modifying their hue with glimpses of white here and there. In the great cup formed by the surrounding mountains there were miles by the score and the hundred where spruce and pine stood in solid ranks; there were other reaches of barren land white with the snow except where a bush or a patch of scrub growth broke the glaring surfaces with a speck of black.

Above the sun blazed cold as ice from a sky pellucid blue at the zenith, shading imperceptibly into a cold white mist that blurred a little the horizon—a mist that suggested sparkling crystals of frost suspended in the air above the winter-prisoned world. The sunlight rebounded from the earth, reflected from billions and billions of snow particles in a blinding torrent of radiance, no more to be endured by human eye than a glance from the sun itself. Against the mountain flanks there were scars, bare slopes of rock swept clean by wind or slide, and these scars assumed fantastic and unbelievable colors in the interplay of light, sometimes black, sometimes gray, sometimes crimson, sometimes purple, sometimes as white as the snow itself.

Here and there the forest gave way to an expanse of swamp where the pointed plumes of the tamaracks rose above the level of the surrounding cedars, and here and there stood the stark trunk of a tree long since dead, waiting the completion òf those processes of decay which, eating at its roots, would level it to earth again. A tree three hundred years in the growing, condemned to stand like a skeleton at the feast among its still living fellows, fated to sweep down at last in a single splitting, crashing second, ruining so swiftly the structure centuries had built!

A thread of more even white, now visible, now broken by intervening forest growths, marked where the river ran.

Irregularly it widened; lakes lay with breathless bosoms bound in a scarf of snow. And between the eye and all these things hung the air; a definite thing, a thing to be taken into account; not the forgotten and disregarded air of more kindly scenes, but a biting, needlelike, razor-edged substance fit to wound and maim. This still and cold air was like a faint blue curtain drawn across a gigantic canvas; a canvas which bore a scene that might fitly have been called "Solitude."

There was, near the southern end of one of the more extensive tracts of white which might be recognized as the snow-covered surface of a lake, a small spot; a dark spot, appearing black against the snow. This spot was infinitely small.

The lake itself was not large—it may have been as large as your hand—and diverging coves at the northern end suggested this simile. The thumb was not apparent, but at least three fingers of the hand could be seen. This small dark spot, appearing black against the snow, was at a point corresponding to the ball of the thumb. It was very small, no more than a pin prick—so small that the eye swept over it without stopping, had to return and search to discover it again; as hard to see as a flock of geese disappearing in the mist miles away along the shore; as hard to keep within the focus of one's vision as an airplane going straight away from the beholder, a mile in every thirty seconds' time. Even more difficult, perhaps, to see this spot and keep it in view, for the geese move and the airplane moves, though it be so slightly, but this spot did not move at all! Visible now at a certain point upon the frozen surface of the lake, its position an hour later had not perceptibly changed. It was, to all intents and purposes, motionless.

Yet that it was not altogether motionless time at length revealed. Toward midday it seemed to have descended from the ball of the thumb into the palm of the hand which the lake represented; by dusk it had approached the base of the index finger. A little after daybreak the next morning it was apparent that the spot was certainly moving, following the index finger toward its end. Toward mid-afternoon it disappeared, merging in the shadows of the forest which cloaked the lake's end and lay like a slipping mantle up the steep slopes of a ridge of higher ground, perceptible from a distance only as a hair line of snow between the forest in the one valley and in the next. On the third day the spot was for a time visible upon this ridge; then it disappeared once more. But the day subsequent, upon a wide expanse of barren land beyond the ridge, the painfully advancing speck of black again came into view.

There was a suggestion of persistence about this spot. It did not wander to and fro, as an animal might be expected to wander; instead it moved steadfastly and in a line more or less direct, suggesting that it was guided by intelligence. It became necessary to suspect that this moving spot was a man. The spectacle of a single man set alone in the immensity of this solitude inevitably excited a certain ironic mirth; it was so ridiculous that it was somehow sublime.

The spot was, in fact, a man—a man alone. His progress across the face of this enormous wilderness was, on any comparative basis, superlatively slow, but as a matter of fact the man seemed to be making what haste he could. A somewhat closer view revealed the fact that he was evidently accustomed to such journeys as this one was. His heavy garments, increasing his apparent breadth, made him seem almost squat; the snowshoes on his feet were like heavy clogs, stumbling through the loose snow; his hood muffled his face, and from its opening there appeared only a red glint of a nose burned by the snowlight. Across his eyes a black band was drawn to protect them from the blinding radiance of the snow. In his hand he carried a rifle in a skin case, shifting the weapon from this side to that, occasionally resting it upon his shoulder. There was a small pack upon his back, but he seemed unconscious of its presence there. A cooking pot and a fry pan hung against this pack. The man himself, concealed within such a mass of accouterments, kept a steady, shuffling pace, threading his way among the inequalities of the ground, moving at times circuitously, yet nevertheless advancing day by day. If you had marked his progress by pin pricks on the map, the tiny holes would have been so near together as almost to overlap; yet a week would have shown a perceptible gain.

The colossal forces, at times inert, at times overpowering, with which he was surrounded, seemed unconscious of this man's existence. He was like a Lilliputian among Brobdingnags, a pygmy among giants; and it was forever necessary that he go cautiously lest ever their casual and unstudied movements overwhelm him. Where the giant that was the wind had breathed a gentle sigh, a swath of down timber barred his passage and forced him to a wide detour. Where the giant that was the snow had played at sliding downhill, it was necessary that he pick a cautious way lest he be precipitated into a gulf full of destruction.

He crawled across the sleeping bosom of the giantess who was the earth; he became entangled in the thickets of her hair; he had to go a day's walk out of his way to avoid the precipice that was her chin, and it required another day for him to descend into the ravine formed by her lips and climb out to level ground once more. The fact that the universe seemed to slumber made his task no easier, for one of the colossal forces asleep about him might so easily turn in its sleep. The twitch of one of their fingers was, for the man, calamity; and even in sleep they presented almost insurmountable difficulties to his passage.

The snow itself had fallen in a mood of riot, playing with the wind a game which left them both exhausted, so that the snow lay in the tumbled abandon of a sleeping child, and the wind too was still. But passively sleeping though it might be, the snow dragged at his feet, reared lofty drifts like ridges which he could not pass, concealed pits into which he might by a careless movement be precipitated, slid down from either side in a swift stroke as a sleeping child brushes at a troublesome fly. His way was beset by these perils, by the peril of a tree falling in the still forest, by the peril of a mishap to his own tiny but effective mechanism. A twisted ankle would destroy him.

The man within his wrappings, inching his way across the face of the universe, felt himself completely at the mercy of these colossal forces among which he picked his way. It was not that they were malicious; it was simply that they disregarded him. He was in their eyes of no account at all; the snow slide that buried him would lie as serenely waiting for the suns of spring as that which he escaped by the most desperate and scrambling haste. The trees, whispering above his head, did not observe his passage past their feet; the mountains never knew he crawled across their flanks; the winds blew over him without feeling that his head tickled their bellies as they passed, and he thought they were huge and reptilian monsters scurrying to and fro above him, whose feet might descend upon him crushingly and lift again without knowing what they had done.

During the day his consciousness of the world about him was not so overwhelming; it was at night, when he made his camp in the forest, that he was most utterly alone. He was lonely because he was so naked and so helpless and so completely disregarded. There is no loneliness like that of one caught up in a throng of persons engaged upon their own affairs; and this was his portion.

When he made his little fire and huddled over it, he could hear the wind rushing toward him from a thousand miles away; he could look up through the interlocked branches of the trees and discover the stars, so like eyes. But the wind rushed past him, and these stars seemed to the man to be looking not at him but just beyond his brow, as though he did not exist, as though his existence were merely a delusion under which he suffered. The great trees over his head brushed together, whispered together; they were full of little murmurous voices, calmly discussing matters beyond his knowledge or understanding.

If he had had a tent he might have shut out the universe, for this is the function of a habitation. Not to shut ourselves in, but to shut the world outside the door. But he had no tent. He was traveling light. He had a little food, and he was able to shoot some game as he advanced; he had matches and an ax and cooking gear, and he had a single blanket. At night he scooped away snow to make walls around his little fire, and he bedded himself, half recumbent, on boughs laid upon this heaped snow; and he woke every few minutes to replenish his fire. But the walls of snow did not shut out the forest. The trees over his head could look down upon him if they chose to do so; it was the more maddening because they did not choose. The stars could see him, but their attention seemed to be fixed on a point just past his brow.

He could not even banish the cold with his little fire; the air, full of icy particles, wreathed itself around him; crystals of ice formed and grew upon his beard and the collar of his hood; cold stole up into his body from the snow; cold stabbed him from above; he had not sufficient food, and he ate sparingly, so that not even when he was moving did warmth fill his veins. He was always in this embrace of the cold, and though he fought against her like a sluggish lover, she still twined her arms about him and he felt her cold breast forever against his own, beseeching him to yield himself to her.

He began at last to permit himself to look forward to the end of his journey. Four days would do it; then three; then two; and finally, huddling shiveringly beside his fire, he saw the dawn of the day that, barring mischance, should bring him to haven.

Impatience began to stir in his blood; he was in such haste to be forward that at noon he did not even stop to boil the kettle, but pressed on. A little after noon he came down into the ravine of a brook where once he had set his

traps, and as he moved steadily forward he saw now and
then a leaning tree, an old windfall, or a great bowlder
which marked the location where one of these sets had
been. The very familiarity of these scenes comforted him
like a home-coming. There was, he knew, no one trapping
here now; the man with whom for two winters he had
shared the cabin ahead had gone to other fields. But he
and his partner had left provender in the hidden cabin;
he counted on being able to sustain himself there, to live
through the winter. The stout walls would shut out the
vastness of the wilderness, and within the cabin he would
have memories for companions—would not be so lonely
there.

He debouched from the ravine into a wider, where the
small stream joined a greater, and so pursued his way,
and he came to the dead water above the beaver dam
where he and his partner had once taken many beaver.
His glance turned that way as he passed, and then abruptly the man stopped and tried to focus his weary eyes.
For better vision he removed from his face the dark handkerchief which he had worn like a veil, as a protection
against the glare from the snow. Out in the pond a stake
protruded through the ice; a stake to which he had secured traps. The thing which had caught his eye was the
fact that about this stake there were low mounds of snow.
A moment's scrutiny satisfied him that his first glance had
told the truth. Some one had been trapping here this winter; had been here, no doubt, before the last fall of snow;
must be in the cabin now.

The discovery awoke in the desperate and lonely man
a tumult of conjecture. His need was great and instant;
he must find shelter and warmth and food. Yet he was
under the necessity of avoiding his fellow men, avoiding

their accusing eyes, avoiding their rumor and report. The alternatives confronting him were critical and he tried to weigh them in cold blood, but his weariness was too great. His attempts to think clearly, to judge accurately, resulted merely in a more complete fuddling of his mental processes. He was not even conscious that he had moved forward until he discovered that his feet were following an old trail beneath the later fallen snow.

The fact that this trail must lead to the cabin he sought came home to him with maddening force, destroying all his caution, nullifying his inhibitions, as the first sip of water wakes a devil of desire in one dying of thirst. Even though destruction lay just ahead, this man had no strength left to avoid it; he plunged onward more swiftly along the trodden trail.

By the cabin door he kicked off his rackets, threw himself down the tunnel-like slope of snow and grasped the latch. Even then, before opening, he hesitated once more, despairingly certain that his own destruction lay within.

But when he opened the door and the man in the cabin turned to look at him, the fugitive suffered such a flood of relief that it was almost more than he could bear. He had been so unutterably lonely; he had striven so desperately to reach the poor comfort of familiar scenes, of a once-known shelter, of a solitude a little less alien than the vast solitude through which he journeyed; he had known despair in the discovery that this goal of his had already been seized upon by another, presumably a stranger; had taken counsel of desperation and chosen to risk destruction for the small portion of comfort he might find within these walls; and then, when all his hopes were at an ebb, fortune had granted him an inexpressible reassurance and relief.

For the man in the cabin, who looked up at his entrance, was his partner, a friend he counted stanch and true.

His name was Mat Rullen, this patient and indomitable traveler through the wilderness. A rude, strong man, who had known the rough spots of the North. He had washed gold and he had mined gold; he had worked for hire and he had slaved like a serf for his own ends; he had fought and won; he had fought and been vanquished. He had striven through a long winter to earn the price of a week's debauch; he had won and lost a fortune in a dozen hours' across a split-slab table littered with greasy cards. He had loved a woman, his mother, and she died; he had loved another, his wife, and she died. He had loved men and they died or went away from the place in which he dwelt. He had moved restlessly from one camp to another, one post to another.

There was in him a curiously sensitive imaginative streak; it made him the prey of hours of bitter depression, when he was but poor company. It made him draw back when those among whom his days were cast would have gone forward; it made him go forward when they drew back. In the casual encounters of life it had lost him many friends; but one man had understood and borne with him; one man he had served well and loved as we love those whom we serve.

This man was Charlie Day; and Charlie Day it was whose countenance he saw when his dazed eyes learned to see through the gloom within the cabin.

They had met in a barroom brawl; had found themselves by chance back to back while a whirling group of men fought all about them; they had buffeted their way into the clear and struck hands and bunked that night together in Mat Rullen's tent. They worked a placer one long summer; they thawed and dug and washed a winter through; they abandoned that enterprise for this trapping territory and wintered together without a bitter hour; they parted at last when one of his moods of black regret drove Mat to harsh and ugly words—parted in a surface hatred. But that hatred on Mat's part was forgotten now; he only remembered the Charlie Day whom he had loved; and he saw Charlie's face with a great lump of happiness choking in his throat, with eyes so moisted that he could not see the lack of response in Charlie's steady glance returning his.

He said through cracked and swollen lips, "Charlie, old man!" and sat down limply upon the floor, half crawling toward the beautiful warmth of the stove. And Charlie stood by, neither assisting nor opposing him, while he warmed himself back to life again and while he eased off the pack and tugged the heavy parka over his head. And Mat talked to his old partner garrulously, senselessly, rejoicing in the sound of his own voice and in the certainty that there was some one to hear what he said; some human ear at hand attending to his words. He was at first conscious of no lack, no failure on the other's part; he desired merely to talk and to be heard.

"I heard you'd gone outside," he said over and over. "I never looked to find you here. I heard you'd gone outside, Charlie, old man. They said so. They said you'd took the last boat out." He looked at the other more attentively. "Somebody said you'd broke a leg; said you went out on crutches, Charlie; said you went home with a crutch under your arm."

Charlie asked at last, in a stony voice, "How come you here?"

And Mat told him, rambling and incoherently. "Overland," he said. "Overland. From the gulch. I had a placer there, working it alone. I come from there. Two weeks on the way. I pulled out of there and headed for the cabin here. I never looked to find you here, Charlie."

"What made you pull out of there?" Charlie insisted.

Mat made a gesture of despair. "One of those things," he explained. "It was old Willie Beam. Old Willie. He always was an old fool, and too much of a fool this time. He kep' pestering at me, in Nick's place, one night. There was a crowd there, but I didn't want to do with any of them. They bothered me; all I wanted was to be left alone. And Old Willie was drunk. Yes, he was drunk—and making big talk to me and the others; and they laughed at him. But he made me sick, Charlie. He made me sick. I didn't want him bothering. I tried to tell him so, Charlie." His tone was a plea. "I told him to leave me alone. I tried to get away from him, and I started to go out and go down to Dave's. But they laughed at that, and they said Old Willie was running me. So I stayed and he crowed over it. Yes, sir, Old Willie was right tickled because he bothered me."

He wiped a hand slowly across his forehead. "I got mad at him—and madder," he said laboriously. "And I talked to him. Yes, sir; I laid him out, talking to him. And Old Willie began to hop. He got mad, his own self. He hopped like a crow. And I was sick of him. And I told him so; and then he dragged that gun of his. Tried to stick it on me. I was too mad to fool with him. And then he was down, and the smoke in my nostrils, and my gun in my hand.

And Old Willie down and gasping and dying on the floor
—and hard looks for me."

He seemed to shudder. "He had his gun out," he repeated. "Had his gun on me. It was up to him. But they
said Old Willie wouldn't harm anybody; said I knew it;
said I ought to have took his gun and slapped his face and
left him be. I dared them all to take it up, but none of
them did. They wouldn't go after their guns, Charlie.
They just pulled back from me and lugged Old Willie
home and buried him. Folks liked him, Charlie; and they
never liked me."

"You hadn't any need of killing him," said Charlie.

Mat looked up at his old partner curiously. "He had
his gun on me," he protested. "That's what they said too,
but he had his gun on me. There wasn't anybody would
take it up with me, Charlie. They just let me alone. Never
come near me. Pulled back when I come around. I tried
to laugh at it, and then I begun to get lonesome, and nobody can stand that, Charlie. I couldn't talk to them.
They'd say, 'Sure, you had a right to. If you wanted to,'
they'd say. 'If you wanted to,' they'd say. But he had his
gun on me, Charlie."

He sat a moment silent, squatting on his hunkers, warm-
ing his hands about the stove, embracing it with his whole
body, bathing in its heat. "They wouldn't talk to me,
Charlie," he repeated. "They wouldn't even listen to me.
The story went down-river. It went around. Nick told me
it would go all over. 'They'll know about you anywhere
you go,' he told me. 'You better go outside,' he said.
'There won't anybody hook up with you here.' And I said
to him, 'He had his gun out,' I said. 'I had a right to drop
him.' And Nick just spit and says, 'Sure, if you wanted
to,' he says. So I couldn't stick it there, Charlie. And I hit

out for the cabin here. Figured to stay here the winter and make a stake of fur maybe and go outside in the spring."

He suddenly beamed with recollection. "But I never looked to find you here, Charlie. It's great, finding you. We can work together this winter now."

His wits were returning; he had the wit to expect an answer from Charlie, agreeing to this plan. But no answer came, so that he looked up at his old partner querulously; and Charlie met his eyes and said at last, steadily enough, shaking his head:

"No, Mat; you can't stay here."

Mat Rullen seemed not to hear this; he muttered, "Like old times, together here, Charlie."

And Charlie said again, more steadily, "You can't stay here."

There was silence then for a time while Mat chewed this and savored its bitter flavor. "Can't stay here, Charlie?" he repeated at last.

Charlie Day shook his head. "Why not, pardner?" Matt asked gently.

"Moll's here with me," said Charlie.

"Moll?"

"She's here with me," the other repeated; and Mat fell silent again, to chew upon this for a while.

She had no other name, this Moll. But Mat knew her. A woman. A woman impossible in any other surroundings save those which for years had been the background of his life—a woman large, ample, mild and beneficent: stalwart as a man, strong as a man, and as tender as a woman too. Not a promiscuous woman, but an itinerant.

She had come north with a man by the name of Sladen, a small man, a weakling, ill, who nagged at her unceasingly, fretted at her in an ill-tempered and irascible way.

In spite of which she lived with him and took care of him,
cooked for him and tended him till his cough disappeared
and his flabby muscles hardened and he became able to
hold his own with men. And one day he told her he was
sick to death of her, and Moll left him. She ran for a
season a rude boarding house, till one Wally Hurd drank
himself into dementia and became her charge; for him she
gave herself fully, sleeping neither night nor day so long
as he needed her solicitude.

There must have been much of the mother in this
woman, this Moll. To her, it was evident enough, men
were children still; she cared for them, humored them, disciplined them in mild ways, gave them what they desired,
all with the same large, impersonal and benign generosity,
always forgetful of herself, seeking only the need that she
might fill. Men spoke of her with scorn—until they fell
ill and needed her. She was unlovely—had too much the
appearance of a man for beauty's sake—but there was in
her broad countenance something eternal and calm and
full of peace. Yes, Mat remembered Moll.

His eyes searched the cabin. "Where's she at?" he
asked.

And Charlie Day explained. "She went out yesterday
morning on the south loop of traps," he said. "My leg's
bad still; I can't cover much ground. She does the heft
of it."

"Here with you?" Mat asked uncertainly.

"She took care of my leg," Charlie replied, as though
this would explain all to the other. "Staked me then and
fetched me in here. Freighted our grub and all up the
river before the freeze. I could get around now if I had
to, but she's willing. Works more'n a man would. I let

her." His eyes shone with a curiously petty light. "Might as well, long as she wants it so," he explained.

"The south loop?" Mat repeated. "She's due back here any time."

Charlie nodded. "So you got to move along," he repeated.

"I figured on staying here," Mat urged helplessly. "When I see you, I figured you'd want me. I can get along with Moll."

"We got only just enough to carry us," Charlie insisted. "Need what we've got."

"I can take some grub we left here," Mat insisted, clinging to straws.

"We allowed for that when we outfitted," Charlie told him. "Figure on using all there is. There ain't room for you here, Mat. You better hit for outside."

Mat sat for a moment very still; then a long shudder ran through his body and he huddled to the stove. "It's damned lonesome traveling," he pleaded.

"I never asked you to come here. I never asked you to kill Old Willie."

"I had a right to," Mat insisted plaintively.

"If you wanted to," Charlie agreed, unmoved.

And there was again silence then, and at its end Mat got slowly to his feet and began to beat the snow off his garments and off his pack traps. He said thoughtfully, "I was glad, finding you here, Charlie."

"You can see yourself you can't stay," Charlie implacably replied.

So Mat got into his gear, with slow and labored movements. "I might rest up a night," he suggested.

"She'll be back any time."

Mat glanced at the two bunks. "I can roll up on the floor."

"You'd do a lot of talking," Charlie told him.

Mat nodded. "I get a comfort out of talking," he agreed. "Ain't had anybody to listen for a long time now."

But Charlie showed no yielding, and Mat saw he would not yield. So a little later he went out through the cabin door and found a little wind was blowing, a little whispering, jeering wind which struck at his warmed cheeks with stabbing fingers and slashed at them with knives of driven snow. He stuck his feet into the loops of his snowshoes and looked down at the cabin door for a last glimpse of Charlie.

But Charlie Day had shut the door; so Mat turned patiently away.

It was late afternoon when he left the cabin; dusk was already fallen, but the snowlight guided his footsteps. And at first he went uncertainly with no definite goal in mind. This cabin had been his goal; in his thoughts for a fortnight past the world had ended here; there was nothing beyond.

But here he could not stay; instead must venture into that world beyond, that world which was nothing. And till now he had been sustained by the knowledge that his infinitely laborious progress was directed to a certain end, but now there was no such knowledge to support him. He was going nowhere; was simply going away from the cabin. There had been no time for a new plan to form in his thoughts. He was purposeless—and alone—and his estate was forlorn as Adam's, fleeing from the flaming sword.

His thoughts kept turning backward to the cabin and

to Charlie; to the warm cabin, with its stores of food and its soft bunks and Charlie comfortable there. Another man might have felt anger, but Mat Rullen was broken past resentment. He was in the full grip of overpowering loneliness and melancholy sorrow; his faltering footsteps lagged; it was only the habit of progress which kept him from halting, slumping down in the snow, submitting himself to be trodden by the galloping hoofs of the wind-driven snow. So he moved on, a derelict, adrift, lacking either home port or destination; and about him lay the great wilderness, calm in its own concerns, and the wind that blew disregarded him, brushed him carelessly; and the hurrying snow drifting on the wind stumbled and jostled past him, scurrying on. The trees over his head whispered pleasantly together like old women gossiping.

He came to a little corner under a bank where there was some shelter from the wind; and he made camp there, moving automatically. Kicked aside the snow with his rackets till he could tread down a more solid area; then removed the snowshoes and completed his excavation. Almost within reach of his hand two or three young pines, dead from overcrowding, stood ready for his fire. He broke a handful of twigs and started the little blaze and huddled over it, melting snow to boil his tea. The provisions in his pack were low. He thought he should have begged matches and salt and tea; these at least Charlie might have spared. For more substantial food he would have to trust his rifle, watch a chance on the morrow.

He ate a little, and broke some green boughs from a low-growing spruce and bedded them against the snow blanket about his fire and so lay down, seeking what measure of warmth he could find. Overhead the interlacing branches whispered; between them he could see the far, impersonal glances of the stars; past him flowed the wind. The pale light of his fire seemed to escape him, to radiate far through the night, through the branches into the bitter current of the outer airs, over the banked snow into the forest. There was nothing to keep it here where it would comfort him; the room in which he slept was the universe; his bed-fellows were the trees in their ranks for miles, the mountains on the horizon's rim, the infinitely distant stars. He was no more than a mote fallen from a sunbeam, a speck of dust waiting to be obliterated or swept away.

He drew his head within his blankets and tried thus to secure a counterfeit of privacy; to build for himself a small world in which though he might be alone he would still be of some consequence. But snow dusted against his cheek and the cold night wind burned him bitterly and the trees still whispered above his bed and the far stars pierced him with their gaze. He huddled closer, pressing the blanket against his eyes, and a stupor crept over him, a stupor that was no more than the noisome counterpart of sleep.

This man, this Mat Rullen, woke from his miserable slumber and dragged the blanket off his face and opened his eyes to see a figure revealed in the light of the fire—the figure of a woman, of the woman called Moll.

He rubbed at his face with his hands, and he watched while the woman busied herself. She put fresh boughs upon the fire till it crackled warmly. He saw beyond her a light hand sledge, upon which there was a load. Food, perhaps; blankets; the necessities of existence.

She did not speak, but he at last found words. "That you, Moll?" he asked.

She nodded. "Charlie told me," she explained briefly. "Don't you bother now."

"Where's Charlie?" he asked.

"He can get along," she replied.

She had, he saw, a kettle boiling; presently held toward him the scalding tea and bade him drink. "You'll sleep better," she said.

"What did you come for?" he asked.

"I'm coming to take care of you," she replied.

The tea ran through him like revivifying fire. It raced through his veins in a scorching flood; he welcomed the agonizing pain. Peace stole through him.

He was surprised to discover a curious phenomenon. The radiance and the heat of the fire no longer escaped into the illimitable universe. It was reflected from the lowest branches of the trees over his head; it rebounded from the banked snow; it clotted about the little fire itself. He could bathe his hands in it. The stirring wind went past them overhead, but it did not dip into the hollow where they were. He found that he could not even see the stars.

Moll took a fur robe from the sledge. She spread it over him and beside him, and she lay down and took him in her arms. He nestled against her warm body. Her coming had driven out the world; it was as though she brought with her a habitation, a haven, a home. And in this home the man was no longer lonely.

He slept in her arms, safely and secure.

EDWINA STANTON BABCOCK

MOOD AND IMPRESSION

I have never had a very conscious method in writing. I trust chiefly to the emotional strength of an impression, keep that impression by me, mull it over and speculate upon it a long time before I write an initial sentence. I have done very successful stories out of swift, slight, but sharp impressions. After I have written my introductory sentence, sometimes not for two years after I have had the "impression," the game is on and it is then merely a matter of mechanical adjustments to get carved out of the mass the things that seem to cohere with the impression.

In my story "Gargoyle" (republished three times) the whole story was written from an initial glimpse of a strange a-typical boy looking intently into the interiors of some tiger lilies. I did not write the story until after the death of some one I loved.

In "Dunelight" I saw the two people in the rain in Oxford, night after night, and heard them play and sing. I wrote the story, eight drafts of it, to see if I could make apparent to the reader the way some one conviction about life adheres to various emotional states . . . "Dunelight" being in reality remembered light on a sandy dune that gave the girl courage for all life.

In "The Eggwoman" (*Classmate*) I built the story around an actual character and actual surroundings, but it was the curious charm and the delight in the *shapes* of eggs of all kinds that dynamoed the story.

I thought once of attending some of the more recent short-story courses but refrained because I saw the tendency to pattern in the work that was turned out. I don't like pattern to be repeated. It seems to me that all structure is fascinating and of significance only as long as it builds itself out of the raw material by some uncodified, unstandardized urge within its creator . . . It is true that wasps seem to like repeating to build their nests the same way, but I am not a wasp.

SCROGGINS and his young wife lived in "proper" lodgings in London until they found out that what was considered "proper" wages no longer paid for "proper" lodgings. By that time it was spring, so they bought the caravan that Slobbers of Bickley was willing to part with for three pounds. Red and blue window glass and a cooking stove were put in by a Maida Vale glazier.

They harnessed to it the lame white horse that Uncle Darbey of Shepherds' Bush wanted to turn out to grass. The two started caravaning along the country roads until they came to Oxford.

London chaps had advised Scroggins.

"Why not do as London chaps were doing? Were the sidewalk artists to have it all their own way? Such swank, with their white ships, blue seas, and red sunsets, they always sitting down to it!" London chaps, like Harry Scroggins, unemployed, had zoned the city musically, apportioning to this square a quartet, to that avenue a trio of harp, violin, and clarinet. The lavender venders and white heather women were warned that they must keep to morning hours. After dinner, below windows where tourists sipped their coffee, the street musicians came.

"London chaps made seven or eight pounds a night in the fog and bad weather as well."

Nobody in all England could pay a living wage. But the tourists had begun again. The great steamships were bringing whole villages over. There were Americans everywhere—especially women, with young hats, indulgent smiles, flat voices. They were all the same—dingy skins,

[1] From *Ladies' Home Journal*, June, 1925. Reprinted by permission of the author.

white frills, summer furs; the Americans liked sentimental songs.

"Harfter they've been spending money hall day, it makes 'em feel good to feel sad," observed one British Museum bobby.

The tried and true policeman at Westminster remarked that "the more the chaps sing 'Somewhere a Voice Is Calling,' or some other gloomy matter, the better the Americans caught on, which was strange, as in speaking they liked their joke."

"My wife can sing," said Harry Scroggins. "I can play the flute then. I play fine. We might take to the street stuff."

He repeated this when the caravan drew up at the Crown and Thistle in Hediston, again when they stopped at the Black Horse on the Iffley Road, again when they halted on the outskirts of Oxford.

"Do 'ee," remarked Oxford advisers.

So Scroggins and his wife "took to it." They took to it with method. They left the caravan in a field by a deep lane on the High Wycombe Road and walked in past Magdalen Bridge down to Carfax Tower, where they mingled with the throngs of Oxford. Once there they had supper at a carmen's pull-up near Folly Bridge, then plodded up to the Hotel Randolph opposite St. John's College in St. Giles Place.

Here they paused. Before the great dark iron doors they stared at the hotel opposite. It was raining a fine light rain, hardly more than a mist. The weather-stained stone buildings were bruised white and black. The hotel opposite looked importantly comfortable. A fat Welsh porter, with an air something between a bishop and a general, was ushering in a newly arrived auto party. The two street musicians could see this party enter the dining room, take their seats with the American air of cosseted fatigue.

Joan and Harry wore raincoats and pulled-down felt hats, from which the moisture dripped. The Northumberland girl dared not lift her solemn dark eyes to the plate-glass windows, nor to the windows above. After their slow travel of country summer, all this city life seemed hard and forbidding.

They shyly consulted.

"Will you sing then?" demanded Harry. He fumbled with the fingers that put together his flute.

"Eh, I'm too muckled," confessed the young wife.

Joan Scroggins was dismayed. She kept her head down, trying hard to control the furious beating of her heart.

"I'll play first." Scroggins was protecting.

"Ho, 'Arry, will 'ee?" His wife was grateful.

Harry, without answer, tuned his flute. He was cool and superior, the assured, highly rated musician, not at all doubting his skill, merely fussy and slightly off key.

The opening of the overture to "Zampa"! Scroggins felt sure of this piece. He had played it as a little boy to admiring friends in a tea room back of the fruit shop kept by his mother in Plymouth. He had played it as a youth under raspberry vines in the sloping fields back of the river Tamar, and to galoots and sailors along the promenade by the Hove. He had played it in the trenches to war-broken youth on rat-worried nights, and had at last played it triumphantly to Joan in Pinnacle, by the Sea of Northumberland, where the romance of old castles was in the air, and where the lighthouse flowered among the rocks that walled one great white dune. "Toot-toot, toot, tee, toot, tee."

The bicycle bells of Oxford sounded cheerily in the street back of them. White-bearded scholars in knickers pedaled studiously by; automobiles passed in sedate slowness. There was a sober sidewalk throng taking its way to the cinema. A man with a wag's face passed trundling a hand-wagon full of carefully scrubbed turtles and calling: "Egyptian turtles for gardens." Indeed, these turtles were Egyptian in so far as they were taken from the Oxford river called Isis.

Another waggish man sauntered by with a basketful of little puppies, which he shouted cheerfully were "just now out of Ireland." Whether by Ireland he meant dog-mother or doggèd country no one stopped to inquire.

Two girls stood in the light evening drizzle selling flowers from English gardens. They wore broad hats, roughly turned up in the back; their dark summer dresses had short sleeves; their arms were coarse and red; but their slender feet were neat in black stockings and well-polished shoes.

The man and woman in the tattered raincoats were somber figures against this rainy-cheerful background. "Zigzag zig" went the feeble flute opening of "Zampa." In the hotel hardly any one turned to hear. At last, however, a leisurely automobile salesman strolled from his table to have a look at the weather. He had a well-considered cigar in his mouth. As he lighted this his eyes took in the two forlorn street figures. He motioned to another man and two women, who joined him. Two girls appeared at a window higher up and a white-haired woman at a window on the corner.

"It was too bad," the Americans thought. No employment. These two young figures stark on the rainy street. So glum. Different from the street singers one saw in

Spain and Naples! That ridiculous little flute, and "Zampa," commonplace "Zampa," done to death already by a thousand whirling disks, a million hotel orchestras and bands and amplifiers, pooh-pooh-poohed out there in the rain!

"Toss 'em a coin." The automobile salesman, chuckling, removed his cigar, felt in his pockets. "Rotten, that flute. Toss 'em a coin, then they'll go away."

He opened the window and cast forth two coppers. "Huh, huh, huh!" the automobile salesman chuckled. "That feller looks like a rube; Bacchus playing on a clothespin." The auto salesman had learned his classics from advertisements of auto tires. Upstairs the two American girls looked soberly down into the darkening street. One of them waved to the street singers. This girl wore an orange jersey; a wide orange felt hat at a daring angle made her dark hair and eyes of a histrionic depth. In her belt was a loose bunch of blue flax flowers, over her shoulders a scarf of the same Aegean blue. She was smileless, with the grave, critical look of present-day youth. The other girl threw down some sixpences wrapped in a bit of newspaper.

At this Joan looked up. Scroggins had instructed the Northumberland wife that no matter how small the coins were, one should nod and smile politely. But he had not said what one should do for sixpences—several. Slowly the North of England girl raised solemn eyes. Again the Americans waved. Scroggins looked at his wife. "You've to sing now," he said shortly. He was not rough, but the quiet English intonation meant obedience.

The tall Coast girl winced. "Ho, 'Arry." She had long ago adopted London cockney.

Her broad figure, already a little misshapen and uncouth in the long ragged raincoat, the felt hat pulled down over her firmly built face, made a strong contrast to that slender orange-and-blue figure above. Womanhood questioned womanhood. What did that girl up there think of this girl below? The rain began to pelt; Joan's feet in the great rough shoes were wet and cold.

"Ho, 'Arry. Don't mike me. I can only gugg along," she faltered. "It's not good singing, mine; I niver sang only to you." Forlornly in the rain she pleaded with him.

Harry moved one step toward her; his tall thin figure in the raincoat was severe. But his light mellow voice had rare English tenderness as he admonished, "Now—now, miss! 'Tisn't as if it was only us two. Carn't you think of something?" Harry's smile to her was shy. "Of the Little Him," coaxed the young fellow. "It might help."

He had chosen the right rallying. The North Coast woman steadied to her job. "Right y'ar." Joan did not plead longer; she stood submissive while Scroggins blew feelingly a tootling prelude to her song.

"I'll sing thee songs of Araby."

Joan knew nothing about Araby; indeed, thought that Araby was some kind of tobacco. But sensing that when you sang you must have something in your mind, and something you liked—as well—she had gotten the habit when singing of thinking about the dune at home.

The dune had been her one marvel; a silver patch in the black rocky coast. It had stayed in her mind long after she had left the sea.

It had been the dune that she invariably had in mind when she had sung to Harry the first days of their marriage; that must be why Harry had come to like the singing.

The dune! Always unclimbable, always white samite, mirage. Almost singing of itself as the wind shifted it and the foam ran up to it. When the hot sun shone and there was mist off the sea it looked like a smoking mountain of white fire.

It was by the dune all through the last summer of the war that Joan had prayed for Harry. The dune had swallowed her terrified horror of death when her mother went from her. The dune had given white breast of comfort after her stern father's beatings. She had played house by it, thinking of Harry.

After that the effort to live in London; then spring fields of England, newborn lambs, colts, and kids, brooks full of forget-me-nots.

While their little caravan halted in deep lanes or by gray ivied walls or in star-roofed fields, the girl had thought dreamily of the dune. The tremulous shimmering shape seemed to follow her.

Now, as she sang, she went over in her slow mind dune pictures—a single gull, his white wings balancing, his shadow on the crest; the sea at the foot, a lazy blue weave of bright ripple ropes, surflike white dogs, leaping to catch the shore as it ran away, a hunted thing, straining from the water's white nets. At other times just Dunelight, white glimmer of sand and heat. The rain fell thicker during Joan's song. The windows of St. John's College were orange in black-and-gray walls. The Martyr's Memorial lifted its venerable challenge into muffled gray.

"I'll sing thee songs of Araby."

The great untrained voice soared out over the houses fronting St. Giles Place. The tones were round, smooth, curiously fresh and deep. There were no phrasings nor cultivated blendings. Joan chopped off her lines with remorseless peasant logic. Harry fluted trim little patterns around her stiff melody. The street for her had become a welter of dim rain, the bright knockers stood out, the wooden college doors with their studded nails seemed shut sternly against her; she noticed the fresh-faced summer-school boys yawning the inevitable Oxford yawn.

"I'll Sing Thee Songs of Araby," then "Somewhere a Voice Is Calling," and then Tosti's "Good-bye." For these songs, London chaps said, were what the Americans liked after they had had ice water and open fires and banana splits and the other things they liked.

At last Dunelight wavered; suddenly Joan knew the flute had ceased its accompaniment. She stood there, head down, miserable. The people up there in the windows were no doubt thinking it shameful that a North Coast girl in this state should wander around the streets singing instead of staying modestly home. Then she grew gladder than it is often given human beings to be glad.

For there was Harry picking up a perfect shower of half-crowns and sixpences, little packets of coppers and, unbelievable, one twisted pound—one pound for the Little Him!

It was the girl in the orange jersey who threw down the pound. Up there in the window her dark face in its daring, dramatic hat brooded down on that other woman-face. She leaned out and called down into the rain. "Lovely," she said. *"Lovely!"*

"Lovely?" Singing like that in the rain! "Aw!" Joan was incredulous.

Then the two left St. Giles Place. They wandered around to Wellington Square, which was "in" the University, and where they knew there would be more tourists and motorists. Again they sang and played until the evening grew late, and they relievedly took themselves to Boffin's, down by Carfax, where all the busses started. Here with hot tea and scones they heartened themselves before they walked out home over the High Wycombe Road where the rain fell on the caravan and the old white horse staggered up from under a wet tree.

All the long plodding way the two serious souls were, for them, ecstatic, for if it went on as it had begun there would be fifteen or twenty pounds a week. So far they had all Oxford to themselves; the Americans scattered money; the field was wholly theirs. A pound a week to live on, and the rest put by for the Little Him!

It grew warm summer, but cool winds came down from Chiltern Hills. The fields were dry stubble that smelled sweet; yew hedges ran high to larch lanes. Great wedges of gold and silver haystacks were sliced like half-cut cakes. There were fringes of rosy willow herb and forget-me-nots and foxglove along the shining curve of the willowed rivers. Massive trees shadowed the slopes where once the Scholar-Gypsy strayed.

It was easy living in summer. Harry got milk and fresh eggs from Godstow, and bread and cheese could be bought at a dairy in Hediston. Near them was Forest Hill, and the little gray church where Milton was married. Here, following dim human promptings, they sometimes went to kneel and pray. There was excitement here for Joan; she would listen with awe while Harry read the list of persons a man must not marry:

"A man must not marry his grandmother," and so forth.

The North Coast girl would question Harry as to such

things. They lay out under a little holly tree and the silver tumble of unbound Oxford bells would come faintly to them.

One night Harry motioned to those far-off Oxford towers crocketed with stars.

"There's a college down there for laboring men. It's not harf bad. Learning puts heart into a man so he can take his own part."

"A man's more better with an education than with a gun." The young things out of their bitter World War learning decided this. They therefore decided that the Little Him, when he grew up, should go to that laboring man's college at Oxford.

Joan's dark eye in the round, simple face turned inquiringly to Harry's keener gaze. "The mothers in the States never plan for their babies to be workin' men. They tell them: 'You're to be President,' and the babies believe it."

"Everybody carn't be President, you know," objected Harry, then true to tradition: "He shall take his work and his smackings like a man."

"Aw! I'll never smack him. And when there is no work in all the world with fair pay?" Joan was passionately sarcastic. "Look at it!" she demanded.

Harry smoked. He did not at once answer. His face had that stony, oblivious calm against which many an English wife must beat in vain.

"You're not to get hexcited," he reproved her. "Would you like a sweet?" He asked it with indulgent cadence, but his voice was austere and sure; it was his belief that women should be comforted and controlled, not understood.

Harry held out the bag of penny sweets. Joan humbly took one. The bag was returned to Harry's pocket. She knew that she was to be quiet now and quit planning for her baby until such time as Harry said the word. And so in silence she obediently ate the sweet.

Her husband waited patiently while she sucked it, then as patiently and parentally he taught her a new song. It was one he had heard while acting as waiter in a London hotel. An American singer had sung it.

> "In the deep night a little bird
> Wakens, or dreams he is awake."

They pronounced the last word, "awike." First Harry played the air on his flute. Then over again. Then he made her repeat the words. Finally she must try to sing both air and words.

Clumsily feeling for the thing, her broad honest mouth tried to do his bidding.

> "In the deep night a little bird
> Wakens, or dreams he is awike;
> Cheerily clear one phrase is heard,
> And you almost feel the morning brike.

> "In the deep dark of loss and wrong,
> One face like a lovely dawn will thrill.
> And all night long at my heart a song
> Suddenly stirs and then is still."

At first the girl, indifferent and dulled by the wandering life they had lived, long tramps and insufficient food, the solemn ways of days and nights and rain and wind, rebelled against this learning of new songs. Joan was gradually feeling elemental languor, as if she were a plant around whose roots the soil had stiffened and swelled, shrouding these roots in organic fire. She would look wonderingly at Harry, his long figure, lean in the waist,

strong in back, lying prone under the little holly tree,
his cap off his tousled English hair, his flute to his lips
as he faithfully ran over the difficult passages in "William
Tell." At last, however, the liquid sounds relaxed the
tense woman-being; the strange, communicative strength
of a healthy man, the very relief of this man's stern
masterfulness came soothingly to Joan. Gratefully she
knew a woman's old, contrary, not too civilized joy of being disciplined. The North Coast girl softened and was
submissive.

"Are you ready then?" asked Harry.

The dumb Northern eyes answered. She obediently sang
over and over bars and words as he taught. At last in the
wondering sense of her own conquering came a strange
quiver, an exultant something swimming up to the surface of the great young voice. This something changed the
voice somewhat, somewhat impaired its clarity, but was a
rapturous vibration that caused the severe tutor to eye
his wife with wonder.

"You like it, my girl." Harry was at once cold and
tender, as only an Englishman may be. "Whatever is it
you say you're thinking of when you're at the singing?"
He demanded it suspiciously, yet with indulgent patron-
age.

"Aw!" begged Joan. She colored. She could not
explain.

But again he asserted authority. This thing might be
dangerous to their success, he informed her. It was well
known that Joan had no musical training, whereas he,
Harry, had played in the Plymouth band at the Hove
open-air concerts and had been invited to play in the
Silvertown band in Oxford.

Things went very well all summer, except that Harry

became slightly discouraged. He, who really loved his music and spent many hours painfully trying to recall airs played by the various types of musicians who had visited the war camps, found that when he and Joan performed together his contributions were ignored. Nobody, if they could hear the singer, wanted to hear the piper! "It's your singing they like best, my girl." The husband admitted it with a sigh. Poor Joan was dismayed. In trying to please him she had displeased him!

So, another evening, when they stood before The Clarendon, Joan did her wifely best to sing badly. She fairly shouted her songs with short breath and manifest indifference. Also, the huskiness of pregnancy was evident. But it made no difference. She had become in Oxford a tradition. The tourists passed her from mouth to mouth: "A North Coast girl with a voice like the Giant's Causeway."

The misshapen young figure in the raincoat did the rest. When the great raw voice went up they got the rare quality and enormous range; the possibility of all that lay within the street singer was apparent to a race whose eye and ear are trained to discriminate in all but its own defects. The Americans were crazy over Joan.

"But she's not doing her best tonight. Poor thing, she ought not to be doing it at all."

"Ye gods, how she soared on the Gull, of Sinding's—savage skirling! How did the girl pick it up?"

"How can she sing at all with that bad position—chin down, no knowledge of how to breathe?"

How does a wave know how to gather and curl and tower and topple and—break?

For it was like that with Joan now. At the words of the song "In the Deep Night," the woman was at home in a woman's world. Joan was seeing Dunelight, as on all nights the world is full of women struggling toward it. The half-sick girl built up that tower of shimmering light, saw it in her mind, shimmering, rising like a great white tree, and sang it. But up in the top of the white tree was not that "Little Bird" of the song, but the Little Him— the Little Him, his arms stretched out to her, his baby face something like Harry's, turned to a life that should not, no, should not, be all labor!

It was easy to finish the song with the Little Him, bright and shining in the Dunelight, and the shillings and half crowns spattering, tingling, ringing down!

The season waned. After Bank Holiday, soft English voices sounded less frequently where the punts glided under the willows. The iron-nailed doors of St. John's Gardens were closed, fewer children came to Worcester Garden to feed the swans.

One coldish night in early September Harry stood in Wellington Square alone. Only a few coppers fell, people at the windows soon turned away, though it seemed to Harry that he played much more jauntily than when his wife was with him.

He trudged back along the High Wycombe Road, wroth with the stars because they looked like bright half crowns and there were none of these in his pockets.

"I must learn a new tune," Harry decided. "The Americans are the same with the music as it is with the ice water and fire; when you bring them the one, it's the other they want."

As he turned into the night fields where the caravan was, he realized that henceforth he must go it alone, also that it was Joan's unskilled voice that had brought the money. He was provoked with her that she could no longer sing, yet a certain canniness checked his feeling. He would not scold Joan. "After all, we're not talking of music, we're talking of money," stated Harry gravely to himself. "I'd better not be killing the golden calf—by scolding, I mean."

He said this to Joan, who smiled her slow smile and could not see what he meant at all. And when he mentioned casually, but craftily, that he had never understood just what she meant by all that silly talk about Dunelight, and she might just as well explain again—her words being at the best poor—she merely sulked. "I don't want to," objected poor Joan.

Harry went over to the bunk where she lay under the kerosene lamp wobbling on its bracket. His cold fair face looked down on her.

"So it's balky you are," began the young Londoner sternly, showing grim displeasure.

But the girl put up her hand to him weakly; the pure look of love in her eyes was something to make a man uncomfortable. It struck Harry that Joan looked like something wild, caught in a trap—something wild, whose eyes were liquid fright. He questioned her rather fiercely; he was uneasy, as though he stood in the presence of a mystic.

" 'Arry, it's too much to siy. I feel something strange, as if I was God; all tonight, lying here alone, it hasn't been just me and then God like the two of us. It's been me with God, the Same Person."

"Ow!" remarked Harry with cold English finality. Then he reproved her. "You're not to say a thing like that. God is no woman."

But she replied slowly and obstinately that that might be for him, but for her it was different. For her, all that night, the stars and trees, the very shining rivers and sheep and hills had said: "We're all God together, you and us, Joan—and yet outside of that there is always more of God, always out and beyond everything," muttered Joan a little wearily.

Harry thought it best to deal lightly with this. "Are you God now?" he asked disrespectfully, adding with briskness: "For if you're not, I'd like to teach you another song. I wouldn't be teaching God anything, of course," remarked ironical Harry.

After the rehearsal Harry determined to search out this Dunelight matter. He questioned his wife very closely. She must hide nothing from him. Harry's ambition as a practitioner on the flute was roused. It was this young person's idea to get the dynamic influence of a dune back of his own accomplishment. If seeing a dune in one's mind made one's music more acceptable, then Harry was willing to see any number of dunes. The thing was, the young fellow decided, to get a precise and correct estimate of Joan's dune, and then if the matter were not too emotionally wasteful, to set up a precise, correct, and superior dune of one's own. "Two dunes," thought practical Harry, "ought to be better than one."

His young wife turned obediently, leaning to him. Under the kerosene light she told him about the white tower of sand, the shimmering bastions of that one great dune on the North Coast. Its crest was like a white tree, at the foot of it the blue hammock of sea-swung, bright ripple-ropes. Recently, so Joan confessed, she had got a little confused, for now on the top where the green grass waved against the sky, there was a little form different to a bird—no bird, indeed, but a little form that waved and smiled and called to her—the Little Him.

"Dunelight—" Suddenly the girl threw herself forward on Harry's breast. There was a pitiful catching of the breath—the great, submerged, sobbing voice. Maybe she wouldn't—

"Now, we haren't going to hexcite you," said Harry calmly.

He was convinced that he knew how to deal with a wife who had fears. He reached up into the pocket of his coat, hanging on a nail under the little tin kerosene lamp, and extracting another sweet, gave it to his wife, watching her suck it as one watches a child. Joan, though the sweet upset her, was grateful. After that Harry went out into the night where the holly tree blotted the stars. He sat down and smoked, deciding that soon it would be time to have a doctor for Joan, and that on their next trip for the singing he would himself try out the Dunelight. He might do worse!

At last came the night that brought the terror of Creation on them both. Joan had become some one Harry did not know. She was a frantic woman, turning fiercely, gaspingly on him. "Ho, 'Arry, don't stand there! Are we doin' right, alone here in the woods and fields?" With shuddering breath, with age-old desperation: "I—need help."

Harry broke then; knelt to her almost like primitive savage, so suddenly of earth and sky and sea she seemed, like no woman Harry had ever known, yet so elementally of every woman and man that had ever been. For a moment he let his young wife cling, then gently put her down again; his voice had cold English tenderness. That mastery took her. "Steady you are! They have a telephone at the pub out on the High Wycombe Road. I'll meet the chap who drives the bus goin' by. He'll get the message right into Oxford, and the doctor will come."

With British slowness and faithfulness this was accomplished. The doctor came, a nurse and ambulance with him. At the hospital they seemed a little hurried. There were signs and indications. It was agreed the baby would in all likelihood live. The surgeon had them give Joan something to soothe the paroxysms. She remained conscious, however, as he worked with her. Soon he encouraged, looking into the dilated eyes: "Your little fellow will soon be singing himself."

The surgeon, however, accustomed to these things, was arrested by her deep, passionate look of elemental pride.

"He's to go to college," gasped Joan.

Then the groveling pains sprang on her. The surgeon could not know that at his few encouraging words the white shimmer of the light over the dune slowly rose, that there flowered with many towers and bastions that Tree of Life that was like a castle, a castle that for the moment seemed blind to her in the glare of a setting sun. The Little Him stood waving—"I'll sing thee songs of Araby." . . . Ah, who was to tell a baby that Araby was undoubtedly only some kind of tobacco?

They let Harry come in from that trance in the corridor where husbands wait, looking down into the pit of conjecture. Dunelight had done some things for Joan; the surgeon and nurse had done some things; but another Practitioner had stepped in. No one told the young father the exact truth; they knew how the truth gets to one who loves.

Two feelings cut across Harry's heart like taut ropes sawing. There was that little thing that already sprawled and kicked, certainly the beginning, a very good beginning, of the Little Him—their Little Him!

"Joan, don't you care?"

Harry, staring at his wife, saw that expression he had

sometimes seen on her face when she sang. He flung himself down by the bed; the two clasped as they had clasped under the holly tree, only Joan let go so soon. It was no longer summer; Harry suddenly realized that—Joan was cold.

There was plenty of kindness for him that week. There was also the dole tardily given indeed; but that wasn't the thing.

Harry, sitting dazed on a bench in Christ Church Gardens, watched the swans trimly pass and repass while he tried to work it out. How to keep near Joan? At last he decided that there would be more of her left by the little holly tree out in the field by Forest Hill than here. So out there in the autumn silence he smoked his pipe in November dusk, watching rooks spraddling through the stubble and gray sheep move into grayer distance. "I'll do well to play the songs she sang," decided Harry.

Late in November, though the street musicians had fallen off in London, Harry stood in Wellington Square where the window boxes had ceased blooming and the curtains had been taken from before the green doorways, where fuel was scarce and food high, but where all the brass knockers and door plates were brightly polished and the stone entrance steps whitewashed.

Harry stood there almost apologetically, for it had long ago been borne in upon him that people did not care much for his flute. He had grown timid, also very brave, because the Little Him at a day nursery in Oxford was flourishing and Harry must provide a good home for him and a good caretaker. Money must somehow come showering down from those windows.

"We're not thinking of Joan, we're trying to get money," Harry reminded himself.

His heart then winced like a thing kicked to death. Not thinking about Joan? Every building on the street thought of her, the bicycle bells rang her, the lights in the windows blurred like eyes looking for her.

There had once been a woman who tramped the rainy streets with him, and because she was a woman saw a thing called Dunelight. Harry now, estimating himself very carefully, knew that he was no musician, nothing but a poor English wastrel, a bit of wreckage from the war, a scarecrow that tooted on a little stick that broke up into three pieces for which music, though he had been called a good player, he never got more than half a crown an evening. It was Joan who had gotten the money and had then gone out and gotten the Little Him. Did that—did everything by this queer thing she called Dunelight!

"Last Night the Nightingale Woke Me!" It was the only thing Harry had the heart to try. He stood there in Wellington Square, the rainy park behind him, before him the enigmatic lights of windows.

The young gentlemen were back for the winter term now. He could see here and there a curly pompadour, a long gawky neck, with white silk Henley collar. Some one in an upper apartment was playing from Elgar's "Dream of Gerontius." Harry got the storm and stress of the thing as the lad's hobbledehoy hands pounded it out.

When it ceased, the street musician deliberately put his flute to his lips. Harry raised dull eyes to those inhospitable windows. The light rain pattered dry leaves in Wellington Square. Suddenly, half-nervous trembling seized the street player. It was all changed; a whole submerged reflex of human sorrow took Harry by the throat. His mind became a great cave of black sorrows like bats

winging through. But Harry was English; he began
calmly to play:

> "Last night the nightingale woke me
>   Mid moonlight's silv'ry gleam.
> It sang from the shady hillside
>   And soft as in a dream. . . .
> I opened my window to hear it
>   And softly the song came through.
> The bird was thrilled, with rapture it trilled
>   And sang, dear, it sang, dear, of you."

The man, standing in the black rain-spattered street,
almost shuddered at what the thing brought back to him.
He was kicked all over now, not only that inert thing, his
heart, but his body. He dared not to look to one side, for
surely because of this sorrow kicking, some one tender and
pitying stood by him. Was it Joan? The flute notes waver-
ing out into the wet night were to Harry despairing and
remote, anguished human sorrow that he himself knew
about but could never make known. Did Joan stand by
him then? Harry's mind saw her, saw her more clearly
than ever before—in her old hat and raincoat, looking
her North Coast look of mild wonder and love.

"It's for the Little Him," said Joan very gently. Was
it her voice or the flute notes fluttering to this soft conclusion?

Harry did not look up at the windows, where now one
or two faces appeared; he was trying to remember what
things they two had done together; what songs had they
done best— For if Joan were to be with him in the music
—like this—

"Good-bye," was the one she had sung so well—Good-
bye to Summer. Well, it had been good-bye to summer for
them.

The rain thickened. This made the flute notes sound curiously dim; many faces came to see this street musician who played on such a dismal night.

"How that flute gets to you! It's surely not the same man we heard here last spring. There was a woman then."

Some one answered: "Poor thing, she died! There's a baby!"

The group was silent. Through the rain the flute notes strayed.

"In the deep dark of loss and wrong."

Harry was thinking that the flute seemed to say the very words as Joan had said them. It had been very hard to teach her to say these words correctly.

"One face like a lovely dawn will thrill."

That was how Joan had thought of the Little Him.

"And all night long at my heart a song—"

"The poor fellow. The war—English youth—broken—hungry—futureless. That picayune little flute—"

Windows one by one opened, half crowns and shillings and ten shilling notes in cigarette boxes! Many heads leaned out to call "Thank you" in the kindly American way. Even one or two English students cast down a copper, peering out, remarking authoritatively: "Right-o! That's all; thank you—and now you quit, you know."

But the Americans cast down more coins; they leaned out into the wet darkness repeating: "Thanks, thanks; lovely!"

English Harry raised his voice quite distinctly and said, "Thank you!" He said it curtly and politely.

They kept on pointing to the strewn money. He shut

up his flute very carefully and put it in the box; then stood there, looking up at the windows.

Again they pointed: "The money—the money."

Harry could not touch money, not just then—not for a moment. He had touched something else—Dunelight!

FANNIE HURST

CHARACTERS CREATE SITUATION

It is extremely difficult for me to trace a story back to its seedling stage. Nothing so concrete as "the moment of conception" ever seems to happen to me. I think this is mainly due to the fact that almost without exception I do not lift my characters or plots from concrete human beings or situations. I seem to say to myself something like this: given a certain type of human being how will he react under certain conditions?

In that way I find my characters come to life first and it is they who create their own situation and plot, so to speak. My characters invariably come first. I am somewhat inclined to think that this is true of most fiction writers except of course in the picaresque, detective and adventure story.

Or perhaps the wish is father to the thought because it seems to me the surer psychological tackle.

SHE WALKS IN BEAUTY [1]

By that same mausolean instinct that was Artemesia's when she mourned her dear departed in marble and hieroglyphics; by that same architectural gesture of grief which caused Jehan at Agra to erect the Taj Mahal in memory of a dead wife and a cold hearthstone, so the Bon Ton Hotel, even to the pillars with red-freckled monoliths and peacock-backed lobby-chairs, making the analogy rather absurdly complete, reared its fourteen stories of "elegantly furnished suites, all the comforts and none of the discomforts of home."

A mausoleum to the hearth. And as true to form as any that ever mourned the dynastic bones of an Augustus or a Hadrian.

It is doubtful if in all its hothouse garden of women the

[1] Reprinted by permission of the author and of the International Magazine Company (*Cosmopolitan Magazine*). Published August, 1921. Copyright, 1921.

Hotel Bon Ton boasted a broken finger-nail or that little brash place along the forefinger that tattles so of potato peeling or asparagus scraping.

The fourteenth story, Manicure, Steam-bath, and Beauty Parlors, saw to all that. In spite of long bridge-table, lobby-divan and *table d'hôte* séances, "tea" where the coffee was served with whipped cream and the tarts built in four tiers and mortared in mocha filling, the Bon Ton Hotel was scarcely more than an average of fourteen pounds over-weight.

Forty's silhouette, except for that cruel and irrefutable place where the throat will wattle, was almost inter-changeable with eighteen's. Indeed, Bon Ton grand-mothers with backs and French heels that were twenty years younger than their throats and bunions, vied with twenty's profile.

Whistler's kind of mother, full of sweet years that were richer because she had dwelt in them, but whose eyelids were a little weary, had no place there.

Mrs. Gronauer, who occupied an outside, southern-exposure suite of five rooms and three baths, jazz-danced on the same cabaret floor with her granddaughters.

Fads for the latest personal accouterments gripped the Bon Ton in seasonal epidemics.

The permanent wave swept it like a tidal one.

The beaded bag, cunningly contrived, needleful by needleful, from little colored strands of glass caviar, glittered its hour.

Filet lace came then, sheerly, whole yokes of it for *crêpe de Chine* nightgowns and dainty scalloped edges for cami-soles.

Mrs. Samstag made six of the nightgowns that winter, three for herself and three for her daughter. Peachblowy pink ones with lace yokes that were scarcely more to the skin than the print of a wave edge running up sand, and then little frills of pink satin ribbon, caught up here and there with the most delightful and unconvincing little blue satin rosebuds.

It was bad for her neuralgic eye, the meanderings of the *filet* pattern, but she liked the delicate threadiness of the handiwork, and Mr. Latz liked watching her.

There you have it! Straight through the lacy mesh of the *filet* to the heart interest!

Mr. Louis Latz, who was too short, slightly too stout, and too shy of likely length of swimming arm ever to have figured in any woman's inevitable visualization of her ultimate Leander, liked, fascinatedly, to watch Mrs. Samstag's nicely manicured fingers at work. He liked them passive, too. Best of all, he would have preferred to feel them between his own, but that had never been.

Nevertheless, that desire was capable of catching him unawares. That very morning as he had stood, in his sumptuous bachelor's apartment, strumming on one of the windows that overlooked an expensive tree and lake vista of Central Park, he had wanted very suddenly and very badly to feel those fingers in his and to kiss down on them. He liked their taper and the rosy pointedness, those fingers, and the dry, neat way they had of slipping in between the threads.

On this, one of a hundred such typical evenings in the Bon Ton lobby, Mr. Latz, sighing out a satisfaction of his inner man, sat himself down on a red velvet chair opposite Mrs. Samstag. His knees, wide-spread, taxed his knife-pressed gray trousers to their very last capacity, but he sat back in none the less evident comfort, building his fingers up into a little chapel.

"Well, how's Mr. Latz this evening?" asked Mrs. Samstag, her smile encompassing the question.

"If I was any better I couldn't stand it"—relishing her smile and his reply.

The Bon Ton had just dined, too well, from fruit-flip *à la* Bon Ton, mulligatawny soup, *filet* of sole, *sauté*, choice of, or both, Poulette *émincé* and spring lamb *grignon* and on through to fresh strawberry ice-cream in fluted paper boxes, *petit fours* and *demi-tasse*. Groups of carefully corseted women stood now beside the invitational plush divans and peacock chairs, paying twenty minutes after-dinner standing penance. Men with Wall Street eyes and blood pressure, slid surreptitious celluloid toothpicks, and gathered around the cigar stand. Orchestra music flickered. Young girls, the traditions of demure sixteen hanging by one inch shoulder-straps and who could not walk across a hardwood floor without sliding the last three steps, teetered in bare arm-in-arm groups, swapping persiflage with pimply, patent-leather haired young men who were full of nervous excitement and eager to excel in return badinage.

Bell hops scurried with folding tables. Bridge games formed.

The theater group got off, so to speak. Showy women and show-off men. Mrs. Gronauer, in a full length mink coat that enveloped her like a squaw, a titillation of diamond aigrettes in her Titianed hair and an aftermath of scent as tangible as the trail of a wounded shark, emerged from the elevator with her son and daughter-in-law.

"Foi!" said Mr. Latz, by way of—somewhat unduly perhaps—expressing his own kind of cognizance of the scented trail.

"Fleur de printemps," said Mrs. Samstag in quick

olfactory analysis. "Eight ninety-eight an ounce." Her nose crawling up to what he thought the cunning perfection of a sniff.

"Used to it from home—not? She is not. Believe me, I knew Max Gronauer when he first started in the produce business in Jersey City and the only perfume he had was seventeen cents a pound, not always fresh killed at that. Cold storage *de printemps*."

"Max Gronauer died just two months after my husband," said Mrs. Samstag, tucking away into her beaded hand-bag her *filet* lace handkerchief, itself guilty of a not inexpensive attar.

"*Thu-thu*," clucked Mr. Latz for want of a fitting retort.

"Heigh-ho! I always say we have so little in common, me and Mrs. Gronauer. She revokes so in bridge, and I think it's terrible for a grandmother to blondine so red; but we've both been widows for almost eight years. Eight years," repeated Mrs. Samstag on a small scented sigh.

He was inordinately sensitive to these allusions, reddening and wanting to seem appropriate.

"Poor, poor little woman!"

"Heigh-ho," she said, and again, "Heigh-ho."

It was about the eyes that Mrs. Samstag showed most plainly whatever inroads into her clay the years might have gained. There were little dark areas beneath them like smeared charcoal and two unrelenting sacs that threatened to become pouchy.

Their effect was not so much one of years, but they gave Mrs. Samstag, in spite of the only slightly plump and really passable figure, the look of one out of health.

What ailed her was hardly organic. She was the victim of periodic and raging neuralgic fires that could sweep the right side of her head and down into her shoulder blade with a great crackling and blazing of nerves. It was not unusual for her daughter Alma to sit up the one or two nights that it could endure, unfailing, through the wee hours, with hot applications.

For a week sometimes, these attacks heralded their comings with little jabs, like the pricks of an exploring needle. Then the under-eyes began to look their muddiest. They were darkening now and she put up two fingers with a little pressing movement to her temple.

"You're a great little woman," reiterated Mr. Latz, rather riveting even Mrs. Samstag's suspicion that here was no great stickler for variety of expression.

"And a great sufferer, too," he said, noting the pressing fingers.

She colored under this delightful impeachment.

"I wouldn't wish one of my neuralgia spells to my worst enemy, Mr. Latz."

"If you were mine—I mean—if—the—say—was mine, I wouldn't stop until I had you to every specialist in Europe. I know a thing or two about those fellows over there. Some of them are wonders."

Mrs. Samstag looked off, her profile inclined to lift and fall as if by little pulleys of emotion.

"That's easier said than done, Mr. Latz, by a—a widow who wants to do right by her grown daughter and living so—high since the war."

"I—I—" said Mr. Latz, leaping impulsively forward on the chair that was as tightly upholstered in effect as he in his modish suit, then clutching himself there as if he had caught the impulse on the fly—"I just wish I could help."

"Oh!" she said, and threw up a swift, brown look from the lace making.

He laughed, but from nervousness.

"My little mother was an ailer too."

"That's me, Mr. Latz. Not sick—just ailing. I always say that it's ridiculous that a woman in such perfect health as I am should be such a sufferer."

"Same with her and her joints."

"Why, I can outdo Alma when it comes to dancing down in the grill with the young people of an evening, or shopping."

"More like sisters than any mother and daughter I ever saw."

"Mother and daughter, but which is which from the back, some of my friends put it," said Mrs. Samstag, not without a curve to her voice, then hastily: "But the best child, Mr. Latz. The best that ever lived. A regular little mother to me in my spells."

"Nice girl, Alma."

"It snowed so the day of—my husband's funeral. Why, do you know that up to then I never had an attack of neuralgia in my life. Didn't even know what a headache was. That long drive. That windy hill-top with two men to keep me from jumping into the grave after him. Ask Alma. That's how I care when I care. But of course, as the saying is, time heals. But that's how I got my first attack. Intenseness is what the doctors called it. I'm terribly intense."

"I—guess when a woman like you—cares like—you—cared, it's not much use hoping you would ever—care again. That's about the way of it, ain't it?"

If he had known it, there was something about his own

intensity of expression to inspire mirth. His eyebrows lifted to little gothic arches of anxiety, a rash of tiny perspiration broke out over his blue shaved face and as he sat on the edge of his chair, it seemed that inevitably the tight sausage-like knees must push their way through mere fabric.

"That's about the way of it, ain't it?" he said again into the growing silence.

"I—when a woman cares for—a man like—I did—Mr. Latz, she'll never be happy until—she cares again—like that. I always say, once an affectionate nature, always an affectionate nature."

"You mean," he said, leaning forward the imperceptible half-inch that was left of chair, "you mean—me?"

The smell of bay rum came out greenly then as the moisture sprang out on his scalp.

"I—I'm a home woman, Mr. Latz. You can put a fish in water but you cannot make him swim. That's me and hotel life."

At this somewhat cryptic apothegm Mr. Latz's knee touched Mrs. Samstag's, so that he sprang back full of nerves at what he had not intended.

"Marry me, Carrie," he said more abruptly than he might have, without the act of that knee to immediately justify.

She spread the lace out on her lap.

Ostensibly to the hotel lobby, they were casual as, "My mulligatawny soup was cold tonight" or "Have you heard the new one that Al Jolson pulls at the Winter Garden?" But actually, the roar was high in Mrs. Samstag's ears and he could feel the plethoric red rushing in flashes over his body.

"Marry me, Carrie," he said, as if to prove that his stiff lips could repeat their incredible feat.

With a woman's talent for them, her tears sprang.

"Mr. Latz—"

"Louis," he interpolated, widely eloquent of posture.

"You're proposing—Louis!" She explained rather than asked, and placed her hand to her heart so prettily that he wanted to crush it there with his kisses.

"God bless you for knowing it so easy, Carrie. A young girl would make it so hard. It's just what has kept me from asking you weeks ago, this getting it said. Carrie, will you?"

"I'm a widow, Mr. Latz—Louis—"

"Loo—"

"L—Loo. With a grown daughter. Not one of those merry widows you read about."

"That's me! A bachelor on top but a home-man underneath. Why, up to five years ago, Carrie, while the best little mother a man ever had was alive, I never had eyes for a woman or—"

"It's common talk what a grand son you were to her, Mr. La—Louis—"

"Loo!"

"Loo."

"I don't want to seem to brag, Carrie, but you saw the coat that just walked out on Mrs. Gronauer? My little mother, she was a humpback, Carrie, not a real one, but all stooped from the heavy years when she was helping my father to get his start. Well, anyway, that little stooped back was one of the reasons why I was so anxious to make it up to her. Y'understand?"

"Yes—Loo."

"But you saw that mink coat? Well, my little mother,

three years before she died, was wearing one like that in sable. Real Russian. Set me back eighteen thousand, wholesale, and she never knew different than that it cost eighteen hundred. Proudest moment of my life when I helped my little old mother into her own automobile in that sable coat."

"I had some friends lived in the Grenoble apartments when you did—the Adelbergs. They used to tell me how it hung right down to her heels and she never got into the auto that she didn't pick it up so as not to sit on it."

"That there coat is packed away in cold storage, now, Carrie, waiting, without me exactly knowing why, I guess, for—the one little woman in the world besides her I would let so much as touch its hem."

Mrs. Samstag's lips parted, her teeth showing through like light.

"Oh," she said, "sable. That's my fur, Loo. I've never owned any, but ask Alma if I don't stop to look at it in every show window. Sable!"

"Carrie—would you—could you—I'm not what you would call a youngster in years, I guess, but forty-four ain't—"

"I'm—forty-one, Louis. A man like you could have younger."

"No. That's what I don't want. In my lonesomeness, after my mother's death, I thought once that maybe a young girl from the West, nice girl with her mother from Ohio—but I—funny thing, now I come to think about it —I never once mentioned my little mother's sable coat to her. I couldn't have satisfied a young girl like that or her me, Carrie, any more than I could satisfy Alma. It was one of those mamma-made matches that we got into because we couldn't help it and out of it before it was too late. No, no, Carrie, what I want is a woman near to my own age."

"Loo, I—I couldn't start in with you even with the one little lie that gives every woman a right to be a liar. I'm forty-three, Louis—nearer to forty-four. You're not mad, Loo?"

"God love it! If that ain't a little woman for you! Mad? Just doing that little thing with me raises your stock fifty per cent."

"I'm—that way."

"We're a lot alike, Carrie. At heart, I'm a home man, Carrie, and unless I'm pretty much off my guess, you are, too—I mean a home woman. Right?"

"Me all over, Loo. Ask Alma if—"

"I've got the means, too, Carrie, to give a woman a home to be proud of."

"Just for fun, ask Alma, Loo, if one year since her father's death I haven't said, Alma, I wish I had the heart to go back housekeeping."

"I knew it!"

"But I ask you, Louis, what's been the incentive? Without a man in the house I wouldn't have the same interest. That first winter after my husband died I didn't even have the heart to take the summer-covers off the furniture. You can believe me or not, but half the time with just me to eat it, I wouldn't bother with more than a cold snack for supper and every one knew what a table we used to set. But with no one to come home evenings expecting a hot meal—"

"You poor little woman. I know how it is. Why, if I used to so much as telephone that I couldn't get home for supper right away I knew my little mother would turn out the gas under what was cooking and not eat enough herself to keep a bird alive."

"Housekeeping is no life for a woman alone. On the other hand, Mr. Latz—Louis—Loo, on my income, and with a daughter growing up, and naturally anxious to give her the best, it hasn't been so easy. People think I'm a rich widow and with her father's memory to consider and a young lady daughter, naturally I let them think it, but on my seventy-four hundred a year it has been hard to keep up appearances in a hotel like this. Not that I think you think I'm a rich widow, but just the same, that's me every time. Right out with the truth from the start."

"It shows you're a clever little manager to be able to do it."

"We lived big and spent big while my husband lived. He was as shrewd a jobber in knit underwear as the business ever saw, but—well, you know how it is. Pneumonia. I always say he wore himself out with conscientiousness."

"Maybe you don't believe it, Carrie, but it makes me happy what you just said about money. It means I can give you things you couldn't afford for yourself. I don't say this for publication, Carrie, but in Wall Street alone, outside of my brokerage business, I cleared eighty-six thousand last year. I can give you the best. You deserve it, Carrie. Will you say yes?"

"My daughter, Loo. She's only eighteen, but she's my shadow—I lean on her so."

"A sweet, dutiful girl like Alma would be the last to stand in her mother's light."

"She's my only. We're different natured. Alma's a Samstag through and through, quiet, reserved. But she's my all, Louis. I love my baby too much to—to marry where she wouldn't be as welcome as the day itself. She's precious to me, Louis."

"Why, of course. You wouldn't be you if she wasn't. You think I would want you to feel different?"

"I mean—Louis—no matter where I go, more than with most children, she's part of me, Loo. I—why, that child won't so much as go to spend the night with a girl friend away from me. Her quiet ways don't show it, but Alma has character! You wouldn't believe it, Louis, how she takes care of me."

"Why, Carrie, the first thing we pick out in our new home will be a room for her."

"Loo!"

"Not that she will want it long the way I see that young rascal Friedlander sits up to her. A better young fellow and a better business head you couldn't pick for her. Didn't that youngster go out to Dayton the other day and land a contract for the surgical fittings for a big new hospital out there before the local firms even rubbed the sleep out of their eyes? I have it from good authority, Friedlander & Sons doubled their excess-profits tax last year."

A white flash of something that was almost fear seemed to strike Mrs. Samstag into a rigid pallor.

"No! No! I'm not like most mothers, Louis, for marrying their daughters off. I want her with me. If marrying her off is your idea, it's best you know it now in the beginning. I want my little girl with me—I have to have my little girl with me!"

He was so deeply moved that his eyes were moist.

"Why, Carrie, every time you open your mouth, you only prove to me further what a grand little woman you are."

"You'll like Alma, when you get to know her, Louis."

"Why, I do now. Always have said she's a sweet little thing."

"She is quiet and hard to get acquainted with at first, but that is reserve. She's not forward like most young girls nowadays. She's the kind of a child that would rather sit upstairs evenings with a book or her sewing than here in the lobby. She's there now."

"Give me that kind every time, in preference to all these gay young chickens that know more they oughtn't to know about life before they start than my little mother did when she finished."

"But do you think that girl will go to bed before I come up? Not a bit of it. She's been my comforter and my salvation in my troubles. More like the mother, I sometimes tell her, and me the child. If you want me, Louis, it's got to be with her too. I couldn't give up my baby— not my baby."

"Why, Carrie, have your baby to your heart's content. She's got to be a fine girl to have you for a mother and now it will be my duty to please her as a father. Carrie, will you have me?"

"Oh, Louis—Loo!"

"Carrie, my dear!"

And so it was that Carrie Samstag and Louis Latz came into their betrothal.

None the less, it was with some misgivings and red lights burning high on her cheek-bones that Mrs. Samstag, at just after ten that evening, turned the knob of the door that entered into her little sitting-room, but in this case, a room redeemed by an upright piano with a green silk and gold-lace shaded floor lamp glowing by it. Two gilt framed photographs and a cluster of ivory knickknacks on the white mantel. A heap of hand-made cushions. Art editions of the gift-poets and some circulating library novels. A fireside chair, privately owned and drawn up, ironically enough, beside the gilded radiator, its head-rest worn from kindly service to Mrs. Samstag's neuralgic brow.

From the nest of cushions in the circle of lamp glow, Alma sprang up at her mother's entrance. Sure enough, she had been reading and her cheek was a little flushed and crumpled from where it had been resting in the palm of her hand.

"Mamma," she said, coming out of the circle of light and switching on the ceiling bulbs, "you stayed down so late."

There was a slow prettiness to Alma. It came upon you like a little dawn, palely at first and then pinkening to a pleasant consciousness that her small face was heart-shaped and clear as an almond, that the pupils of her gray eyes were deep and dark like cisterns and to young Leo Friedlander, rather apt his comparison, too, her mouth was exactly the shape of a small bow that had shot its quiverful of arrows into his heart.

And instead of her eighteen she looked sixteen. There was that kind of timid adolescence about her, yet when she said, "Mamma, you stayed down so late," the bang of a little pistol-shot was back somewhere in her voice.

"Why—Mr. Latz—and I—sat and talked."

An almost imperceptible nerve was dancing against Mrs. Samstag's right temple. Alma could sense, rather than see the ridge of pain.

"You're all right, mamma?"

"Yes," said Mrs. Samstag, and plumped rather than sat herself down on a divan, its naked greenness relieved by a thrown scarf of black velvet, stenciled in gold.

"You shouldn't have remained down so long if your head is hurting," said her daughter, and quite casually took up her mother's beaded hand-bag where it had fallen in her lap, but her fingers feeling lightly and furtively as if for the shape of its contents.

"Stop that," said Mrs. Samstag, jerking it back, a dull anger in her voice.

"Come to bed, mamma. If you're in for neuralgia, I'll fix the electric pad."

Suddenly Mrs. Samstag shot out her arm, rather slim looking in the invariable long sleeve she affected, drawing Alma back toward her by the ribbon sash of her pretty chiffon frock.

"Alma, be good to mamma tonight! Sweetheart—be good to her."

The quick suspecting fear that had motivated Miss Samstag's groping along the beaded hand-bag shot out again in her manner.

"Mamma—you haven't?"

"No, no. Don't nag me. It's something else, Alma. Something mamma is very happy about."

"Mamma, you've broken your promise again."

"No. No. No. Alma, I've been a good mother to you, haven't I?"

"Yes, mamma, yes, but what—"

"Whatever else I've been hasn't been my fault—you've always blamed Heyman."

"Mamma, I don't understand."

"I've caused you worry, Alma—terrible worry. But everything is changed now. Mamma's going to turn over a new leaf that everything is going to be happiness in this family."

"Dearest, if you knew how happy it makes me to hear you say that."

"Alma, look at me."

"Mamma, you—you frighten me."

"You like Louis Latz, don't you, Alma?"

"Why, yes, mamma. Very much."

"We can't all be young and handsome like Leo, can we?"

"You mean—"

"I mean that finer and better men than Louis Latz aren't lying around loose. A man who treated his mother like a queen and who worked himself up from selling newspapers on the street to a millionaire."

"Mamma?"

"Yes, baby. He asked me tonight. Come to me, Alma, stay with me close. He asked me tonight."

"What?"

"You know. Haven't you seen it coming for weeks? I have."

"Seen what?"

"Don't make mamma come out and say it. For eight years I've been as grieving a widow to a man as a woman could be. But I'm human, Alma, and he—asked me tonight."

There was a curious pallor came over Miss Samstag's face, as if smeared there by a hand.

"Asked you what?"

"Alma, it don't mean I'm not true to your father as I was the day I buried him in that blizzard back there, but could you ask for a finer, steadier man than Louis Latz? It looks out of his face."

"Mamma, you—what—are you saying?"

"Alma?"

There lay a silence between them that took on the roar of a simoon and Miss Samstag jumped then from her mother's embrace, her little face stiff with the clench of her mouth.

"Mamma—you—no—no. Oh, mamma— Oh—"

A quick spout of hysteria seemed to half strangle Mrs. Samstag, so that she slanted backward, holding her throat.

"I knew it. My own child against me. Oh, God! Why was I born? My own child against me!"

"Mamma—you can't marry him. You can't marry—anybody."

"Why can't I marry anybody? Must I be afraid to tell my own child when a good man wants to marry me and give us both a good home? That's my thanks for making my child my first consideration—before I accepted him."

"Mamma, you didn't accept him. Darling, you wouldn't do a—thing like that!"

Miss Samstag's voice thickened up then, quite frantically, into a little scream that knotted in her throat and she was suddenly so small and stricken, that with a gasp for fear she might crumple up where she stood, Mrs. Samstag leaned forward, catching her again by the sash.

"Alma!"

It was only for an instant, however. Suddenly Miss Samstag was her coolly firm little self, the bang of authority back in her voice.

"You can't marry Louis Latz."

"Can't I? Watch me."

"You can't do that to a nice, deserving fellow like him!"

"Do what?"

"That!"

Then Mrs. Samstag threw up both her hands to her

face, rocking in an agony of self-abandon that was rather horrid to behold.

"Oh, God, why don't you put me out of it all? My misery! I'm a leper to my own child!"

"Oh—mamma—"

"Yes, a leper. Hold my misfortune against me. Let my neuralgia and Doctor Heyman's prescription to cure it ruin my life. Rob me of what happiness with a good man there is left in it for me. I don't want happiness. Don't expect it. I'm here just to suffer. My daughter will see to that. Oh, I know what is on your mind. You want to make me out something—terrible—because Dr. Heyman once taught me how to help myself a little when I'm nearly wild with neuralgia. Those were doctor's orders. I'll kill myself before I let you make me out something terrible. I never even knew what it was before the doctor gave his prescription. I'll kill—you hear—kill myself."

She was hoarse, she was tear splotched so that her lips were slippery with them, and while the ague of her passion shook her, Alma, her own face swept white and her voice guttered with restraint, took her mother into the cradle of her arms, and rocked and hushed her there.

"Mamma, mamma, what are you saying? I'm not blaming you, sweetheart. I blame him—Dr. Heyman—for prescribing it in the beginning. I know your fight. How brave it is. Even when I'm crossest with you, I realize. Alma's fighting with you, dearest, every inch of the way until —you're cured! And then—maybe—some day—anything you want! But not now. Mamma, you wouldn't marry Louis Latz now!"

"I would. He's my cure. A good home with a good man and money enough to travel and forget myself. Alma, mamma knows she's not an angel—sometimes when she thinks what she's put her little girl through this last year, she just wants to go out on the hill-top where she caught the neuralgia and lay down beside that grave out there and—"

"Mamma, don't talk like that!"

"But now's my chance, Alma, to get well. I've too much worry in this big hotel trying to keep up big expenses on little money and—"

"I know it, mamma. That's why I'm so in favor of finding ourselves a sweet, tiny little apartment with kitch—"

"No! Your father died with the world thinking him a rich man and it will never find out from me that he wasn't. I won't be the one to humiliate his memory—a man who enjoyed keeping up appearances the way he did. Oh, Alma, Alma, I'm going to get well now. I promise. So help me God, if I ever give in to—to it again."

"Mamma, please. For God's sake, you've said the same thing so often only to break your promise."

"I've been weak, Alma; I don't deny it. But nobody who hasn't been tortured as I have, can realize what it means to get relief just by—"

"Mamma, you're not playing fair this minute. That's the frightening part. It isn't only the neuralgia any more. It's just desire. That's what's so terrible to me, mamma. The way you have been taking it these last months. Just from—desire."

Mrs. Samstag buried her face, shuddering down into her hands.

"Oh, God, my own child against me!"

"No, mamma. Why, sweetheart, nobody knows better than I do how sweet and good you are when you are away —from it. We'll fight it together and win! I'm not afraid.

It's been worse this last month because you've been nervous, dear. I understand now. You see, I—didn't dream of you and—Louis Latz. We'll forget—we'll take a little two room apartment of our own, darling, and get your mind on housekeeping and I'll take up stenography or social ser—"

"What good am I anyway? No good. In my own way. In my child's way. A young man like Leo Friedlander crazy to propose and my child can't let him come to the point because she is afraid to leave her mother. Oh, I know—I know more than you think I do. Ruining your life! That's what I am, and mine too!"

Tears now ran in hot cascades down Alma's cheeks.

"Why, mamma, as if I cared about anything—just so you—get well."

"I know what I've done. Ruined my baby's life and now—"

"No!"

"Then help me, Alma. Louis wants me for his happiness. I want him for mine. Nothing will cure me like having a good man to live up to. The minute I find myself getting the craving for—it—don't you see, baby, fear that a good husband like Louis could find out such a thing about me would hold me back. See, Alma?"

"That's a wrong basis to start married life on—"

"I'm a woman who needs a man to baby her, Alma. That's the cure for me. Not to let me would be the same as to kill me. I've been a bad, weak woman, Alma, to be so afraid that maybe Leo Friedlander would steal you away from me. We'll make it a double wedding, baby."

"Mamma, mamma, I'll never leave you."

"All right, then, so you won't think your new father and me want to get rid of you. The first thing we'll pick out in our new home, he said it himself tonight, is Alma's room."

"I tell you it's wrong. It's wrong!"

"The rest with Leo can come later, after I've proved to you for a little while that I'm cured. Alma, don't cry! It's my cure. Just think, a good man. A beautiful home to take my mind off—worry. He said tonight he wants to spend a fortune if necessary to cure—my neuralgia."

"Oh, mamma, mamma, if it were only—that!"

"Alma, if I promise on my—my life! I never felt the craving so little as I do—now."

"You've said that before—and before."

"But never, with such a wonderful reason. It's the beginning of a new life. I know it. I'm cured!"

"Mamma, if I thought you meant it."

"I do. Alma, look at me. This very minute I've a real jumping case of neuralgia. But I wouldn't have anything for it except the electric pad. I feel fine. Strong! Alma, the bad times with me are over."

"Oh, mamma, mamma, how I pray you're right."

"You'll thank God for the day that Louis Latz proposed to me. Why, I'd rather cut off my right hand than marry a man who could ever live to learn such a—thing about me."

"But it's not fair. We'll have to explain to him, dear, that we hope you're cured now, but—"

"If you do—if you do—I'll kill myself! I won't live to bear that! You don't want me cured. You want to get rid of me, to degrade me until I kill myself! If I was ever anything else than what I am now—to Louis Latz—anything but his ideal—Alma, you won't tell! Kill me, but don't tell—don't tell!"

"Why, you know I wouldn't, sweetheart, if it is so terrible to you. Never."

"Say it again."

"Never."

"As if it hasn't been terrible enough that you should have to know. But it's over, Alma. Your bad times with me are finished. I'm cured."

"But wait a little while, mamma, just a year."

"No. No."

"A few months."

"Now. He wants it soon. The sooner the better at our age. Alma, mamma's cured! What happiness. Kiss me, darling. So help me God, to keep my promises to you. Cured, Alma, cured."

And so in the end, with a smile on her lips that belied almost to herself the little run of fear through her heart, Alma's last kiss to her mother that night was the long one of felicitation.

And because love, even the talk of it, is so gamey on the lips of woman to woman, they lay in bed that night heart-beat to heart-beat, the electric pad under her pillow warm to the hurt of Mrs. Samstag's brow and talked, these two, deep into the stillness of the hotel night.

"My little baby, who's helped me through such bad times, it's your turn now, Alma, to be care-free, like other girls."

"I'll never leave you, mamma, even if—he shouldn't want me."

"He will, darling, and does! Those were his words. 'A room for Alma.' "

"I'll never leave you!"

"You will! Much as Louis and me want you with us every minute, we won't stand in your way! That's another reason I'm so happy, Alma. I'm not alone, any more now. Leo's so crazy over you, just waiting for the chance to —pop—"

"Shh-sh-h-h."

"Don't tremble so, darling. Mamma knows. He told Mrs. Gronauer last night when she was joking him to buy a ten dollar carnation for the Convalescent Home Bazaar, that he would only take one if it was white, because little white flowers reminded him of Alma Samstag."

"Oh, mamma—"

"Say, it is as plain as the nose on your face. He can't keep his eyes off you. He sells goods to Doctor Gronauer's clinic and he says the same thing about him. It makes me so happy, Alma, to think you won't have to hold him off any more."

"I'll never leave you. Never!"

None the less she was the first to drop off to sleep, pink, there in the dark, with the secret of her blushes.

Then for Mrs. Samstag the travail set in. Lying there with her raging head tossing this way and that on the heated pillow, she heard with cruel awareness, the minutiae, all the faint but clarified noises, that can make a night seem so long. The distant click of the elevator, depositing a night-hawk. A plong of the bed spring. Somebody's cough. A train's shriek. The jerk of plumbing. A window being raised. That creak which lies hidden in every darkness, like a mysterious knee-joint. By three o'clock she was a quivering victim to these petty concepts, and her pillow so explored that not a spot but what was rumpled to the aching lay of her cheek.

Once Alma, as a rule supersensitive to her mother's slightest unrest, floated up for the moment out of her young sleep, but she was very drowsy and very tired and

dream-tides were almost carrying her back, as she said:
"Mamma, are you all right?"

Simulating sleep, Mrs. Samstag lay tense until her
daughter's breathing resumed its light cadence.

Then at four o'clock, the kind of nervousness that Mrs.
Samstag had learned to fear, began to roll over her in
waves, locking her throat and curling her toes and her
fingers, and her tongue up dry against the roof of her
mouth.

She must concentrate now—must steer her mind away
from the craving!

Now then: West End Avenue. Louis liked the apartments there. Luxurious. Quiet. Residential. Circassian
walnut or mahogany dining-room? Alma should decide. A
baby-grand piano. Later to be Alma's engagement gift
from, "Mamma and—Papa." No, "Mamma and Louis."
Better so.

How her neck and her shoulder-blade and now her
elbow, were flaming with the pain! She cried a little, far
back in her throat with the small hissing noise of a steam-
radiator, and tried a poor futile scheme for easing her
head in the crotch of her elbow.

Now then: She must knit Louis some neckties. The silk-
sweater-stitch would do. Married in a traveling-suit. One
of those smart dark-blue twills like Mrs. Gronauer
Junior's. Top-coat—sable. Louis' hair thinning. Tonic.
Oh, God, let me sleep. Please, God. The wheeze rising in
her closed throat. That little threatening desire that must
not shape itself! It darted with the hither and thither of
a bee bumbling against a garden wall. No. No. Ugh! The
vast chills of nervousness. The flaming, the craving chills
of desire!

Just this last giving-in. This once. To be rested and

fresh for him tomorrow. Then never again. The little
beaded hand-bag. Oh, God, help me. That burning ache
to rest and to uncurl of nervousness. All the thousand,
thousand little pores of her body, screaming each one, to
be placated. They hurt the entire surface of her. That
great storm at sea in her head; the crackle of lightning
down that arm—

Let me see—Circassian walnut—baby-grand—the
pores demanding, crying—shrieking—

It was then that Carrie Samstag, even in her lovely pink
night-dress, a crone with pain, and the cables out dread-
fully in her neck, began by infinitesimal processes to swing
herself gently to the side of the bed, unrelaxed inch by unrelaxed inch, softly and with the cunning born of travail.

It was actually a matter of fifteen minutes, that breathless swing toward the floor, the mattress rising after her
with scarcely a whisper of its stuffings and her two bare
feet landing patly into the pale blue room-slippers, there
beside the bed.

Then her bag, the beaded one on the end of the divan.
The slow taut feeling for it and the floor that creaked
twice, starting the sweat out over her.

It was finally after more tortuous saving of floor creaks
and the interminable opening and closing of a door that
Carrie Samstag, the beaded bag in her hand, found herself face to face with herself in the mirror of the bathroom medicine chest.

She was shuddering with one of the hot chills, the needle
and little glass piston out of the hand-bag and with a dry
little insuck of breath, pinching up little areas of flesh
from her arm, bent on a good firm perch, as it were.

There were undeniable pock-marks on Mrs. Samstag's

right forearm. Invariably it sickened her to see them.
Little graves. Oh, oh, little graves. For Alma. Herself.
And now Louis. Just once. Just one more little grave—

And Alma, answering her somewhere down in her heart-
beats: "No, mamma, no, mamma. No. No. No."

But all the little pores gaping. Mouths! The pinching
up of the skin. Here, this little clean and white area.

"No, mamma. No, mamma. No. No. No."

"Just once, darling?" Oh—oh—graves for Alma and
Louis. No. No. No.

Somehow, some way, with all the little mouths still
parched and gaping and the clean and quite white area
unblemished, Mrs. Samstag found her way back to bed.
She was in a drench of sweat when she got there and the
conflagration of neuralgia, curiously enough, was now
roaring in her ears so that it seemed to her she could hear
her pain.

Her daughter lay asleep, with her face to the wall, her
flowing hair spread in a fan against the pillow and her
body curled up cozily. The remaining hours of the night,
in a kind of waking faint she could never find the words to
describe, Mrs. Samstag, with that dreadful dew of her
sweat constantly out over her, lay with her twisted lips to
the faint perfume of that fan of Alma's flowing hair, her
toes curling in and out. Out and in. Toward morning she
slept. Actually, sweetly and deeply as if she could never
have done with deep draughts of it.

She awoke to the brief patch of sunlight that smiled into
their apartment for about eight minutes of each forenoon.

Alma was at the pretty chore of lifting the trays from
a hamper of roses. She placed a shower of them on her
mother's coverlet with a kiss, a deeper and dearer one
somehow, this morning.

There was a card and Mrs. Samstag read it and laughed:

> Good morning, Carrie.
> Louis.

They seemed to her, poor dear, these roses, to be pink with the glory of the coming of the dawn.

On the spur of the moment and because the same precipitate decisions that determined Louis Latz's successes in Wall Street determined him here, they were married the following Thursday in Greenwich, Connecticut, without even allowing Carrie time for the blue twill traveling suit. She wore her brown velvet instead, looking quite modish, and a sable wrap, gift of the groom, lending genuine magnificence.

Alma was there, of course, in a beautiful fox scarf, also gift of the groom, and locked in a white kind of tensity that made her seem more than ever like a little white flower to Leo Friedlander, the sole other attendant, and who during the ceremony yearned at her with his gaze. But her eyes were squeezed tight against his, as if to forbid herself the consciousness that life seemed suddenly so richly sweet to her—oh, so richly sweet!

There was a time during the first months of the married life of Louis and Carrie Latz, when it seemed to Alma, who in the sanctity of her lovely little ivory bedroom all appointed in rose-enamel toilet trifles, could be prayerful with the peace of it, that the old Carrie, who could come pale and terrible out of her drugged night, belonged to some grimacing and chimeric past. A dead past that had buried its dead and its hatchet.

There had been a month at Hot Springs in the wintergreen heart of Virginia, and whatever Louis may have felt in his heart, of his right to the privacy of these honeymoon days, was carefully belied on his lips, and at Alma's depriving him now and then of his wife's company, packing her off to rest when he wanted a climb with her up a mountain slope or a drive over piny roads, he could still smile and pinch her cheek.

"You're stingy to me with my wife, Alma," he said to her upon one of these provocations. "I don't believe she's got a daughter at all, but a little policeman instead."

And Alma smiled back, out of the agony of her constant consciousness that she was insinuating her presence upon him, and resolutely, so that her fear for him should always subordinate her fear of him, she bit down her sensitiveness in proportion to the rising tide of his growing, but still politely held in check, bewilderment.

One day, these first weeks of their marriage, because she saw the dreaded signal of the muddy pools under her mother's eyes and the little quivering nerve beneath the temple, she shut him out of her presence for a day and a night, and when he came fuming up every few minutes from the hotel veranda, miserable and fretting, met him at the closed door of her mother's darkened room and was adamant.

"It won't hurt if I tiptoe in and sit with her," he pleaded.

"No, Louis. No one knows how to get her through these spells like I do. The least excitement will only prolong her pain."

He trotted off then down the hotel corridor, with a strut to his resentment that was bantam and just a little fighty.

That night, as Alma lay beside her mother, fighting sleep and watching, Carrie rolled her eyes sidewise with the plea of a stricken dog in them.

"Alma," she whispered, "for God's sake. Just this once. To tide me over. One shot—darling. Alma, if you love me?"

Later, there was a struggle between them that hardly bears relating. A lamp was overturned. But toward morning, when Carrie lay exhausted, but at rest in her daughter's arms, she kept muttering in her sleep:

"Thank you, baby. You saved me. Never leave me, Alma. Never—never—never. You saved me, Alma."

And then the miracle of those next months. The return to New York. The happily busy weeks of furnishing and the unlimited gratifications of the well-filled purse. The selection of the limousine with the special body that was fearfully and wonderfully made in mulberry upholstery with mother-of-pearl caparisons. The fourteen-room apartment on West End Avenue, with four baths, drawing-room of pink brocaded walls and Carrie's Roman bathroom that was precisely as large as her old hotel sitting-room, with two full length wall-mirrors, a dressing-table canopied in white lace over white satin and the marble bath itself, two steps down and with the rubber curtains that swished after.

There were evenings when Carrie, who loved the tyranny of things with what must have been a survival within her of the bazaar instinct, would fall asleep almost directly after dinner, her head back against her husband's shoulder, roundly tired out after a day all cluttered up with matching the blue upholstery of their bedroom with taffeta bed-hangings.

Latz liked her so, with her fragrantly coiffured head, scarcely gray, back against his shoulder and with his newspapers—Wall Street journals and the comic weeklies which he liked to read—would sit an entire evening thus, moving only when his joints rebelled, and his pipe smoke carefully directed away from her face.

Weeks and weeks of this and already Louis Latz's trousers were a little out of crease and Mrs. Latz after eight o'clock and under cover of a very fluffy and very expensive négligé, would unhook her stays.

Sometimes friends came in for a game of small-stake poker, but after the second month they countermanded the standing order for Saturday night musical comedy seats. So often they discovered it was pleasanter to remain at home. Indeed, during these days of household adjustment, as many as four evenings a week Mrs. Latz dozed there against her husband's shoulder, until about ten, when he kissed her awake to forage with him in the great, white porcelain refrigerator and then to bed.

And Alma. Almost, she tiptoed through these months. Not that her scorching awareness of what must have crouched low in Louis' mind ever diminished. Sometimes, although still never by word, she could see the displeasure mount in his face.

If she entered in on a tête-à-tête, as she did once, when by chance she had sniffed the curative smell of spirits of camphor on the air of a room through which her mother had passed, and came to drag her off that night to share her own lace-covered and ivory bed.

Again: upon the occasion of an impulsively planned motor trip and week-end to Lakewood, her intrusion had been so obvious.

"Want to join us, Alma?"

"Oh—yes—thank you, Louis."

"But I thought you and Leo were—"

"No, no, I'd rather go with you and mamma, Louis."

Even her mother had smiled rather strainedly. Louis' invitation, politely uttered, had said so plainly: "Are we two never to be alone, your mother and I?"

Oh, there was no doubt that Louis Latz was in love and with all the delayed fervor of first youth.

There was something rather throat-catching about his treatment of her mother that made Alma want to cry.

He would never tire of marveling, not alone at the wonder of her, but at the wonder that she was his.

"No man has ever been as lucky in women as I have, Carrie," he told her once in Alma's hearing. "It seemed to me that after—my little mother, there couldn't ever be another—and now you! You!"

At the business of sewing some beads on a lamp-shade, Carrie looked up, her eyes dewy.

"And I felt that way about one good husband," she said, "and now I see there could be two."

Alma tiptoed out.

The third month of this, she was allowing Leo Friedlander his two evenings a week. Once to the theater in a modish little sedan car which Leo drove himself. One evening at home in the rose and mauve drawing-room. It delighted Louis and Carrie slyly to have in their friends for poker over the dining-room table these evenings, leaving the young people somewhat indirectly chaperoned until as late as midnight. Louis' attitude with Leo was one of winks, quirks, slaps on the back and the curving voice of innuendo.

"Come on in, Leo, the water's fine!"

"Louis!" This from Alma stung to crimson and not arch enough to feign that she did not understand.

"Loo, don't tease," said Carrie, smiling, but then closing her eyes as if to invoke help to want this thing to come to pass.

But Leo was frankly the lover, kept not without difficulty on the edge of his ardor. A city youth with gymnasium-bred shoulders, fine, pole vaulter's length of limb and a clean tan skin that bespoke cold drubbings with Turkish towels.

And despite herself, Alma, who was not without a young girl's feelings for nice detail, could thrill to this sartorial svelteness and to the patent-leather lay of his black hair which caught the light like a polished floor.

The kind of sweetness he found in Alma he could never articulate even to himself. In some ways she seemed hardly to have the pressure of vitality to match his, but on the other hand, just that slower beat to her may have heightened his sense of prowess. His greatest delight seemed to lie in her pallid loveliness. "White Honeysuckle," he called her and the names of all the beautiful white flowers he knew. And then one night, to the rattle of poker chips from the remote dining-room, he jerked her to him without preamble, kissing her mouth down tightly against her teeth.

"My sweetheart. My little, white carnation sweetheart. I won't be held off any longer. I'm going to carry you away for my little moon-flower wife."

She sprang back prettier than he had ever seen her in the dishevelment from where his embrace had dragged at her hair.

"You mustn't," she cried, but there was enough of the conquering male in him to read easily into this a mere plating over her desire.

"You can't hold me at arm's length any longer. You've maddened me for months. I love you. You love me. You do. You do," and crushed her to him, but this time his pain and his surprise genuine as she sprang back, quivering.

"You—I—mustn't!" she said, frantic to keep her lips from twisting, her little lacy fribble of a handkerchief a mere string from winding.

"Mustn't what?"

"Mustn't," was all she could repeat and not weep her words.

"Won't—I—do?"

"It's—mamma."

"What?"

"You see—I—she's all alone."

"You adorable, she's got a brand-new husky husband."

"No—you don't—understand."

Then, on a thunder-clap of inspiration, hitting his knee, "I have it. Mamma-baby! That's it. My girlie is a cry-baby, mamma-baby!" And made to slide along the divan toward her, but up flew her two small hands, like fans.

"No," she said with the little bang back in her voice which steadied him again. "I mustn't! You see, we're so close. Sometimes it's more as if I were the mother and she my little girl."

Misery made her dumb.

"Why, don't you know, dear, that your mother is better able to take care of herself than you are? She's bigger and stronger. You—you're a little white flower."

"Leo—give me time. Let me think."

"A thousand thinks, Alma, but I love you. I love you and want so terribly for you to love me back."

"I—do."

"Then tell me with kisses."

Again she pressed him to arm's length.

"Please, Leo. Not yet. Let me think. Just one day. To-morrow."

"No, no. Now."

"Tomorrow."

"When?"

"Evening."

"No, morning."

"All right, Leo—tomorrow morning—"

"I'll sit up all night and count every second in every minute and every minute in every hour."

She put up her soft little fingers to his lips.

"Dear boy," she said.

And then they kissed and after a little swoon to his nearness she struggled like a caught bird and a guilty one.

"Please go, Leo," she said, "leave me alone—"

"Little mamma-baby sweetheart," he said. "I'll build you a nest right next to hers. Good night, little White Flower. I'll be waiting, and remember, counting every second of every minute and every minute of every hour."

For a long time she remained where he had left her, forward on the pink divan, her head with a listening look to it, as if waiting an answer for the prayers that she sent up.

At two o'clock that morning, by what intuition she would never know, and with such leverage that she landed out of bed plump on her two feet, Alma, with all her faculties into trace like fire-horses, sprang out of sleep.

It was a matter of twenty steps across the hall. In the white-tiled Roman bathroom, the muddy circles suddenly out and angry beneath her eyes, her mother was standing before one of the full-length mirrors—snickering.

There was a fresh little grave on the inside of her right fore arm.

Sometimes in the weeks that followed, a sense of the miracle of what was happening would clutch at Alma's throat like a fear.

Louis did not know.

That the old neuralgic recurrences were more frequent again, yes. Already plans for a summer trip abroad, on a curative mission bent, were taking shape. There was a famous nerve specialist, the one who had worked such wonders on his little mother's cruelly rheumatic limbs, reassuringly foremost in his mind.

But except that there were not infrequent and sometimes twenty-four hour sieges when he was denied the sight of his wife, he had learned with a male's acquiescence to the frailties of the other sex, to submit, and with no great understanding of pain, to condone.

And as if to atone for these more or less frequent lapses there was something pathetic, even a little heart-breaking, in Carrie's zeal for his well-being. No duty too small. One night she wanted to unlace his shoes and even shine them, would have, in fact, except for his fierce catching of her into his arms and for some reason, his tonsils aching as he kissed her.

Once after a "spell" she took out every garment from his wardrobe and kissing them piece by piece, put them back again and he found her so, and they cried together, he of happiness.

In his utter beatitude, even his resentment of Alma continued to grow but slowly. Once, when after forty-eight hours she forbade him rather fiercely an entrance into his wife's room, he shoved her aside almost rudely, but at Carrie's little shriek of remonstrance from the darkened room, backed out shamefacedly and apologized next day in the conciliatory language of a tiny wrist-watch.

But a break came, as she knew and feared it must.

One evening during one of these attacks, when for two days Carrie had not appeared at the dinner table, Alma, entering when the meal was almost over, seated herself rather exhaustedly at her mother's place opposite her stepfather.

He had reached the stage when that little unconscious usurpation in itself could annoy him.

"How's your mother?" he asked, dourly for him.

"She's asleep."

"Funny. This is the third attack this month and each time it lasts longer. Confound that neuralgia."

"She's easier now."

He pushed back his plate.

"Then I'll go in and sit with her while she sleeps."

She who was so fastidiously dainty of manner, half rose, spilling her soup.

"No," she said, "you mustn't! Not now!" And sat down again hurriedly, wanting not to appear perturbed.

A curious thing happened then to Louis. His lower lip came pursing out like a little shelf and a hitherto unsuspected look of pigginess fattened over his rather plump face.

"You quit butting into me and my wife's affairs, you, or get the hell out of here," he said, without changing his voice or his manner.

She placed her hand to the almost unbearable flutter of her heart.

"Louis! You mustn't talk like that to—me!"

"Don't make me say something I'll regret. You! Only take this tip, you! There's one of two things you better do. Quit trying to come between me and her or—get out."

"I—she's sick."

"Naw, she ain't. Not as sick as you make out. You're trying, God knows why, to keep us apart. I've watched you. I know your sneaking kind. Still water runs deep. You've never missed a chance since we're married to keep us apart. Shame!"

"I—she—"

"Now mark my word, if it wasn't to spare her, I'd have invited you out long ago. Haven't you got any pride?"

"I have. I have," she almost moaned and could have crumpled up there and swooned in her humiliation.

"You're not a regular girl. You're a she-devil. That's what you are! Trying to come between your mother and me. Ain't you ashamed? What is it you want?"

"Louis—I don't—"

"First you turn down a fine fellow like Leo Friedlander, so he don't come to the house any more and then you take out on us whatever is eating you, by trying to come between me and the finest woman that ever lived. Shame. Shame."

"Louis," she said. "Louis," wringing her hands in a dry wash of agony, "can't you understand? She'd rather have me. It makes her nervous trying to pretend to you that she's not suffering when she is. That's all, Louis. You see, she's not ashamed to suffer before me. Why, Louis—that's all. Why should I want to come between you and her? Isn't she dearer to me than anything in the world and haven't you been the best friend to me a girl could have? That's all—Louis."

He was placated and a little sorry and did not insist further upon going into the room.

"Funny," he said. "Funny," and adjusting his spectacles, snapped open his newspaper for a lonely evening.

The one thing that perturbed Alma almost more than anything else, as the dreaded cravings grew, with each siege her mother becoming more brutish and more given to profanity, was where she obtained the drug.

The well-thumbed old doctor's prescription she had purloined even back in the hotel days, and embargo and legislation were daily making more and more furtive and prohibitive the traffic in narcotics.

Once Alma, mistakenly too, she thought later, had suspected a chauffeur of collusion with her mother and abruptly dismissed him. To Louis' rage.

"What's the idea?" he said out of Carrie's hearing, of course. "Who's running this shebang anyway?"

Once after Alma had guarded her well for days, scarcely leaving her side, Carrie laughed sardonically up into her daughter's face, her eyes as glassy and without swimming fluid as a doll's.

"I get it! But wouldn't you like to know where? Yah!"

And to Alma's horror she slapped her quite roundly across the cheek.

And then one day, after a long period of quiet, when Carrie had lavished her really great wealth of contrite love upon her daughter and husband, spending on Alma and loading her with gifts of jewelry and finery to somehow express her grateful adoration of her; paying her husband the secret penance of twofold fidelity to his well-being and every whim, Alma, returning from a trip, taken reluctantly, and at her mother's bidding, down to the basement trunk-room, found her gone, a modish black-lace hat and the sable coat missing from the closet.

It was early afternoon, sunlit and pleasantly cold.

The first rush of panic and the impulse to dash after,

stayed, she forced herself down into a chair, striving with the utmost difficulty for coherence of procedure.

Where in the half hour of her absence had her mother gone? Matinée? Impossible! Walking. Hardly probable. Upon inquiry in the kitchen neither of the maids had seen nor heard her depart. Motoring? With a hand that trembled in spite of itself, Alma telephoned the garage. Car and chauffeur were there. Incredible as it seemed, Alma, upon more than one occasion, had lately been obliged to remind her mother that she was becoming careless of the old pointedly rosy hands. Manicurist? She telephoned the Bon Ton Beauty Parlor. No. Where, O God, where? Which way to begin? That was what troubled her most. To start right, so as not to lose a precious second.

Suddenly, and for no particular reason, Alma began a hurried search through her mother's dresser-drawers of lively personal appointments.

A one-inch square of newspaper clipping apparently gouged from the sheet with a hairpin, caught her eye from the top of one of the gold backed hair-brushes. Dawningly, Alma read.

It described in brief detail the innovation of a newly equipped Narcotic Clinic on the Bowery below Canal Street, provided to medically administer to the pathological cravings of addicts.

Fifteen minutes later Alma emerged from the subway at Canal Street and with three blocks toward her destination ahead, started to run.

At the end of the first block she saw her mother, in the sable coat and the black-lace hat, coming toward her.

Her first impulse was to run faster and yoo-hoo, but she thought better of it and by biting her lips and digging her fingernails, was able to slow down to a casual walk.

Carrie's fur coat was flaring open and because of the quality of her attire down there where the bilge waters of the city-tide flow and eddy, stares followed her.

Once, to the stoppage of Alma's heart, she halted and said a brief word to a truckman as he crossed the sidewalk with a bill of lading. He hesitated, laughed and went on.

Then she quickened her pace and went on, but as if with a sense of being followed, because constantly as she walked, she jerked a step, to look back, and then again, over her shoulder.

A second time she stopped, this time to address a little nub of a woman without a hat and lugging one-sidedly a stack of men's basted waistcoats, evidently for home-work in some tenement. She looked and muttered her un-understanding of whatever Carrie had to say and shambled on.

Then Mrs. Latz spied her daughter, greeting her without surprise or any particular recognition.

"Thought you could fool me! Heh, Louis? Alma."

"Mamma, it's Alma. It's all right. Don't you remember, we had this appointment? Come, dear."

"No, you don't! That's a man following. Shh-h-h-h, Louis. I was fooling. I went up to him (snicker) and I said to him, 'Give you five dollars for a doctor's certificate.' That's all I said to him, or any of them. He's in a white carnation, Louis. You can find him by the—it's on his coat lapel. He's coming! Quick—"

"Mamma, there's no one following. Wait, I'll call a taxi!"

"No, you don't! He tried to put me in a taxi, too. No, you don't!"

"Then the subway, dearest. You'll sit quietly beside Alma in the subway, won't you, Carrie? Alma's so tired."

Suddenly Carrie began to whimper.

"My baby! Don't let her see me. My baby. What am I good for? I've ruined her life. My precious sweetheart's life. I hit her once—Louis—in the mouth. God won't forgive me for that."

"Yes, He will, dear, if you come."

"It bled. Alma, tell him mamma lost her doctor's certificate. That's all I said to him—give you five dollars for a doctor's certificate—he had a white carnation—right lapel—stingy! Quick! He's following!"

"Sweetheart, please, there's no one coming."

"Don't tell! Oh, Alma darling—mamma's ruined your life. Her sweetheart baby's life."

"No, darling, you haven't. She loves you if you'll come home with her, dear, to bed, before Louis gets home and—"

"No. No. He mustn't see. Never this bad—was I, darling—oh—oh—"

"No, mamma—never—this bad. That's why we must hurry."

"Best man that ever lived. Best baby. Ruin. Ruin."

"Mamma, you—you're making Alma tremble so that she can scarcely walk if you drag her back so. There's no one following, dear. I won't let any one harm you. Please, sweetheart—a taxicab."

"No. I tell you he's following. He tried to put me into a taxicab."

"Then, mamma, listen. Do you hear! Alma wants you to listen. If you don't—she'll faint. People are looking. Now I want you to turn square around and look. No, look again. You see now, there's no one following. Now, I want you to cross the street over there to the subway. Just with Alma, who loves you. There's nobody following. Just with Alma who loves you."

And then Carrie, whose lace hat was crazily on the back of her head, relaxed enough so that through the enormous maze of the traffic of trucks and the heavier drags of the lower city, she and her daughter could wind their way.

"My baby. My poor Louis," she kept saying. "The worst I've ever been. Oh—Alma—Louis—waiting—before we get there—Louis."

It was in the tightest tangle of the crossing and apparently on this conjuring of her husband, that Carrie jerked suddenly free of Alma's frailer hold.

"No—no—not home—now. Him. Alma!" And darted back against the breast of the down side of the traffic.

There was scarcely more than the quick rotation of her arm around with the spoke of a truck wheel, so quickly she went down.

It was almost a miracle, her kind of death, because out of all that jam of tonnage, she carried only one bruise, a faint one, near the brow.

And the wonder was that Louis Latz in his grief was so proud.

"To think," he kept saying over and over again and unabashed at the way his face twisted, "to think they should have happened to me. Two such women in one lifetime, as my little mother—and her. Fat little old Louis to have had those two. Why, just the memory of my Carrie —is almost enough—to think old me should have a memory like that—it is almost enough—isn't it, Alma?"

She kissed his hand.

That very same, that dreadful night, almost without her knowing it, her throat-tearing sobs broke loose, her face to the waistcoat of Leo Friedlander.

He held her close. Very, very close.

"Why, sweetheart," he said, "I could cut out my heart to help you. Why, sweetheart. Shh-h-h, remember what Louis says. Just the beautiful memory—of—her—is—wonderful—"

"Just—the b-beautiful—memory—you'll always have it too—of her—my mamma—won't you, Leo? Won't you?"

"Always," he said, when the tight grip in his throat had eased enough.

"Say—it again—Leo."

"Always."

She could not know how dear she became to him then, because not ten minutes before, from the very lapel against which her cheek lay pressed, he had unpinned a white carnation.

HENRY G. DWIGHT

RIGHTNESS OF LANGUAGE AND CHARACTER

At first sight your suggestion that you would like to put before your classes "the writer's views about his medium and about those problems of technique which he has solved in the making of his story" sounds rather alarming. So far as this writer is concerned, that may be because he has written no great number of stories. Or is it because he is not conscious of entertaining very definite theories about that particular medium or of having solved many problems of technique? That is no reason why one should be high-hat about it, though. Especially toward a fellow-craftsman whom it amuses to compare notes on the tricks of the trade. So why shouldn't I pull a mechanical toy to pieces to find out how it was made?

As to generalities—"views about his medium"—I don't think I could say anything that would be of the slightest interest. I have tinkered with more than one medium, and hold no brief for one above another. Neither in my reading is one kind of short story likely to enthrall me above another—except that I prefer the better ones to the worse! What chiefly catches me about them is just what you now have in mind: the way they are done. But I like a great many ways; and some of the ways I like best are the ones I myself can least do. Chekhov's, for instance, or Maupassant's, or Henry James', or Kipling's, or Ernest Hemingway's. I almost added Thornton Wilder because I admire him so much and because so many of his chapters are short stories in themselves. What catches me very quickly in any man's way is his style. About Chekhov, alas, I am not competent to speak on that point, for I read no Russian. A story which is awkward in construction, however, or commonplace in theme, is often saved by nothing more than its language—which need not have charm or originality but which must have some intrinsic rightness. Yet, of course, the rightness may be so utterly in the character, in the situation that portrays him, that the language doesn't matter. On the whole the power to create a character seems to be the greater gift. Happy (and few) are they who possess both!

To descend to the plane of the personal: In a book of mine

419

called *Stamboul Nights* there is a sketch entitled "The Leopard of the Sea," which might do for the laboratory experiment you propose. Some of the others went by themselves, because I merely had to put on paper a tale that some one told at dinner. That one, however, being put together out of a number of small pieces, cost me a good deal of trouble. Just how many pieces there were I couldn't say. I remember that a man who lived in a lighthouse on the Black Sea told me about seeing a Turkish steamer suddenly stand on her head in a storm and plunge out of sight. Another man told me about some Turkish sailors who sold a couple of portholes out of their ship, or rather the interior fittings of a porthold, and lived to regret it. A third man told me about a Palace official who was exiled to Arabia and ordered to be gone before morning—in a ship which hadn't moved from her moorings for ten years. A fourth man told me about a regiment of Turkish soldiers on their way home from Mesopotamia, who forced the captain of their ship to put into an intermediate port and then forced the local commandant to produce their back pay. And in those days there were many quaint yarns to be heard about the sketchy discipline, provisioning, and navigation of Turkish ships. One such vessel was really called *The Leopard of the Sea*.

Well, these odds and ends suggested a tradition of the sea entirely different from our own. It occurred to me that a hint of it might be evoked by stringing the various pieces together in some consecutive or plausible way. The Palace official would do for a beginning, the incidents of the portholes and the soldiers getting their pay might find a place in the middle, and the foundering would naturally come at the end. Then there arose the problem of how to deal with events extending over a considerable length of time. A novel is the real answer to that. A short story, being limited to as few thousand words as possible (or less!) and requiring a unity of effect, cannot manage too many characters or incidents. To compress a narrative of months or years into too narrow a space destroys the illusion of time and the result is less interesting than a mail-order catalogue. What to do—unless you throw the illusion of time overboard, with a thousand details you might use, and resort to some such device as a letter or a reminiscence? But having done so, you must invent a new illusion. You must find a credible moment of time and not too objectionable a place for telling your story, which must not too visibly be dragged in by the ears.

That difficulty held me up the longest. However, it happened that I had taken a night photograph in Stamboul during Ramazan, and while waiting in a vacant lot for my effect I had had several conversations with people who stopped to look at my camera. None of them were about ships; but it suddenly struck me that that might do for a setting of my story. After which the thing was more or less plain sailing. The ship of light hanging over the mosque was an afterthought (although a true piece of local color), introduced not only as a bit of decoration but as a means of heightening, if possible, the illusion of unity. And I have to thank certain unsympathetic editors—who to be sure did not suggest it in so many words—for one improvement. Every time they sent the sketch back to me I chopped off more of the beginning, which was originally much longer drawn out.

THE LEOPARD OF THE SEA [1]

AFTER it was quite dark, a man who strolled by happened to catch sight of my camera. He stopped and began to examine it. I discreetly lit a cigarette in order to show him that the camera had a proprietor. He continued his inspection, as much as to show me that he had known I was there. Then he took out his tobacco box, rolled a cigarette with deliberation, came up to me, saluted me politely, and lighted his cigarette from mine. It is the custom of the country, you know. Nobody has any matches. I suppose somebody did once, but since then everybody has gone on taking the sacred fire from everybody else.

Having made the second salutation of usage, the stranger showed no haste to be off. Indeed, after standing a moment, he sat down on another stone near me—not so

[1] From *Stamboul Nights*, by H. G. Dwight, copyright, 1916, by Doubleday, Page and Company. By permission of the author and the publishers.

near as the Greek had done. From that, and from his silence, and from a certain easy awkwardness about him, I guessed he was a Turk.

"Do you make postcards?" he asked at last.

"No," I said, "I am just taking a picture."

"Ah, you have a whim."

"Yes," I assented, "I have a whim." And I smiled to myself in the dark at the pleasant idiom.

"Why do you take pictures now, when it is dark?" pursued my companion. "There is a very pretty view from here in the daytime, but can your machine see it at night?"

I did not mind his inquisitiveness. There was nothing eager or insistent about it. It was simple and natural, and there was a quality in it that I often feel in the Turks, of being able to take the preliminaries of life for granted. The man was evidently not of the higher classes, but neither was he of the lowest. I could make out that he wore European clothes and no collar.

"I want to get the lights of Ramazan," I explained to him. "I took one picture at sunset, so as to get the shape of Yeni Jami and the way the Golden Horn lies behind it, and afterward I shall take another on the same plate, for the lights."

"Ah!" he uttered, as if perfectly comprehending my whim. And after a pause he added: "They must make a great feast at Yeni Jami tonight. They have not lighted one lamp yet."

It was true. The minarets of St. Sophia, the Süleïmanieh, all the other great mosques that ride the crest of Stamboul, already wore their necklaces of gold beads, while mysterious pendants began to twinkle between them. We watched one spark after another spell "O Mohammed!" above the dome of St. Sophia, and a golden flower grew out of the dark between the minarets of Baïezid.

"Do you come from far?" suddenly asked my companion.

"Yes," I said, "from America."

"From America," he repeated. I could see by his tone that the name did not suggest very much to him. "I have been to many countries, but I have not been to America. How many days does it take to go?"

"Eh," I replied, "if you pay very much and go half the way by train you can do it in eight or nine days. If you go all the way by steamer it takes about three weeks."

"Then it is not so far as Yemen," remarked my companion.

"Oh, have you been to Yemen?" I asked in return. "I have been to many countries too, but I have never been to Yemen."

"I never would have gone if I had known. But now they go most of the way by train."

"Didn't you like the sea?" I ventured.

"Fire is for the brazier and water is for the cup," returned my companion somewhat enigmatically.

A flicker came out against one of the dark lances of Yeni Jami, and then three small lamps—which were glass cups of oil with a floating wick—dropped into place one above another. Presently three more appeared beside them, and three more, until the lower gallery of the minaret was set off with its triple circlet of light. There was an interval, during which one could imagine a turbaned person picking his way up a corkscrew stair of stone, and the second gallery put on a similar ornament. I was wondering whether the turbaned person would have to climb all the way down to the ground and up into the other minaret, when lights began to flicker there too. But what I really wondered was what my companion meant by his odd proverb.

"Have you been much on the sea?" I asked, hoping to find out.

"Eh, my father was a stoker on the *Leopard of the Sea,* and when I was thirteen or fourteen I went on board too. The captain took a fancy to me, and when I grew up they made me a lieutenant. But we only went outside once: that time we went to Yemen."

"Oh!" I exclaimed, beginning to be interested in my man and resolving to seize him by the leg if he got up from his stone. "What sort of a ship was the *Leopard of the Sea?*"

"Didn't you ever hear of her?" he asked in surprise. I didn't answer and he went on: "She was not a battleship, if that is what you mean. They called her a cruiser. She was an old steamer they bought in Europe. Sometimes she carried soldiers to the Dardanelles, but most of the time she lay in the Golden Horn."

"How did she happen to go to Yemen?"

The experience of a lengthening career has taught me that information may sometimes be obtained by asking for it, and this time my strategy was successful.

"It was an idea of Sultan Hamid. One night, late late, an aide-de-camp from the Palace came on board with an officer in chains, and said that he was to be taken at once to Yemen. Ten minutes later another aide-de-camp came to say good-bye to the officer, from the Sultan, and to give him his promotion as general, and to make him a present of five hundred pounds. They said he was a Circassian prince and that he had been plotting. It was a lie. But Sultan Hamid believed it. And how was he to know that you cannot start for Yemen like that, in ten minutes? It was not his trade. It was ours; but none of us was on board, and we had no coal, and no food, and nothing, and the people from the Palace said we must be gone before morning. So sailors came to wake us up—as many of us as they could find—and there was great calamity. And we did start before morning. We got a tug to pull us, and we went around to Küchük Chekmejeh, in the Marmora, and there we stayed till we were ready to start. It took us three or four weeks. The machine was old and broken, and we had to get an Englishman to mend it. And the *Leopard of the Sea* had been lying so long in the harbor that no one could find her bottom. It was all grown with bushes and trees, like a garden. And what mussels grew in the garden! And what *pilaf* they made! We picked off all we could, and we ate them ourselves till we were sick of them, and we sold the rest. The mussels of the *Leopard of the Sea* were famous in Constantinople. Afterward we were sorry we had sold the mussels though. When at last we started for Yemen each one of us had ten loaves of bread and some olives and cheese. We didn't know how long we would be on the way. At the end of three days we had only just passed the Dardanelles and the cheese and olives were gone. A day or two later the bread was gone too, though we were still far from Yemen.

"Water we had, thanks to God! We had a machine for making the water of the sea sweet. It was only food we didn't have. We had to stop at an island and get some."

"What island was it?" pursued I, in curiosity, wondering how far the *Leopard of the Sea* got on ten loaves of bread a man.

"How should I know? It was an island in the White Sea." By which he meant not our White Sea but the

Mediterranean. "I didn't ask the name. Greeks lived on it. The governor of course was a Turk. We were very sorry when we left it. The sea began to show himself after that. Until then we had not known him."

"Were you sick?"

The darkness hid on my face the grin without which this question may not be asked.

"My soul! Who is not sick when the wind blows on the sea—unless he is accustomed? We were not accustomed. How should we be? We had never put our noses outside the Dardanelles. It was worst for the captain and me, because we had to stay on deck and steer whether we were sick or not. But we got accustomed by and by. And the captain taught me a little about the machine which points its finger at the Great Bear, and about the papers wherein are written all the lands and islands of the earth. And after two or three weeks we found Egypt. It seemed to me a miracle. When I saw it lying white and flat on the edge of the sea and the captain said it was Egypt, I said to myself: How do we know that it is Egypt? It may be Persia. It may be England. But it was Egypt, thanks to God! And if it had not been for the Circassian I don't know what we would have done.

"He was a very good man. The aide-de-camp who brought him from the Palace said that he was to be kept shut up in a small room and that he was to eat nothing but bread and water. But we were all shut up and none of us had anything but bread and water, and not always that. And so the captain very soon let the Circassian do what he liked. And when we got to Egypt the Circassian bought food and coal for us, out of the money the Sultan had given him. For we had none. We had spent all we had at Küchük Chekmejeh and at the island. Then we went on, through the river that goes into the Arabian Sea. We had orders to take the Circassian to Jiddeh; but at Suez they brought us a telegram telling us to go on without stopping to Hodeïda, and afterward to bring the Circassian back to Jiddeh. At Hodeïda, however, we found another telegram which said that we were to go on to Basra, for some soldiers."

"To Basra!" I exclaimed.

I began to feel hopelessly choked up with questions. I wanted to know more about the Circassian. I wanted to know more about everything. The man whom chance had brought for a moment to a stone beside me had an Odyssey in him, if one could only get at it.

"To Basra, *ya!*" he said before I could stop him. "And a time we had getting to Basra—more than two months. It was so hot we could not sleep at night, and again we had nothing to eat. And worst of all, the machine that made the water of the sea sweet got a hole in it, we used it so much, and after that the water was only partly sweet. And it was so bad we tried to find water on the land, and one night we went too near and sat." By which the mate of the *Leopard of the Sea* meant that they ran aground.

"We sat for two weeks, trying to get away. It was good that the wind did not blow in that time. In the end I don't know whether more water came into the sea or what happened, but all of a sudden we found that we could move. Then another calamity came on our heads. Although we had been sitting for two weeks we had been burning coal most of the time, trying to get away. So before we got to Basra no coal was left. The Circassian had bought more than we needed to get to Jiddeh or even to Hodeïda, but we never expected to go any farther. So we spent all our time finding wood for the machine. We burned up all the doors, all the chairs, all the tables, all the boats. We cut down walls in the ship, we tore up decks. And then we only just got into the river of Basra.

"At Basra how good it was to put our feet on the earth! And if you knew what a country that is—hot, flat, dirty! They speak Arabic too, which none of us could understand but the Circassian. And thieves! We had already burned up most of the ship, but they would have stolen the rest if we had let them. So although we had come to land we still had no peace. And twelve hundred soldiers were waiting for us and expected to be taken away immediately. They had been in Arabia seven years, poor things, although when they went the government promised that they should stay only three. There had been three thousand of them in the beginning. More than half of them had died, not from bullets but from the sun of that country and its poisonous air. And not one of them had been paid or had had a new uniform in seven years. You would have wept to see them—how ragged and thin they were, and how they begged us to pay them and take them away.

"How could we take them away or pay them? We had not been paid ourselves for four or five months, and we had no food or water or coal, and nobody would give us any. We went to the governor, we went to the general, we went to everybody; but not a *para* could we get. The Circassian still had a little money, most of which we used in telegraphing to Constantinople. And still no money came. We had to sell our watches, our clothes, anything we had left. One day we even sold two windows—you know the little round windows in the wall of a ship? A fat Arab wanted them for his house. What could we do? We had to live. We couldn't find any others to take their places and so we nailed kerosene tins over the holes—one inside and one outside. They looked very funny, like blind eyes. They were at the bow, one on each side."

My companion paused a moment, as if musing over the blind eyes of the *Leopard of the Sea*. Then he rolled himself another cigarette. I noticed for the first time that the minarets of Yeni Jami were fully alight, and that other lights were beginning to hang in the darkness between them.

"In the end it was the Circassian again who got us away from Basra. He gave the captain the last money he had and told him to telegraph to Sultan Hamid and say five hundred pounds must be sent to us immediately or we would go to Europe and set the Circassian free. How was Sultan Hamid in his palace to know that we had no coal and could not go to Europe if we wanted to? But the next day the governor came to the captain with five hundred pounds and a decoration, which he pinned on his coat with much speech, and invited him not to let the dangerous Circassian go. The dangerous Circassian was there listening with the others, and the governor liked to speak with him more than with any of us, because he was an *effendi* and knew all the people of the Palace. The governor after all, poor man, was no better than an exile himself.

"So at last we started back to Jiddeh, with money in our pockets and bread in the cupboard and coal in the machine. The captain took care to put a lot in the place where the windows had been that he sold, to keep the tin tight against the wall of the ship. We got along very well that time. We reached Jiddeh in forty-five days. Before we got there the captain told the Circassian that he would not give him to the governor but that he would give another man, one of the soldiers, and say it was the Circassian, and bring the Circassian back to Egypt and let him go. But the Circassian would not allow him. He said it was not just that another man should be punished in his place, and that they would find it out in Constantinople and punish the captain and the governor and there would be many calamities. Even when the captain wept and kissed his feet, the Circassian would not allow him. You see they had lived together for so many months and had suffered so much together that they had become friends. Ah, he was a very good man. Because he was a good man God rewarded him, as you will see."

I did not see at once, however, for my companion stopped again. And when he went on it was not to give me any essential light on the history of the mysterious Circassian.

"I told you about the soldiers we brought from Basra, who had been in Arabia seven years and who had never been paid. They were so glad to leave Basra that they made little noise about their money, and the general promised them that they would get it in Jiddeh. But when they heard the story of the Circassian, how he telegraphed to Sultan Hamid and got money for us, they said it was a shame that he didn't get money for them too: they had gone seven years without a *para*. And when the general of Jiddeh told them that they would be paid in Constantinople they made much noise. They would not believe that the general had no money, and they brought the Circassian into it again and said he must telegraph to Sultan Hamid. They could not understand! It was only when the general threatened to keep them in Yemen and send the *Leopard of the Sea* home without them that they were quiet.

"We were sorry to leave the Circassian in Jiddeh, but

we were to start away at last. It is the country of the
Prophet, but *vallah!* it is a dirty country! We came
quickly enough up to Egypt. The *Leopard of the Sea*
walked more slowly than ever, because the hole in the machine for making the water of the sea sweet spoiled the
water, and the bad water spoiled the machine of the ship.
Still, we went forward all the time. And in Egypt, thanks
to God, there was no telegram. And our hearts became
light when we came once more into the White Sea, where
it seemed cold to us after Yemen.

"The captain said he would stop nowhere till we got to
the Dardanelles, lest he should find a telegram. But our
calamities were not quite done. It was because of the soldiers again. After they smelled the air of their country
once more and ate bread every day, something came to
them. They went to the captain one morning and said,
'We wish to go to Beïrout.' The captain told them he
couldn't go to Beïrout. He had orders to go to Constantinople. What did they wish in Beïrout? They merely answered, 'We wish to go to Beïrout.' And in the end they
went to Beïrout. What could the captain do? They were
a thousand, with guns, and we were forty or fifty; and
they were very angry. They said they were fools ever to
have left Arabia without their money and they were tired
of promises.

"So we went to Beïrout. The soldiers told the captain
that he need not mix in their business: they had thought
of a thing to do. Only let him wait till they were ready to
go. And half of them stayed on the steamer to see that
he did not go away and leave them. The other half went
on shore and asked where was the governor's palace. Every
one was much surprised to see six hundred ragged soldiers
going to the governor's palace, and many followed them.

When they reached the palace the soldiers asked for the governor. A servant told them that the governor was not there. 'Never mind,' said the soldiers, 'we are six hundred, and on the ship there are six hundred more, and we will find the governor.' Then they were told to wait a little and the governor would come. And the governor did come. For I suppose he was not pleased that there should be scandal in the city. Also it happened that he had very few soldiers of his own, because there was fighting in the Lebanon.

"He received the six hundred very politely, and gave them coffee and cigarettes, and asked them what he could do for them. And they told him their story, and what they had suffered, and how many of them had died, and that they had never been paid, and they said their hearts were broken and they wished their money. The governor said they were right, and it was hard for a man to go seven years without being paid. Still, he was not their general: how could he pay them? 'You can telegraph to Sultan Hamid,' they said, 'and he will send you the money. We shall wait here till the answer comes.' And they waited, the six hundred of them.

"They made no noise and frightened no one, but they sat there on the floor with their rifles on their knees, and smoked cigarettes with the soldiers of the governor—who pitied them and said they would never drive them away. And by and by the governor came back and said he had heard from Sultan Hamid, who said it was a sin that his children should be treated in that way, and they should have their money. And then he called a scribe, and they made an account, and the soldiers took the money. It came to eight or nine thousand pounds. And a mistake was made by the scribe, and some soldiers got too little, and the governor gave them what was owed. And the soldiers said they were glad they had not been paid in seven years —to get so much now.

"The captain was not pleased by this work, for it put us back many days and he thought Sultan Hamid might be angry if he got too many telegrams asking for money. However, the captain was pleased and we were all pleased to get away from Beïrout with no more trouble. But of course the soldiers were the most pleased, who smelled their own country again after seven years, and who had their money at last. They sat on the deck all day counting it, and singing, and some had pipes which they played, and those who were Laz or Kürds or Albanians danced dances of their country. But before long the sea began to dance, and then they stopped. And by and by the wind blew so hard they could not stay on deck. We did not mind, because we were accustomed; and the wind was from the south, which helped us. But they were not accustomed, and they were very sick. The ship was so small and they were so many that downstairs there was no room to turn without stepping on a sick soldier. And water poured down from above, and they all got soaked as they lay on the floor. Even if we had not burned up all the sofas and tables and chairs in the sea of Basra there never would have been beds enough for them. And at last there came a night when the captain and I began to think. The ship went this side, the ship went the other side, waves rolled back and forth in the cabin, everywhere there were cracks and macks till we thought the *Leopard of the Sea* would crack in two. By God, it was a night of much fear. But what is there more than *kismet?* It was our *kismet* that that also should pass."

I saw it was time to open the shutter of my camera, for

the lights between the minarets of Yeni Jami had grouped themselves into the image of a ship. It seemed an odd co-incidence. When I sat down again on my stone, after pinching the bulb, the mate of the *Leopard of the Sea* continued to stare abstractedly at the little bark of gold sailing in the dark sky.

"Who shall escape his destiny?" he uttered at length. "For six months we had had no peace. We had lacked bread. We had suffered storms. We had sat on the floor of the sea. We had been burned and frozen. We had been robbed. We had been worse off than beggars. We had been unjustly treated. We had eaten all manner of dung. But no harm had come to us, thanks to God! And the morning after that night was like a morning of paradise. The sun was bright and warm. The sea was blue blue. There was no wind. There were hardly any waves, for we were among the islands again. We could see on them the flowers of almond trees and peach trees. The soldiers said they heard the birds. They had forgotten all their calamities, the sol-diers, and were sitting on the deck again, counting their gold, singing, playing pipes, dancing. And in front of us we could see the mountains of the Dardanelles."

He sighed, telling the beads of the string he carried as he went over the memory in his mind.

"There was only one thing: the *Leopard of the Sea* sat very low in the water. Why not, after the rivers that came in the night before? I thought nothing of it. We pumped, but we didn't mind, because we were so near home. I saw, though, that the captain was thinking. I asked him if he was afraid they would make trouble for us about the tele-grams and the money. Sultan Hamid often did things for reasons that were not apparent, and he never forgot.

" 'God love you!' said the captain. 'I think nothing of

that. But do you remember those windows we sold in Basra? Those are what make me think. We needed bread then, it is true, and no one can blame us. Also we nailed the tin on very tightly. But in the storm I kept thinking of them. And you see the bow now is lower than the stern. Those blind eyes are under water.'

" 'They will still see the way to Stamboul,' I told him. 'There is plenty of coal behind the tin.'

" 'Yes,' he said, 'but coal is like rice. It drinks up water, more and more, without your knowing it.'

" 'Eh, if we have a *pilaf* of coal in the ship, what matter?' I said.

"He laughed.

" 'I would not mind so much if we had not burned the boats. Just look downstairs and see if there is much water about.'

"I looked, and I couldn't find any to speak of. I went down to the engine room, without telling them why I came, and there was very little. What they were thinking of down there was the machine. It had become more and more rotten, from the bad water, till it would hardly work. The door of our house was open in front of us, but when we would have run to it like boys, the *Leopard of the Sea* could only walk, slowly slowly, like an old man."

He had left out enormously, and I realized in the end that I had small notion what manner of man he was himself. But I am bound to say that he did make vivid, as we squatted there on our neighborly stones, the final case of the *Leopard of the Sea*.

"Why should I make much speech? The old man never found the door of his house. It was because of his blind eyes. But until the last moment we hoped we might get to the Dardanelles. The sea became more and more quiet.

It was more beautiful than anything I have ever seen, like jewels with light shining through them. A great purple island stood not far away, and white houses were on it. And sails played like children on the blue of the sea. It was so beautiful and so still that the soldiers were not frightened. They noticed that the ship settled in the water, but the captain told them it was nothing. He asked me what we should do—whether we should let off steam to keep the machine from bursting. We finally decided not to. We might reach land after all, and steamers and ships were all about us. While if we let off steam and signaled for help, there would be much confusion and the soldiers might make another calamity; for they were very simple. 'Akh! if they only hadn't made us go to Beïrout!' the captain said. 'We would have been at home by this time.' But we were very sorry for them."

He stopped again for a moment. Yet I knew in my heart that it was wholly without melodramatic intent.

"The sun set. Night came—a warm night of stars. I remember how they looked, and how the soldiers sang on the deck, and then how the *Leopard of the Sea* suddenly began to run—but down, pitching forward."

I wondered many things, but chiefly if he would say anything more. It seemed indecent to ask him—with that picture in my eyes of a lighted steamer suddenly lurching, bow foremost, out of sight. Presently he did say something, though not just what I hoped. First, however, he leaned over and patted the ground.

"The earth!" he said. "The earth! I like to feel that under my feet!"

Then he got up, made me a courteous salaam, and left me on my stone to stare at the little ship of light hanging over the dark mosque.

GERTRUDE DIAMANT

ORCHESTRATION OF WORDS

My method of writing a short story does not follow any plan. As nearly as I can approximate them, however, these are the rules which govern my writing:

1. I do not think in terms of character and plot. These seem to me academic categories, used by critics as an expedient of criticism. If I should consciously say: "I shall write about such a character and devise this sort of plot," it would result, in my case, in an unsatisfactory and superficial performance. In so far, however, as the term "character" may be used in this discussion (and it is hardly possible to discuss a theory of writing without being forced to resort to it), it is used with a special connotation. A "character" to me is never a type, never subject to classification. Nor am I interested in analyzing character in terms of motives (love, greed, ambition, etc.). The people whom I write about might easily be pigeon-holed from the realistic point of view by Sinclair Lewis, let us say; or, from the scientific point of view, by the Freudians. But I do not care about how a character impresses *me;* I care, rather, to write about how the world impresses *him;* to follow the flux of impressions that register on his mind, to enter his consciousness and look out on the world from that consciousness. And no person, in his own consciousness, can ever be to himself a classified character.

2. Usually, before I begin work on a story, I have a hint in my notebook. This may take the form of a title, a bit of dialogue, a phrase, a description. From such inchoate material the story develops . . . sometimes by a process of accretion—jottings recorded in the notebook over a period of months; sometimes a single note is sufficiently provocative to furnish a whole story.

3. In so far as a plot may be deduced from the finished product (and, of course, plot must always be present in every work of fiction to a greater or less extent) my plots may be defined as psychological plots. My interest lies primarily in analyzing mind, not in terms of motive, however, but in terms of mood. An emotional climax which may take only three or four minutes in the consciousness of a character, may interest me to

such an extent that I develop a minute analysis of that climax into a long story (as in my story "Pregnant," *The American Caravan,* 1928). Or I may take a segment of somebody's mind, and make a story of following the unconscious flux of impressions, thoughts and emotions that occur there. The visible world exists only secondarily, only as it enters into this flux of mind. Often the names of my characters do not interest me, and, if it is possible to leave them without names, I do so. Often the plot and characters of a story are both subordinate to a third element, which in a certain way is even more fundamental and important to writing than either of these. This is rhythm, the orchestration of words and sensory impressions. In "Channa Makes Her Bed" (*Menorah Journal,* February, 1925) neither Channa, nor the plot of her receiving immortality and renouncing it, is important. My aim was to convey in writing the mood of an old ladies' home, a mood of age which is past all passion and has almost reached non-being in life. The success of a story of this kind depends wholly on the turn of the phrase, the choice of words, the images.

In looking back on the genesis of my story "Adventure" (which appeared in *The American Caravan,* 1927) I find in my notebook the first sentence recorded, without further comment. I remember also that at the time the story suggested itself to me, I had occasion to pass a factory every day, and to observe the workers entering it. There was also in my mind at the time the thought of Fritz Yuhrman, though I had not chosen a name or local habitation for him. (In fact the story was almost complete before I decided to give him these.) In my mind, however, was the idea of writing a story about a grown-up man whose perceptions were still childlike, and yet often more profound than the perceptions of those apparently brighter; who was sensitive but inarticulate, pitting himself against a world that he could not understand. Having him work in a factory and meet his doom there afforded both a foil for his character, and evidence of how the world took its toll of him. There is in this story no plot in the conventional sense, no climax, or rising or falling action. It is the flux of Fritz Yuhrman's mind which makes the plot, and the accident in the factory is secondary.

These rules, of course, are only very inaccurate approximations of the forces which unconsciously govern my work. It is difficult to make a truthful analysis, but I hope this will prove helpful.

ADVENTURE [1]

ALL pleasant things were in the future. He would rise every morning at five, rumble to work on the crosstown, feed his machine all day, then rumble home again. Meanwhile he could dream. Rumbling to work on the crosstown, feeding squares of white paper to his machine, eating lunch while it watched him, he could always dream. He could think of the blueness of his eyes, and the careful, sweet pose of his lips. He was Fritz Yuhrman. He could taste those syllables, their finality, and the mystery that they were he. There would never be a change, he did not want one. His days now were like an avenue of trees, and he had nothing to do but march past them.

Yes, all pleasant things were in the future. Early in the morning, the shop windows. Ineffable ladies powdering themselves with large white puffs. Gloves and ties and derbies . . . a mysterious symbol of maleness. Pink and blue women's things, that curled under the show-glass like careless hair under water. The city was clean in the morning, a nut just plucked from the shell. It was pleasant and lonely to rumble along in the crosstown, always under the elevated, that straddled the street with a hundred squat legs. And all the signs were mysterious. He read them over and over like poetry. "V. Capri, Cleaner . . . Plumbers' Supplies, Delaney." It made him think

---

[1] From *The American Caravan,* The Macaulay Company, 1927. Reprinted by permission of the author and of the publishers.

of a time when he used to sit in a churchyard, reading epitaphs.

Meanwhile the light crept down from the housetops, slowly, a blonde screen unrolling. Gold triangles wedged into the purple pavements. People came out of the asphalt, all dressed, with definite faces, knowing where they were going. The car turned at last—the car and the tracks stopped together. He was dropped like a leaf into the stream of workers.

That was good. Every morning it was good, to be going with them, one step in a rhythm of many steps. Better than standing alone on street corners, not seeing the light creep down from the housetops—or listening to his hunger—a song buzzing too long in his brain. Now he heard it—the syncopating tap of women's heels, the music of full limbs straining against tight skirts. Nobody turned. It would be like putting a knot into a taut chain going forward.

The factory, too, was a thing to wonder at—a domino of black windows on white walls. Every morning it baffled him. When he saw it from the crosstown, bright and floating in the sun, there was no building at all. It was a flag, black and white in squares, gay and relentless. Nearer, and the flag curled up—but the blackness and whiteness were still there, matched against each other like a game being played. Yes, a domino, meaningful and grotesque like all dominoes. And then nothing but a door, and they going in. So the day began. A gong now would ring him to his machine—a gong would ring him away from it. There would never be a change, he did not want one. Once when Fritz Yuhrman was a boy walking in the woods, he saw a cat measure a space, and walk it back and forth. This space he measured for himself.

Fritz Yuhrman had not always wanted to work in the factory. Long ago, he thought of becoming a singer. He was a little boy then, liking to sing. He had a thin, straight voice, enough thread of a voice to string a few notes on: and he wandered all day alone in the woods, weaving his thin thread of song in and out of the trees. Going home he did not stop singing. And the people of Ledyard who passed him shook their heads. Ah, well, one might sing. But this Fritz Yuhrman, if he wasn't singing—there he was! Not a sound from him! A young pine in the wind had more to say. But Fritz went on singing. It was his way of breathing.

"Hi, Fritz! Where have you been all day?" his father asked him. "Tramp! Let me look at you!"

With his stump of candle held close, old Michael saw his son—the ripe color of air playing on his cheeks, the tangled dance of his straight hair, his blue eyes that the wind had polished. Bad! That was the way to come from a naked woman.

"Well, there's the supper, and there's the milk." At everything he pointed his candle, like a stubby finger flaming greedily towards things.

Fritz did not answer. He stood there knowing that something round and thin as a soap bubble was breaking into fragments. And in some way old Michael was causing it.

"I'm not hungry. I'm going to bed."

At first Michael assented cheerfully. "Well, there's the bed, and there's your nightshirt." But as Fritz gave his flaming finger wide berth, Michael's voice rose in a soft volley of questions.

"Not hungry," he said thoughtfully. "You say you're

not hungry, Fritz? But how can that be? How can you not be hungry?"

He moved forward, eating the space between them slowly, as if it tasted good. He was not taller than Fritz: but his shortness was old, and his body rhythm different. His shortness had the hurling power of a squat projectile. As he stood before his son, there was a wayward innocence in his face. He seemed to be waiting for that click in his anger which should be the signal to hurl himself.

Suddenly Fritz shouted. "I'm not!" It came from the distance, a clear, taut shout, like the flash of a knife between them. Michael looked at him. Then he clicked himself round, and took his candle. In the air was the after-image of the shout, and Fritz stood under it, trembling.

But there were worse things than going hungry to bed. They said in the village that only old Michael and his son lived in the house. Yet at night Fritz knew better. Why did the pump wait for him to lie down, and then turn into a reared-up snake, looking at him all night, with the profile of its eye? And one star always came to the window, and stayed there, fastened like a bright bug on a petal. He knew he could touch it. But first it would make a hissing sound, and then sting him. Neither was that the worst of it. Outside was the pine tree, always there, with one great palm held over the flat roof. It was a sour pine, and it stood there hating the house. Some night, he knew, it would happen. A rustling sound first—then a terrible creaking. The pine was lifting its palm! Ah, God, it was happening! He heard it! The pine slapped the roof. . . .

Meanwhile old Michael came to bed, and Fritz had a new game to play. He hated his father. He could lie awake, and play it like a game.

Sometimes, in the morning, it was hard to get away. That was when three boys who lived near him saw him going. They came out on the road, and stood in his way, shouting. "Clam-face!" "Fritz-without-a-tongue." Words that fell into a marvelous rhythm: one could even march to them. And it was true. He *had* no tongue! His face quivered into a knot. It flamed and sputtered at them. But he could not answer them, he had no tongue.

Better run away from them—to the hill today. Now up, up to its back. "Lie quiet, my hill, while I mount you." Here the arched back—there the flat neck and the snout, always pressed close to the earth. It was an old animal, this hill—an animal so old that no one had ever seen it. But he wasn't afraid. He sat on it—he rode it all day. . . . If he could live forever alone on the hill, away from *them*. He would stay there always, quiet as a leaf, until the leaves would not even know he was there. How strange was the going to bed—the unlacing of his shoes— the close room under the blankets. Here, no strangeness.

One day when Fritz was lying alone on the hill, he saw suddenly a little furry pyramid, with two long, quivering ears in front. It moved, and four boys were stalking a rabbit. He saw them through the grass, a small, moving forest of brown legs. He heard stiff grass snapping between their toes. He heard their breathing, heavy and dry, the sound of sweat in it. Until they were gone, Fritz lay still. His heart was knotting itself so that nothing could untie it. Straight and rigid he lay, as if they had stepped on him, a living thing in the grass. Then he was up shouting: "You. . . ." He was down, beating the earth, tearing it in fine, straight lines—biting dry, bitter mouthfuls. He hated them! He would pull them to pieces! He would run down the hill and throw himself on them. He would take them each in turn, and sit astride of them, and beat them with both fists, as if they were drums for him. There would be no one else in the world but Fritz Yuhrman. God would make it so. . . .

But when he rose at last, he did not understand it all. There were four boys chasing a rabbit. Robert's right foot had a wart on it. He had seen the wart riding through the grass on Robert's foot. And Peter could not keep up with the others—the little boy who always breathed so hard it sounded like sobbing. He was lying in the grass, he saw these things. That was all.

"It is time now, Fritz," his father said that night. "No more loafing for you. I need a man."

He didn't care. No use going there again. When he looked at the hill, it was like looking at words that he had forgotten how to read.

All day Fritz worked in the fields. Days became months and years, but Fritz was not aware. He no longer saw anything, he no longer sang. He moved in the rhythm of his work, as in an active numbness. His movements were like sounds that he could not hear. But sometimes, when he was alone, working and bending away from the sun, the brightness of the sky and the earth flowed on him suddenly, raping his senses. He felt the floating of the earth—but the floating and the brightness were unbearable. To save himself, he looked towards the house—over acres of fluid earth, rolling away from the spot where he stood, from his feet that had become the navel of a vast fountain. And he saw the house clinging to a slope. It was a small gray shell, clawing the earth with its walls, trying to stay erect in the floating brightness. He saw himself and old Michael going into the shell and coming out, and only in the darkness inside were they safe. He must go towards the house, now . . . carefully, to prevent himself from falling . . . into the darkness between the walls. But as he went down, it seemed to him that he was not walking, but plunging in space: and the vast, green deck of earth was plunging with him. He saw the house soaring away from him high into air, swooping down again, yet always clutching the earth with desperate walls. And when he entered it at last, he felt weary and glad, like a boy who has caught a ball out of a rough sea.

Inside the house, Fritz drank cold water and cooled his forehead. For a while, now, his numbness was shattered. He saw the shapes and colors of things again. But the shapes and colors were like a plaid cloth of terrible distinctness, waving in front of his eyes and torturing them.

Sometimes he was aware that he hated his father. Michael seemed to be everywhere. And at night they lay down together in one bed, like cattle sharing the stall. Between one breath and another, sleep came to old Michael. In the morning he was bending over Fritz, with a stump of candle in his hand. "Hi, Fritz! Wake up, it is day already." Never another word—never a word to show they were father and son. That didn't matter. Day and night mattered—two acres, one to be sown with work, and the other with sleep. Yes, Fritz knew his father, he knew what he was. When he swept the stable floor into a golden pyramid of manure—when he saw the flesh of cows quiver and come to rest—swiftly and mysteriously, in those moments, Fritz knew his father.

"Come, Fritz, faster," old Michael was shouting to him.

Fritz paused with an umbrella of hay over him. Now, now he would pitch it up, let it fall wildly, nowheres. Then to spring off the hay pile, run the length of the grass path, hurdle the fence—so into the road.

From under his umbrella of hay, Fritz saw the legs of old Michael Yuhrman, short and lumpy in their brown overalls. They were two stumps of earth, planted wherever they stood. And they could move, and plant themselves again. If one thread of hay blew down from the wagon, they knew it. And if he ran away, they would come after him, and be planted wherever he turned. Faster, then! Hay into the wagon! An upward waterfall of hay.

But that night Fritz woke with a singing in his hands. Now it could be done! In some way, quickly, it could be done! He rose on his knees and looked at Michael. His father was rolled tightly into the blankets, round and small like a bottle, with his little red nipple of a face sticking out. There was a singing in his hands. He felt joyful again, as if he were alone on the hill. . . .

One night Fritz found himself walking towards the village. He wanted to speak to some one. When the other young men of Ledyard saw him coming, the laughing and talking among them trailed off. They were quiet, but they left a little flame of gayety burning, so that it could flare up when he left. With nothing to say, Fritz went towards them, and stood, for a while, timidly with them. Then they saw that it was a miracle, and it was comical—some one who had nothing to say! Their eyes flashed word of it to each other. They burst out laughing.

It was that way every night. He became a stage direction to them. They said: "It's Fritz Yuhrman," and they formed a circle around him. Soon Fritz also understood.

He was not to meet them, but in this way. It was the pattern into which they fell. And they laughed at everything he said. He laughed himself. That, too, was in the pattern. But all the time he hated them.

He hated them, until that hatred became for him a fresh numbness. Because they had cast him out with laughing, they had made his loneliness whole. Now he loved his loneliness, as a bond between them. And they had given it to him as a man gives a child to a woman and leaves her. It was a reproach to them, and yet he thanked them for it.

He stopped seeking them, but spent his time cherishing his loneliness. He moved about his work with careful movements, conscious of his wholeness. He grew afraid of his own voice. He never spoke, but seemed always to be listening. He listened intently to the voice of the ropes when he raised a bucket of water. He listened to the rusty hinges sounding in the ducks' throats; to the wind, raging softly and ceaselessly around his silence. He herded the cows with frantic hurlings of his arms and legs, rather than raise his voice. Speech seemed to him a remote and difficult thing.

Often he looked into the mirror and identified himself. He became aware of the blueness of his eyes, and the careful, sweet pose of his lips. He was Fritz Yuhrman. He did not know that he was a small man, with his head always on one side, as if listening.

And there was no going down to them again. In his mind he could see them, standing there, knotted together with whispering, and blown apart with laughing. They were laughing at him, because he was empty handed. Yet he knew of a way to possess something that they all must respect. Suppose he murdered his father. . . . "Fritz

Yuhrman, he's murdered his father." "Did you hear, Fritz Yuhrman murdered his father!" Once there had been a murderer in the village, and every one spoke of him. Fritz remembered it from the time he was little. They didn't laugh at him, either. No, surely no laughing then. It was clear, then. He must murder his father. And when this was clear, Fritz watched the body of his father wherever it went—riding a mower in the fields, or bending over the grindstone. He knew how the murder would look, from beginning to end. He saw it again and again. But about old Michael's body there was a terrible innocence, because he did not yet know. He saw his father's body yielding to him, and all its attitudes of terror. He thought of it passionately, as if he were about to possess a woman.

When Fritz went down the road at night, he had to pass Susan Beebe's house; and she was sitting on the porch nearly every night, alone. He was afraid of Susan Beebe. Her large red hands came out of her arms so suddenly. And there she was, always alone in the dark. At night he could not see her hands, but he thought he saw her neck, white and large and round, like the wooden church pillars. Suppose one night she should speak to him! It would be terrible, as though the high chiffonier near the sink had spoken to him. And yet it might happen. All day in the fields Fritz thought of it. He seemed to hear the sound of Susan Beebe talking to him everywhere. When he heard it distinctly, he was frightened. And when he did not hear it, he kept on working—for hours, often—until it sounded again. And then, one night, she spoke to him.

"Hello, Fritz."

"Hello, Susan."

She came down with her arms folded on her back, holding her elbows. They walked back and forth on the road, between two lamps that made a cage of light.

Every night after that, for three summer months, Fritz and Susan walked together in the cage of light. Forward they went, from the edge of darkness to the edge of light; and back again, over their own steps. Only their shadows, walking before them, straining away sidewise from their feet, dared pass into the darkness. Quickly, then, they turned, and dragged their shadows back again. There were only a few words to be said. Susan was content to walk beside him, holding her elbows in back; and he was afraid of her.

One night came the first rustle of cold wind, a whip faintly swished. As if some one had spoken, they looked at each other; and the fear of winter looked back at him and at her out of their faces.

"It's going to be cold, soon," Fritz said.

"Yes, it's winter, almost." And she held her elbows tighter. But they turned without other words, and walked back to the verge of darkness. Fritz wondered how he would see Susan in the winter. He would have to sit in her parlor, seeing her in the light. She might be knitting. . . . He saw her large red hands coming out of her arms. She might look at him archly—and her small head would hang back on the white pillar of her neck. Her body was in the rocker, straight and upright; but her long limbs pointed at him under her skirt, and her knees lolled away from each other. He saw them, thin buds raised on her round legs, that grew like trunks from their base of shoes. He was terrified. If only the winter would keep away. But just then a ribbon of leaves blew down before them, like the waving scarf of an enemy.

"The leaves are blowing down," Susan said. As they passed under the lamp Fritz looked at her, and saw meanings in her face that made him afraid. She stopped, and bent towards him a little, still holding her elbows in back. "Fritz!" But he walked rapidly on, into the darkness, and left her there.

He walked with a sudden sense of gayety and flight. He was going away! Why hadn't he thought of that before? It was so simple. It was such a good thing to do. Yes, the sky was going farther away, and the stars were getting smaller. Already the trees looked like masts swaying on a ship, with their black branches for cross-bars, and the wind for waves, and the earth for a deck. The whole earth was blowing like a ship. Every twig on trees, and every board in houses was creaking. The earth was tossing like a ship, and he was walking alone on it . . . sailing it, sailing it, through windy darkness forever. There *were* ships and sailors, of course. There were other places. There were cities, where one did nothing all day. One could stand on a street corner in the city, and see people passing from morning to night—and every person had a different face. Never the same face passed again. Nobody there would know he was Fritz Yuhrman. They would let him alone. In and out of the noise and the faces he could go by himself, neutral as the sound of a drum going in and out of the other music. A great vagueness was the city. . . . Best go there, away from Susan, away from Michael, and the others. Why, if he went, they would have something new to say: "Fritz Yuhrman, he's gone to the city." That was surely a smart thing to do. "Why didn't I go too? He's smart, that Fritz."

He woke his father up to tell him. When old Michael

heard it, he laughed. For minutes at a time, he lay laughing. Yet the next morning Fritz went. Snow lay all over, blurring the shapes of everything. He could not see any place where he used to go as a boy. Of all those landscapes nothing was left but the smell of air.

In that way Fritz came to the factory. Jonah Weisbord, the small man who shared his room, was foreman in the factory, and took him there.

"You don't have to stay, if you don't like it," Jonah said. "But look, the work is easy. You just go like this all day,"—he passed an imaginary something into the air. "No trouble. No brains, no muscles needed. And they pay you for it, into the bargain."

That seemed reasonable. It was clear that if you didn't have to think of what you were doing, you could think of other things. It was like not doing any work at all. Just as Fritz had imagined it. And then to be paid into the bargain. . . . And after his first day Fritz told Jonah he would stay.

On the floor where Fritz worked there were eight machines in a row. They were large machines, always working together. They made Fritz think of eight dancers, moving through the same figures to one rhythm. Often he crawled under them, and crouched in back, where he could see the shuttles, like dancers' backs, flying towards him and away. He liked to stay there as long as they let him. Crouching there, he felt he was part of the dance. Slowly, with a sense of numbness, he let the rhythm of the machines come on him. He felt their methodical ecstasy and their weariness.

In the daytime everything was pleasant. His machine understood him. It let him dream, and it didn't laugh at him. All it wanted was that white squares of paper should be laid on its tongue; and every time it swallowed, it smiled broadly. In the daytime he scarcely heard the noise of the machines. But at night a queer thing happened. They all stood before him, and they were not dancing this time, but singing. They sang with a thousand plunging gestures, as if the song would burst them. And the song and the gestures were obscene. And at night, often, he dreamt that they were laughing at him—the other workmen in the factory. But he knew that couldn't be. Here they liked him. They listened to him respectfully, and thought well of him. It would be that way always. The future was clear and pleasant.

"Come on, Fritz, sing something." It was the half hour for lunch, and at first they were all quiet, as if the sudden silence were darkness, making them ashamed. But Jonah, the shameless one, always called out loudly: "Come on, Fritz, sing something."

Then Fritz sang for them, weaving his thin thread of voice in and out of the still machines. They all winked at each other, and jerked their thumbs toward him. When he saw that, his voice jerked also, as if their thumbs were tweaking his throat. When he did not feel like singing, Fritz went over to talk to them. Listening was Jonah, who stood with his knees slightly bent and wide apart, a base for his hands. That was the way his knees laughed at Fritz. There was Ian Harlan, too, a tall fellow, whose forefinger was always crooked in his hair, scratching away his wonder and admiration. Fritz loved to think of things to say, to make the tall man scratch harder.

"If I saw an old woman," Fritz told them one day, "climbing the steps in the park—and if the day were slippery, why, I would take her right up in my arms, and carry her up to the top. Even if the day were not slippery, I'd do it."

"Sure you would," Jonah answered, with his knees laughing wider. "You couldn't lift an old woman. You're smaller than any old woman. But tell me, Fritz. *Did* you ever see an old woman, climbing the steps in a park?"

Oh, the fine scorn of his answer!

"Good, then!" and Jonah winked at the others. "Now, Fritz, since you really saw such an old woman, why didn't you pick her up, and carry her to the top?"

Jonah straightened his knees archly, and they all looked solemnly at Fritz. Only the tall man was scratching his forelock. Well, Fritz would have to think of something else. But Jonah was thinking too.

"Tell me, you," Jonah said one day. "Would you speak to a half man?"

"And where can half men be found?" Fritz asked loudly.

The small man spat. "Tcht! I know one for sure. Below here, nothing. He walks on all fours. It's a trick. Only George knows how."

"And why shouldn't I speak to him?"

Jonah's knees laughed again.

"Because nobody talks to a half man. See, Fritz? Nobody talks to a half man. Why, he stands near the park every day, and when it looks like rain, he shouts out to the people: 'It looks like rain.' And when it looks like a thunder storm, he shouts: 'It won't storm much . . . may not storm at all.' And he's right! Every time, he's right! He knows the weather, sure. Only nobody listens to him, because he's a half man. They all run away from him. Now, you, would you talk to him?"

Fritz answered: "Tell me where he is, and I'll go to-night, and talk to him."

"But nobody *does*," Jonah concluded in triumph. "Pah! They all run away from him, and he gets angry, and shouts after them: 'Nobody talks to a half man.' That makes them run away harder." Jonah spit between his knees.

But that night, when Fritz was falling asleep, he saw the half man standing near his bed. His forehead was laid to the blanket, as though his head hurt. He was breathing hard, like the little boy, Peter, and he was pointing up at the ceiling. Fritz lay paralyzed. He knew that the half man could leap and dance. It would happen before his eyes. . . .

Yet the days were pleasant enough. He did not want anything to change for all the years to come. He was a full cup. Not a drop of him should be spilled or added.

Then, one day, they discharged him. It was Jonah who tapped him on the shoulder. He said nothing. He just cocked his thumb at the door. The men and the machines all stopped to watch him go. The tongue of his own machine was lolling out, but he had to leave it that way. The sudden silence was like a lifted whip. He went before it fell.

Down . . . down the steps . . . faster . . . or he would hear it . . . the men and the machines laughing. And now he knew! They were laughing at him all the time . . . and when they were tired of him, they whipped him out. With a gesture they whipped him out, though a dog requires words. But he would hurt them . . . soon they were coming out. He waited for them in a doorway. Soon they were coming. . . .

He would flay each one with his eyes . . . thrust his look at them, like poison spewed out of his eyes. He would draw their hearts into a thin line between the tightness of his lips. They would be aware of him. . . . At last they would have to swallow him, each one as he passed—and he would taste bitter for them. But they passed and did not see him. Out of the doorway in which he stood, fell the black domino of his shadow. They walked on the shadow, but they did not see him.

Fritz Yuhrman stepped out of the doorway. He felt joyous, he tried to think why. Then he remembered that he had forgotten his hat. He must go back to the factory and get it. He did not feel himself walking the half block. There was no one on the street but a man talking to them of God. The man lifted his hand, and it burned brightly in the air. His short fingers were five candles, burning of an even length. Fritz was joyful because he had forgotten his hat, and because the man's hand was burning in the air. The door let him in—the stairs lifted him.

The machines were sleeping already. They were sleeping like folded birds, with their heads tucked down and their wings out. He went to his machine. It whined itself awake, and began to swallow the white squares of paper that he laid on its tongue. It swallowed all there was, and Fritz looked around for more. But while he looked, it caught his arm, and would not let it go. It was pulling him, like a playful child, and he had to follow. Somewhere he heard a shout. He saw Jonah running toward him. It was funny the way he ran, with his knees way ahead of his body.

WALDO FRANK

WAITING FOR THE WORD-RHYTHM

The only short stories of mine that strike me as absolutely achieved are those in *City Block*. These were all composed in the following way:

The idea was there for a long time before any attempt at writing: in most cases, for years. When I say Idea, I mean a merger of situation and persons so close that I cannot extricate one from the other. These ideas, with literally hundreds of others, get jotted into a notebook. They are germs: most of them remain germs—i.e., they do not germinate, are never written. In those that got written a rotting process took place: they were forgotten, they changed shape, were forgotten again. Finally, I felt the idea growing organic: exerting pressure on my consciousness. When the time and opportunity were ripe, I then consciously began to think of the embryonic story. I took it about with me, in my head, for a long intensive period: and as I did so it became more and more salient in my mind. I began to feel and see the characters, the rooms, etc., in which they dwelt. Still I did not write—I always resist writing as long as possible. At last comes a time when the story begins to have a word-rhythm in my mind. I sense it musically. Much of the detail of person, etc., fades away—or, rather, is essentialized into rhythmic word-stuff. There comes a time when I hear the story—when it begins to sing and speak in my head. Then I sit down and generally in a few hours it is written. I think the majority of the short stories I've written were actually set on paper in a single day or night. Sometimes there is a false start. I begin writing—and lose the rhythm. This means that I've been in error in believing that the tale was organic. I drop it, perhaps for months —perhaps forever.

When I get to writing, the verisimilitude of persons and situations is gone. I am not recording or narrating a series of facts in time. The stuff of the tale has become a complex of forces, dynamically moving—expressing itself. The persons are not persons, nor the scenes literal scenes: the life-material has been transfigured into essential, abstract art-material. I care nothing about "accuracy," etc., save insofar as that means accuracy of the words that come forth as expressing the art-stuff within me. But I am not passive in this process. The characters do not speak for themselves, nor act out their lives in the conventional romantic-realistic way. I feel, in writing my story, that I am dynamically active through these integers—through these organs that *are* the story. I have no personal feeling toward them: they suffer, experience joy, etc., in a way that while it expresses me is impersonal. The action is *sub specie aeternitatis*. I have often grown personally attached to characters in my books, long after they were published—when I have written other things and can return to them like a reader. In the process of creation I am free of sentiment—I am scarcely a persona at all. I am an engine dynamically at work—and the work *is* the tale. . . . If I have any feeling at all it is one of inevitable power—quite white and pure of personal participation.

I find that if I write while the personal and intellectual connotations of my theme are still extant, the result is not a pure esthetic transfiguration. Creation is a chemical process, as I see it: or an atomic one. The countless personal impulse that goes to make the germ of a work of art has to rot and to be transformed into an esthetic body—whose value lies precisely in the fact that the transfiguration from personal and sentimental elements has been successful.

BREAD-CRUMBS [1]

WHICHEVER way she moved—if it was possible with a turn of her head—Mrs. Silvester looked out on the street. Three children were romping there. They rolled and screamed and twisted gayly. Behind their fragile note was the thick texture of the City.

"I'd give them more sensible clothes to play in," she decided, "if they was mine. And just as nice, too!"

It was closing time—early. But the day had been good, the five o'clock bake was gone, and Joseph Silvester's leg

[1] From *The Seven Arts*, May, 1917. Reprinted by permission of the author.

was troubling him again. So she had sent him home, and the boy away. And as she worked, absently dusting, tidying, locking up, her eyes and her heart dwelt with the romping children. The impress of them was not glad, but it was sharp. Their fascination hurt her.

Still aloof from what she did, she went to the cash-drawer and lifted out the day's receipts. And then, as if by force, she turned her eyes from the children to the money. She counted it. She was smiling vaguely at what it told of success and comfort.

The children's laughter lay above the gray street like a little field of flowers. The woman made a bundle of the coins and bills. Then, she took two quarters from it and slipped them into the pocket of her skirt. Then, she completed the package and bolted the door behind her. She brushed past the children without attention. Quite suddenly they were uninteresting and annoying.

It was a walk of three minutes to her flat—one on the avenue, two on the block. The warm Spring evening tinged the clamorous movement of the City, made it somehow gentle and glad and clean. Its smile was stronger than the street's stridency. Helene Silvester went unconsciously along. The crowd that clotted and upset her way with its thick drab was nothing to her. It was like inconsequential mud beneath her feet. She walked through the Spring evening. She was aware of nothing else. A thought of what she had so inexplicably done in the store strove to be noticed. But the part of her that thought was mute and impotent. She did not care, she did not care to know that she had taken the two quarters. The impulse that had caused her deed kept her from questioning its purpose. It seemed sure of itself. Altogether it ruled her, so that she was in no way troubled.

She found her husband ailing. She cooked his supper, and then made him go to bed. It was too early for her to follow. She put out the light. She sat by the window of her front room. Her eyes and that part of her that dreamed took their course outward through the window.

She seemed strangely strong and her reach had no sense of limitation. Directly before her was the brown mass of buildings, deep in a faint purple haze. Below, the street seethed with its myriad energy that drew in as it rose, and struck her like the sharpened crest of a wave. Her window had a slight square frame, and somehow she perceived herself within it, dull and small in her gray dress, with her cheeks pale against the air. And yet the sky welling above the street, which huddled like a swarming thing beneath it, was a more real measure. The sky seemed to catch her with its gleam that fell upon her window; seemed to carry her up and to unfold her. The frangent street was lost in the silence of her outspreading self. And now she no longer saw her little figure framed by the window. She saw a serene sweep of world, slowly murmurous; and of it she saw her life, a pulse in the wide rhythm . . .

She had been married five years and she had been unhappy. Their trade had thriven. She had seen children romping like flowers in gray soil. She had stolen two silver quarters from herself. And in six months, she was to have —at last—a baby of her own . . .

The great sky rocked the world like a calm mother cradling an infant. The torn noises of the open windows and the block became a cry. Helene Silvester sat without further thought. And then she roused herself. She had been slumbering away, her face sheer to the air. And in her silly dream, she and the sky were one; the playful turmoil of the street was a single voice for which she waited.

Carefully the young woman closed the window.

"It might rain," was her thought.

Then, she went to bed.

The following day, Joseph Silvester remained at home. Helene kept the store herself. The curious impulse of the day before did not return. She brought back her little bundle of money undespoiled. But the two quarters had stayed where she had tucked them.

Joseph was feeling better, so there were two that evening beside the window. The silence was no less. Helene's thrill had become her monotone.

"I feel so glad—so glad . . ." she had said half-aloud. "It's two lives, husband: my own—and—" she stopped.

Joseph sat there, gripping his black pipe with white teeth. They showed behind the dark droop of his mustache. Also faintly as he puffed, his mouth showed and his lips were thin. He was a tall and heavy man. He was ten years older than his wife: a silent man, knotted by his power, stifled in his lack of an outlet. As he sat there, languid and slow, he was the portrait of a veteran, retired and cluttered up in the kind parsimony of the present. His energy was the sort that longs to slumber. Now, he blinked at Helene's words. They were the nonsense that had made him love her.

"He'll be a good, strong lad," he said with effort—the reach of his imagination.

"Husband—husband!" she was disturbed by the prosaic forecast. A good strong lad—? Others had merited that term.

The silence came again. Outside, the street was a harsh pagan a-frolic in the shadow of a church. But Helene's spirit chimed on. She had been thinking of her son. And now, she was reminded of the two quarters she had stolen from herself.

Light burst on her act. She was not amazed by it, now that she understood. But she was caught by the glamor of her impulse, as it came to her, radiant with her deed. That silver was for her son! Everything that she did and had was hers and her husband's together. The child also would be theirs together; and the clothes he wore and the care of him and the hope for his success. But the money was not theirs; it was hers! It was a bond with her child that birth would not sever.

She went no farther in her planning. She had no will to sound the sense of it. Why steal for her child, when everything that was theirs would be his? It was indeed a mute, foolish, guilty impulse. But Helene knew she would abide by it. Merely, since it was foolish, she would put it away. Since it was guilty, she would protect it. Since it was mute, she would love it.

The next day a quarter went into her skirt. At the month's end, Helene secretly opened an account in her own name, at the nearest bank for savings.

By no other thing was her life stirred from the course of waiting and of working. There had been one reason for her unhappiness. And it was going; each day it was going farther. And in its stead, there were a thousand reasons for being glad. Every detail of existence was quick now with a new throb of gladness; was like herself with the early throb of a new being. All life was tense and proud, was reticent and sweet with its sap of birth. She and all life were sisters. The baking and selling of bread, the brushing of her hair at night, the clothing of her breasts at dawn, the preparing of food, the gossip of her neighbors, the gentle pleasure of her husband—in everything was an unuttered song. A melody had come of the clatter and the travail of existence.

Helene walked through the cold sounds of life, outwardly quiet, inwardly a flame. But it was the flame that moved her. And the flame needed fuel. This was the reason of the now regulated theft.

The child was born in October. They baptized him William. It was Joseph's choice.

Helene's mood changed.

More and more, the business of the bakery devolved on her. During the early months of the child's life, Joseph was grumbling in his subterranean way. It was clear to Helene that she must overcome the tense hope of mothering more children. The peace of their life seemed to call for her unfailing presence. Joseph was lovable only when she allowed him to be passive. And only then did he appear to love her child.

He would say: "Work—worry—work—worry—for *him!*" when Helene had wished to stay at home. And such talk was unbearable to her. Besides, it seemed just that her husband should provide the color, the moral standard of their home; and that she should be its life. Gladly, she accepted whatever turn of events made him more the figure-head, herself more the burdened one. And it was not long before this unlevel distribution seemed a part of her comfort. For Helene was a woman with loyal faith in her own hands. Those whom she loved, she loved to feel dependent. Those whom she loved, she did not care to look on as dependable.

But with these full days she had changed. The wistful, the dreamful in her grew more covert. All her activity was an outward feature of her dream. But as work amassed, that gentle strain retired from the surface. At marriage, she had been a girl with tender lines, frail almost —a soft curve to her forehead, and a petulant wave to her hair, and nervous hands. Now, she was ample, sturdy. She had seemed tall with her slenderness; she was now short with her solidity. Only the glamor of her tilted eyes and the elusive tremble of her lips remained as tokens of her nature. . . . And her eyes looked mainly at accounts; and from her lips came capable commands.

It was not hard for Helene to manage a safe arrangement for her secret Fund. It had become an altar with its daily offering. To serve it, Helene had taken over complete charge of the bakery's accounts. The store was entirely her husband's. But even Joseph knew that he no longer ordered it. His was the credit and the atmosphere. Helene held command; and, since the bakery throve, she took her tithe.

The boy grew also, and the boy's Fund, as she now always thought of it. Helene was a careful mother. She was not lavish in attentions which warp and spoil a child. Strictly she measured her boy's nature, and planted a word or a sentiment, where, in her absence, it would grow. In a real way, William was her own. It was her taste and intuition that took root in the soil of his will. And yet, a great part of the mother went yearning and hungry. Helene did not have enough of her son. Almost, it seemed that her son was not enough for her. There were periods of rebellion against the store; hectic flights of her passion beyond life's meticulous plod; times when it was hard not to be altogether mother. But Helene held herself. The bakery needed her; life gripped her and reined her in. Her eager arms straightened against their fever to enclose her son; guarded against the lover in her breast. She remained housewife, manager, the restrained and careful parent. But in such phases, she heightened the daily toll for her secret Fund. This was a way of outlet.

It had sprung from a mute source. It had grown to be a field for all the mute things in her—where they could play, where they could meet a sort of sun, where they could be.

For Helene would not have been so indispensable a help-meet, had she not been many more things first. Into this pent shell she crowded a maze of murmurous life. She was a symbol of the stifled city. Athrob with a deep stream of power, she ran a bakeshop; all woven up in a panoply of dreams the least of which had a bright tip in the stars, she robbed small coins from her own cash-box. Her vision was that the dun streets were strewn with pied and playing flowers, yet she lacked force to win the communion that she needed with her child, to dare the venture of another. In all things, it is her like that had turned the glad fields into dolorous cities; and that give their golden lilt to the shambled gutters.

The Fund grew then; and into it, swelling also, flowed her thought and her impulse. But the sign of all this was merely her more rapt interest in the Fund. She knew of nothing else. She was a quite ordinary woman. Yet, it was the Fund that made her cramped life bearable. It was a way of revolt and of adventure: a way of having a separate life and of doing a silent thing. It had been Romance; it became Reality.

Joseph sat in his rocker and it was Sunday and he was unable to suggest their going anywhere.

"Don't you feel like an outing?"

"I'm tired, Helene. You go—with the boy."

She did not think of the drouth of her husband's life.

A dart of pleasure at the fruitful sum she had put away tinged through her. This was enough.

Joseph plied her with questions, in the store.

"We must get another place for the cakes. Why don't the Martins never come here any more? By the way, Helene, can you send our William with that extra delivery to number 393? I forgot it with the boy's orders."

William went. Helene answered all the questions.

"Ten cents extra for my child's having to do errands," she adjudicated grimly, as she made her theft that evening. So the inner rebellion was sloughed off.

Life was a dead thing. But her live fingers worked on it. Its dross was quick with her spirit.

After ten years, there was the Fund grown to four figures!

And then, Helene fell sick.

Once more her life was unlit, unwoven dross. Its emptiness had a painful, echoing reverberation. And then, all of her limbs were lead; and her thoughts weighted her body which they had lifted up. And the air choked her breathing; and the pavements of the street struck hard against her walking. And her work was a tedium and love was an irony . . . It was the sort of illness Helene could be made to admit—the one sort. It sank her to her bed. And there it held her stricken for half a year, while the world slumbered and dreamed outside, and her spirit beat within. And only her hands were flecked with life, as if life had run down and low to that extremity.

Finally, she was washed up, a blanched shred of herself, with all of world and spirit to be made anew.

For twelve months, Joseph had the store and his son

in his unaided hands. The task was beyond the man. Gradually, all these years, he had let his initiative dry away. He had settled into a state of half-decrepitude, of sweet inertia. It had been as much Helene's fault as his.

He strove heroically. He was all caught up in the stern business of command, and did not know that he was failing. He worked incessantly; he nursed his wife; he tried to be an active father; he got up at dawn. And while he worked, his mind was stiff with fear and worry—mute to recording. . . . When Helene came to herself, the bakery had fallen off from its prosperity. And Joseph Silvester was in debt.

Her healing was a sharp, slow birth. Her illness had been a guilty night. While her senses slumbered there was her household fallen away! All of it was like a mad interlude from faithfulness.

But now she was able to sit in her chair, while Joseph laid the events before her. Not until then was he sure himself of what had happened. What he knew best was that he had fought hard, admitted no breach in his hope. He stood beside her, a large, gentle man with his hair graying and his eyes poignantly moist and his lank hands faintly moving.

"Sit down, dear," she had to tell him. He sank awkwardly, and faced her. They looked calmly at each other. They seemed closer together than they had been. This dread thing, life, had played them an irreverent trick. It had tried to lay silence on them. But they were above the silence.

"I tried, Helene, to keep strict accounts of the business. But I was worried—I was so tired!" He gave her a batch of crumpled papers, blurred over with his pencil.

"Here are bills; I haven't paid them yet." He gave these to her, also.

She took them. "Go back to the store," she said, "while I study these."

Joseph got up and lingered. At the door he spoke.

"Helene—"

"Yes, husband—?"

"I—I wanted to say—it don't matter—none of the trouble—now; when I see you gettin' well."

"Of course, it don't!" she answered. And then she laughed.

The story of the crumpled sheets was an easy one for her trained eyes to read. The business of the bakery was dwindling. At the first outlay due to her illness, Joseph had retrenched. He had forced a diminution of his sales by a curtailment of his supplies. It had been the one way he knew of to save money. And it had its logical result. His trade had shrunk. He had let it shrink. At each reverse, he had cut down the amount and the quality of what he had to sell. The vicious process had gained momentum. Expenses had risen. Everything else had lessened. And for each drop, the foolish man had had no wiser answer than to add a willed retrenchment of his own.

Helene shook her head.

"It's my fault," she said. "If he had been that silly when I married him, he could never have had a bakery at all! I've spoiled him." And then, "I had no business getting sick."

She got up from her chair to see if she was strong enough to walk. A pain shot through her temples; her mind sickened in a swirl of nausea. But her feet held her. She walked the length of the room, three times. Then she sank down in her chair. She wanted to rest on her bed. She had resisted that. That had been giving ground, not gaining it.

"In a week, I'll be good," was her decision. It had no link with the pain in her temples.

She nursed herself carefully, meanwhile. She knew that she was preparing for a battle. And all of that week, she laid her plans, she went over the conditions she would have to cope with, she marshaled her resources. During that week no thought or fact of her life seemed to escape her. All of her was quickened by the sharp emergency of her affairs. All of her was attuned to meeting it. Yet, she did not dream, one moment, of touching her secret Fund.

"If only we had saved some money," Joseph said to her, with a low shake of his big head, looking away. "We should have, wife. We have been foolish."

"It is a pity, husband," was her answer.

And then, the battle.

Her eagerness swept her along. She was content, being full-handed. She had no eye to gauge the direction of her struggle. But even hope had to stop to breathe; and in the pause Helene looked about her. What she found was strangely different from her hope.

The way of their life had been increase. Now, it was loss. To bring about that change, there had come a violent event—her illness. No effort seemed strong enough to turn them back to the old way. Helene learned that there was stubborn growth in a bad direction, even as in a good one. The tide was going out.

And while she labored, hands beating against the ebb, hope weaving a frail garb against the onslaught, her Fund was fat and peaceful with its interest.

There were five years of battle. Into it Helene flung all of her diligence and craft. For it her husband found a new bloom of obdurate resolution. They served merely to prolong the battle.

She had begun to fight, for her health's sake, too soon. She did not regain the full vigor she had lost. Once more, she was pale and thin, and her hands were nervous. Her work and worry ate up each new shoot of strength as it appeared. Again the dreamful fiber of Helene stood at the surface—stripped, like her life, of its substance. Without blossom of youth and lilt of growth, there she was as she had been at the naked outset. Only she had her son beside her, and the secret Fund in the bank for savings.

These, then, served in place of the hope and passion and power of fifteen years before. These alone remained. She clung to them with desperation. And her grip was that of a spent, scared creature in the dark. For Helene did not know what life was fashioning. But, although she did not understand, she thought no more of giving up her Fund than she did of giving up her boy. In some way, one group of feelings bound them.

And inexorably, failure had crept up.

They had worked body to body—she and her husband. The old easeful state of Joseph had shriveled and gone away. He was a strong man, now. His will had burst forth. But the long sleep had atrophied his powers. He was intent on doing; he did not know what to do. He was more helpless in his blindness, because he was more active. His energies were new, but his skill was old. And, after all, even the Helene who had been, the woman merged into the substance of her will, with all of her vigor athrob and her strength unthwarted, had done no greater thing than this: to make a prosperous bake-shop prosper a little more.

But the blight of the year when she lay blighted also, had sunk too deep into the source of their affairs. About them had been too much life, strained to catch the sun where they drooped to the shadow. So now, at last, the time of deferring debts was over. The battle of five years swerved suddenly to a decision.

They sat facing each other, their hard stiff chairs against two walls. Joseph's rocker was empty. He was in no mood for it. Before them, in the center of the room, was a bare table. Their flat was darker, poorer than any they had occupied before. It was a Sunday afternoon. The morrow was the last day for paying certain creditors who had placed their ultimatum on legal paper. Joseph had the paper in his hands. It was his, because the property was his.

Beyond the window was a sordid street that stretched like a funnel to a little treeless park. Here their son was playing.

"Wife," Joseph said, "these are what's going to ruin us. Eight hundred dollars. If we could meet them—"

"The store is picking up."

"Yes; that's the sneering part of it. All of this fight, and the store picking up. And then—" he stirred the paper languidly, "then this."

"What can we do, Joseph?" Only her mouth moved as Helene spoke.

"Yes; that's it—what can we do, Helene?" He seemed to be tracing her words, with a tired care, in order to comprehend them.

"We'll have to go to work," she said.

The big man trembled. He rose partly from his seat. And then, gripping himself, he rested back.

"You mean a job—for *us?*" Still he seemed to grope, fingering over her words.

"What else is there to do!"

Helene left her chair. She wanted to walk.

"Sit down, wife." His tone was an unmistakable command.

Helene caught it, amazed, and her seat found her.

"Do you know what you've said, Helene? Do you know what that'd mean? Do you understand—?"

His voice was shaken, but it was strong. He had out-stretched his hand. It also was both strong and shaken.

"Joseph," Helene said, "how can I help knowing? Have I been outside? You talk—!"

All of her feeling raveled into pain. After his wreckage, had she not given the sinew of her body?

"Listen, Helene. I'm over fifty years old. I've been a sober man. I've been a decent man. Do you want me to go out, like a laborer, now? Could you stand for me to do that, Helene—?"

"I'll be going with you, Joseph."

"Listen some more, Helene. Have I ever harmed you? Have I ever interfered with all you wanted? I know you was clever. I know I was lazy. You was the boss, Helene. And when you was sick, don't you think I was ashamed how I spoiled what you had done? Do you think, wife, I liked to see myself for what I was? This is my fault. That ain't easy, knowing!"

"We're in it together, like one, husband. We'll face it."

His words hurt her. They had driven tears to her eyes. There was a tragic anger in this man's grief which she had never seen; which—of all of him—she could not master.

"You can stop it, Helene."

"What!"

He was standing over her. His big hands were clenched. And his body seemed alive in his flat clothes.

"I'm speaking, now! I watched you. I've known all along. I said nothing. Why should I? You deserved what you took. You would do no harm with it. I trusted you. I trust you, now, Helene. But save us! What's it all been piled up for, else? It's a heap of money, if you ain't spent it!"

His voice had been low. His words came ponderously. Helene was watching his clamped hands.

"Is it spent, Helene?"

"No, husband, it ain't spent."

Joseph lurched back, loosing his hands. "Thank God," he breathed.

"It ain't going to be spent! It ain't mine to spend! It's Willie's!"

Her words were quick. They were more shattering to him than all of his surprise had been to her. Rather than meet them, he contrived to doubt them.

"Then you don't understand."

"I do, husband. Who should understand, if I did not?"

"It's ruin! It's disgrace!" he was shouting now. "Here, with that bank-book!"

He thrust forth his palms. She was also on her feet.

"No."

"Here!" he once more lowered his voice.

"It's Willie's, I tell you."

"It's my money. Where did you get it from? My store—"

"You can't take it, Joseph."

"I don't mean to take it. You'll give it here."

They swayed close to each other. And then, she smiled. She had mastered him again.

"Sit down, husband. And let's talk."

Bewilderment was foremost in his senses. Long he had known of this. But always he had had two habits: a profound respect for the woman that he loved, a profound silence for what was close-woven in his life. He was ready, with the wreck of that life upon him, to listen to her words. With another, doubtless, all his slumbering mute strength would have flamed high with passion and a blind violence. He sat now, his body strained and aquiver, while his wife spoke, slowly.

"I never guessed you knew. Well, you do know. I thought it was my secret. I'm glad you never spoke to me about it. Thanks for that, husband. Your speaking would have spoiled it. I don't know why," she shook her head, "but it would. And it's true. And it's three thousand dollars—" She paused.

He measured his hope with her words, not daring to know their strangeness one to the other.

"Joseph," she went on, "think what it is—all that money—think what it means. It's the difference between you and Willie; it's what you never had. I love you, but what are you? What are either of us? It's what is goin' to make him stronger, better!"

"You see us on the edge of nothing. And you insult your husband."

"I don't. But our life's done. We can plod through, somehow. What'll that money do for us? Pay our debts— yes; and run our bakery. What's that to Willie? And what can it do for him? The money can give him an education! It can send him to college! Oh, don't you see?"

"And we—?"

"We'll work. It's your store. It's my money. I don't have to pay your debts with it. But, Joseph, am I forsaking you? Have I done that yet? I'll work with you, husband. I'm yours, even if this money ain't. I'll care for you. Oh, what won't I go through with you!"

"You can save us."

"At his expense?"

Her face had been soft. It hardened.

"No, I tell you! That's his. That's his chance. If we got to go down, so he can keep on goin' up—why down we got to go!"

She stopped. There was an austere ring in her voice.

Joseph looked at his wife. He came up close to her, in order to look close. She seemed, this moment, the clear, single summary of all that she had been to make him love her:—all this, in what appeared to him the moment of betrayal.

Still, he said: "You're heartless, wife. You steal from me; years, you been stealing from me. And now, you think of making your son better than I was."

"It's true."

"You don't care for me. All your love's there." He waved to the street.

"I'm yours, husband," was her answer.

"Is this honest—for them we owe to?"

Helene smiled: "It's his, now. We'll work to pay off, if that's your will."

"You mean it, Helene."

"What do we count, Joseph? *We* can work—until we die."

The man's face flamed a moment; and from the fire came hardness.

"Where's your love o' life? Are we that old?"

She smiled at him again—a smile this time flushed with a great knowledge that hurt. Her mind raced back. She saw three children romping in the street before the window of her shop. She saw herself, grasping two silver coins. And now, her hands moved vaguely in the direction of the window near which she stood.

"Where's your love o' life?" he had asked her. Her waving was her answer.

She sank into her chair. She held her head in her two hands. She sobbed. For it seemed that she had understood.

Her husband wavered before the agony of her vision. He was disarmed. He, also, understood—but as one separate from life, seeing it, feeling its horrid beauty across a gulf. He stood there, silent.

And then, in Helene's grief-bathed mind the vision came, and her tears made it gleam. She saw herself and her husband. They were aged and bowed, and stained and stricken with dull toil. And they were clad as are the men and women who labor with their hands. And they were going forth through a black swamp. And before them was nothing. But behind them—impelling them to go, driving them on, was a child dressed all in white. It was their child.

BARRY BENEFIELD

RHYTHM OF WORDS AND MATERIAL

I am not at all sure I know the genesis and development of any of the stories I have written. I have a notion that when I am self-conscious about writing fiction I can't do it. All I know is that a story-idea, which may have been lying about in my mind for months or years, which may even have been looked at and rejected time and time again, somehow takes on life and begins attracting all manner of material toward it. I then try to put it into words. Often the first start is a failure, and the second, third and fourth too for that matter; a failure because the material is demanding a rhythm I haven't yet struck. "Rhythm" here sounds arty and moonshiny and silly, I suppose; but I don't know how else to word what I mean.

After a while usually, though sometimes at once, my words get into step with the material and then the march is a steady, rapid and, to me, a thrilling movement to the conclusion.

This is too vague to be helpful, I am sure, but it is the best I can do.

SIMPLY SUGAR PIE [1]

S UGAR PIE carried the last of the three weekly washin's to its owner early Saturday afternoon, and having bought some supplies at a drug store and a grocery store she set out, stumbling wearily along, for her shanty on the ragged southern edge of the little Louisiana town. Though Crebillon had, within the previous five years, increased its population from three hundred to a thousand, chiefly through an influx of derrick and pipe men from Illinois and Pennsylvania having to do with a few oil wells that had been developed in the swampy land on the north side of the town, yet out where Sugar Pie lived

[1] From *Short Turns,* The Century Company, 1926. Reprinted by permission of the author and of the publishers.

there were only five or six one-room shanties. Then came the circling pine forest.

On the way home the young negro woman stopped at one of the neighboring shanties and talked earnestly for some time with old Aunt Viney Lane, who promised to come over right after supper and stay through the night.

December's chill wind, wetted by the swamps on the other side of the railroad track, cut cruel and hard through the air; and as soon as Sugar Pie reached home she began carrying in from the wood-pile all the sticks that could possibly be gotten into her wide-mouthed fire-place, and all the chips and bark she could fumble into her apron. She was too weak now to wield the ax. Not waiting for the falling night, she fried some bacon and cooked a corn-pone in the skillet, and crawled into bed.

There had been two things about Sugar Pie Pickett in her life of twenty-one years that had aroused enough interest in the four or five little towns she had successively loved as home to justify detailed explanation—her name and the shiny, puckered scar in the middle of her right cheek, and in consequence she was very proud of them.

A spider having bitten her when a baby, her superstitious mother, fearing that the bite meant death unless heroic action were taken at once, had rubbed caustic laundry lye on her face to kill the poison. As for her name, nearly all negro babies are called Sugar Pie at first; but that name of loving infancy, perhaps because of her eternally amiable expression, had stuck to her so long now that she had forgotten her more properly Christian name. No one, not even she herself, troubled to remember the surname Pickett as either useful or decorative; so that universally she was, and had always been, simply Sugar Pie.

She lay still in bed, though with her muscles straining tight in the suspense of an awful fear and a tender passionate yearning, one moment staring at the dying fire out to her left, the next at the dying day outside the calico-curtained window to her right.

"Lawdy, Lawdy, I wisht Aunt Viney would come on," she moaned to herself more and more often as the cold damp night closed in on her from within and from without.

Sugar Pie kept telling herself that she would get up in a minute or two and put some wood on the fire, for there would be need of a good blaze for Aunt Viney that night. The little red flames flickered down shorter, and grew weakly paler, until finally they were barely strong enough to cast a ghastly, staggering shadow out to the edge of the rough stone hearth; and Sugar Pie dozed off into a pained, uneasy slumber.

She woke up with a guilty, jumpy start, looking quickly toward the fireplace. The room was black with a thick, icy darkness; there was not even a shadow over the hearth. All she could see out to the left was a single evil-eyed live coal leering at her from a dimly illumined pile of gray ashes. It came to her that some one was, and had been for a good while, knocking furtively at her locked front door.

"Sugar Pie, Sugar Pie, wake up," she heard Aunt Viney's voice calling, and she was vaguely aware of a note of warning secrecy in it. "Is you 'wake now, honey?"

Sugar Pie tried to raise her voice to explain that she couldn't get up to unlock the front door, and would Aunt Viney go around to the back door and push right hard on it and come on in; but her words trailed off into an unintelligible moan. Anyway, the old woman outside was talking on faster, the excitement in her tone overcoming the fear.

"Wake up, chile, wake up," Aunt Viney kept calling insistently. "Jerry Cole—you know dat nigger whut drove Dr. Forchaux's buggy—Jerry shot Constable Larkin tonight, 'count of a crap game Mr. Larkin was tryin' to stop; an' dey done hung Jerry to a telegraft pole. Den dem oil men said to run out all de niggers an' make dis a white man's town, like dat New Era place is.

"Dey done started in on de folks on de yuther side of town. Dey burned Jim Nix's house smack to de groun' 'cause he shot at 'em, an' he scarcely got out with his hide. Some folks is gone on down de railroad track fas' as dey can; some is on de dirt road makin' for Myrtle Manor. Hit ain't but twenty miles away. Plenty of niggers dere; hit's a farmers' town. Is you hearin' me, honey?"

Sugar Pie groaned for answer.

"Dey is comin' on down heah next," the trembling voice of the old woman outside ran on more and more excitedly. "Me an' Hannah Lucky is goin' out by de dirt road toward Myrtle Manor, but we ain't goin' to have time to take nothin' 'cept a little somethin' to eat. You reckon, honey, you could make out to git up an'—"

The words beyond the locked door broke off suddenly, and Sugar Pie heard the scuffle of Aunt Viney's loosely dragging shoes running across her hard front yard. Then she distinguished the explanation of her flight—a low buzzing hum of voices moving across the grassy flat between the main section of the town and this ragged edge on which she and several other negroes lived. The mob was coming.

Once Sugar Pie had seen two bodies hanging under a

railroad trestle early in the morning. They had been there all night, and the necks were stretched out to a hideously unnatural length. Always after that, whenever she recalled the event, she could see plainly, between two heads and two bodies the outlines of which were never clear in her memory, those two long, terrifyingly thin necks that no time could ever dim. Timid, her imagination inflamed by centuries of superstitious thinking, her nerves burning and twisting with fear and pain, the young negro woman there on the bed went through all the torturing horrors of hanging and burning at the stake while the low buzzing voices covered a mere hundred yards of ground coming across the grassy flat.

Suddenly all the terrors that her mind was seeing and her body suffering were swept away by a swift convulsive agony of gigantic pain. It wrenched and lifted her up and half out of bed. Once only she screamed into the sooty, smothering darkness above her, and then fell back on the pillow, mercifully bereft of consciousness.

On Monday morning the door of the shanty opened, and Sugar Pie stepped slowly out on the ground. Though it was seven o'clock, the winter sun so far had merely lightened somewhat the eastern section of the sky, whose bedraggled edges sagged down heavily around the shivering earth. Putting out her left hand to the rough board wall to steady herself, Sugar Pie walked effortfully a few feet, then stopped, leaning her head weakly against the shanty.

"I got to cook somethin'," she kept saying to herself. "I got to cook somethin' to git some stren'th from, else I cain't make out to do it."

A man passing along the path in front of her fenceless yard saw her and halted.

"Why, Sugar Pie, haven't you left town yet?" he called. "Your house was all closed yesterday, an' there wasn't any smoke comin' out of the chimney; so ever'body thought you had got out Saturday night with the others. They tarred an' feathered ole Mary Nimmo because she stayed behind to catch up her four chickens. Three or four of you'all's houses have already been burnt down; the rest will go pretty soon, to keep you all from tryin' to come back, or wantin' to. That's the way it's done these days, with a lot of new men comin' in from ever'wheres. We used to lynch a man now an' then for doin' the worst thing, but we never bothered the innocent ones. Better watch out, Sugar Pie."

Sugar Pie recognized the voice as that of Dick Walters, Crebillon's night watchman, now on his way home, a couple of miles out of town. Grateful for the kindness of his tone, she turned and raised her head to say she was obleeged to him for tellin' her; but he had walked on.

"Oh, I'll be gone befo' dinner-time," she tried to call. Her voice was so strangely thin and feeble that it appeared comical to her, and she summoned one of her good-natured old smiles for her own benefit. It lit up her face, slightly contorting the right side of it where the shiny scar was; and then gradually faded out. "I got to cook somethin' to git some stren'th from," she murmured; and moved toward the corner of the house, and turned it.

"Whew!" she whispered, drawing back from the teeth of the north wind. "Hit shore *is* cold."

Waiting a few minutes behind the protecting south side of the house to gather her courage and strength, she walked staggeringly on to the wood-pile by the well. Out of habit she picked up the ax, but her trembling hands let the cold, slippery handle slide through them. Kneeling on the ground, she filled her apron with chips and splinters and bark, rose unsteadily to her feet, reeled back to the house, and got inside, pushing the dragging door tightly into place.

After a while a little smoke curled out of her mud-and-stick chimney. Three or four men passing along the path in front of her yard heard bacon sizzling over a poor fire. Each of them stopped, looked inquiringly at the house, frowned, walked on.

Along about 9 o'clock the sagging door was again dragged open, and Sugar Pie stepped out with something of her old briskness. The food had begun filtering heat and strength through her. She stood on the hard, white ground, staring wistfully back at the shanty. Suspended from around her shoulders by a stout string was a tin bucket, and in her arms she carried a bundle wrapped in a red shawl. Sugar Pie was ready to obey the law of the mob.

Except for what she wore on her body and bore in her arms, all the things, useful and necessary and merely dear, that she owned in the world were back there in the shanty and out there in the yard. She regretted most a pair of green vases that a grateful customer had given her one Christmas, and the black clothes-boiling pot, with both its ears knocked off, out there in the yard by the well. Her mother had used it before her; it was a good pot, it boiled quickly. The shanty and everything in it would probably be burned down within a week. Where Aunt Viney's home had been there was now nothing except the half-burned body of the locust tree that had shaded her house.

"Tst!" Sugar Pie clicked at herself through her teeth

impatiently. "I got to be movin' on now; I got to finish it befo' *dis* day is done."

Sighing deeply, she gathered the bundled red shawl closer to her, and, turning, walked from her yard and out along the path across the flat land, the wet wind behind her pasting her thin calico dress close against her legs so that she had to step slowly and carefully lest she stumble and fall and drop the red-shawled bundle.

Out in front of her the sweep of close-cropped grass, still tipped with the morning's icy hoar frost, was unbroken except here and there by a round pond, where boys caught crawfish in the spring, and by little dark patches and criss-crossed lanes made by the feet of frolicking calves, and by an occasional stately file of tame ducks or geese on their way to the festal ponds.

Sugar Pie saw a small company of geese crossing her path. One of them had been brave enough to bring off a brood in the autumn. Surrounded by her flock of fluffy yellow toddlers, the old white goose passed the young black woman with the unhurried dignity of majestic motherhood. Sugar Pie turned her eyes away, pulled the red-shawled bundle hard against her, and stumbled on, holding her head down.

Straight out across the grassy flat was the town's graveyard. Because Sugar Pie could not walk fast it was some time before she reached the fence of upright pickets with sharp points. Leaning her head against the whitewashed barrier, she gazed in a long time at the neat, gray mounds.

It was not a large cemetery, not so large even as Mansfield's, where she had last lived, and there were few marble tombstones in it; but everything was very clean inside

there, and quiet, and safe, and there were a good many
cedar trees, and flower bushes that would be sweet and
pretty when the spring came on. Yes, it would be mighty
nice in there. Sugar Pie closed her eyes, as if in pain,
hugging the red-shawled bundle protectingly closer up
into her arms.

After a while she walked down along the fence, took
another longing look in from the corner, and struck out
directly westward, away from Crebillon, towards the circling pine forest. Once behind the trees, she turned north,
crossed the railroad track, and came finally to the dirt
road leading to Myrtle Manor, twenty miles west. Settling
down to a slow but steady gait, she followed that on.

By noon she had not traveled quite beyond the reach
of the drilling engine whistles, signaling the glad time for
dinner. Through the woods they came to her dimmed and
softened by the melancholy magic of distance, awaking a
yearning homesickness for the town that had driven her
out. Sugar Pie judged that she was four or five miles
from Crebillon, far enough away for safety, anyhow;
and she decided to make a stop here.

The ground had been gradually rising higher as she
had come westward. Out to the left rose a gentle hill,
thickly carpeted with the brown straw of several seasons'
shedding, shrouded in the semi-darkness of the grisly gray
sky and the closely-set pines. If she went up a good distance on the hill, no one could see her from the road, and
she could eat and then do what she had planned.

Halfway up the hill her strength seemed to give out
entirely; but she rested a few minutes, then climbed on
to and over the top, stopping eight or nine yards on the
farther side of it. She sank down under a high pine tree,
leaning back against the bole of it, holding the red-shawled

bundle in the hollow of her lap to rest her tired arms.

But the air was icy cold, and soon she stirred herself to make a fire. Rising, she laid her burden tenderly on a heap of straw at the foot of the tree, and unstrung the tin bucket from around her shoulders. She gathered some pine knots, and with the ease of an expert started a leaping little red blaze. Sitting down again, and wrapping her arms around her knees, she stared into the fire, now and then unlocking her hands and holding them up before it to catch quickly in her thin-skinned palms as much heat as possible for her numbed arms.

Presently she drew to her the tin bucket and pulled off its top. Having taken out a knife and fork, she emptied out all at once on the straw the other contents of the pail. The three twisted pieces of bacon were covered thickly with congealed gray grease, and the heavy, solid corn-pone was speckled with black ashes. Sugar Pie looked at the food for a minute, then pushed it aside with surprised disgust, put down the knife and fork, and stared again into the fire, occasionally sweeping the hill as far as she could see with her big, round eyes.

The rushing life of the warm months was gone from the woods. Of the millions and millions of katydids and crickets that then seemed always everywhere fiddling away on their same sad song, not one now lifted a tiny signal above the horizon of the lower silence. Except for the changeless pines, all the trees were without or losing their leaves. Far down the hill one stubborn old blackgum yet held a few tatters of its crimson autumn robe. Out to her left two or three scattered hickories drooped in pale thin gold that seemed to be dissolving into the thick wet air. No sounds of birds were in the middle distance of the humbler trees. Away up above Sugar Pie's head, where the gray clouds writhed and twisted between contending winds, and only a little distance below them, it seemed to her, the dark-headed pines swayed slowly back and forth moaning in long-drawn whispers.

After a while Sugar Pie roused herself with a determined effort, and got hurriedly to her feet. Having replenished the fire, she inspected the ground all around beneath her tree. Finally she came to a decision, halted, sank down on her knees, and scraped away the straw with the knife and fork, laying bare the soft black earth. Marking off a careful rectangle, she began to dig. With the knife and fork she loosened the ground; with her hands she lifted it out into a single regular pile by the side of the slowly deepening hole.

It was not a very large hole that Sugar Pie was digging there, and yet she did not get along very fast with it, for the tools she used were small and weak, and she was very anxious about the evenness of its edges, and then with more and more frequency as she worked along she would stop, throw her apron back over her head and sit all hunched up, her shoulders shaking, pressing her hands, still holding the knife and fork, hard against her heart.

Along about three o'clock, though, Sugar Pie rose to her feet, and going up to the foot of the tree unwound the red-shawled bundle and lifted out on the straw a tiny naked baby, almost white, long stiff in death, his clenched little fists arrested forever halfway to eyes that had never opened. Sugar Pie went back to the hole and put the red shawl down in it first, folding the edges smoothly out over the sides. Then she put in a piece of an old white blanket; and finally, a big blue handkerchief. It had a hole in one corner of it, but it was silk.

All the time as she went about this last business Sugar Pie kept biting at her lip, and every now and then she would say almost fiercely to herself, "Naw, naw, don't you do it now, don't you do it. Wait; time 'nough then."

Presently, standing up, she walked forward to the baby, gathered him silently into her arms, and moved back to the cushioned hole in the soft black earth, kneeling there. She kissed him, and hugged him so close and so long away up in her arms that he seemed to her to be melting into her again, shutting her eyes tight and rocking her bent body waveringly back and forth.

After a while, biting at her lip and often shaking her head violently as if to throw off something that was weakening her for the work in hand, she laid the baby tenderly down into the hole. She tried to straighten out the fingers and the crooked arms; but she soon saw that it was not for her to smooth those clenched little fists, so she let them alone, and folded in over them the edges of the blue silk handkerchief and the white blanket and the red shawl.

Sugar Pie remembered several funerals that she had seen, and she was resolved to give to this one of her baby whatever of ceremonial pomp she could accomplish. Crawling over to the fire, she got a handful of cool ashes, and dragged herself back to the hole in the ground. Filling the other hand with dirt, she raised them both over the infant dead and let some ashes and then some sod fall on the multi-colored shroud.

"Ashes to ashes, Lawd," she said, stopping to gulp. "Dus' to dus', Lawd."

Chewing cruelly at her lip and shaking her head with more violent determination than ever, Sugar Pie began moving by tiny handfuls the loose earth in on and over the body, crumbling the sod fine to make it fall softly. All at once she remembered that there had been music at the graveside in the funerals she had seen, so she decided to sing a popular negro hymn, in which new words have been fitted to an old tune. It was her favorite. She began:

> "Oh, he gwine to hebben on de mawnin' train
> An' ole Saint Peter gwine to—"

But she stopped singing suddenly, bending low her head and covering her face with her hands. After a while she looked up again and went on filling in the grave.

"He *ought* to go to hebben, anyhow," she said. "It ain't none o' his fault whut he is."

When the dirt had been filled in and heaped up Sugar Pie set both hands to smoothing it into mounded shape, stooping over frequently to rub her cheek against the cold earth.

Though it was hardly more than 4 o'clock, already the darkness was falling thickly amongst the trees. Sugar Pie drew her knees up to her chin, wrapped her arms around them and stared out into the blackening woods. As yet her eyes had been dry. A gust of wind came rattling across the hillside with the bodies of dead autumn leaves, and one of them, a little figure in red-gold, hovered over the rounded mound, and dropped, and started up again, and then fell back, the wind gone on without it. Seeing that, Sugar Pie bent her head forward and gave herself to the relief that was her due.

It was all black in the woods when the distant whistles of dear Crebillon blew for 6 o'clock—for 6 o'clock and the going home of the workmen, and warm suppers, and lights, and laughter and friendliness among themselves.

Sugar Pie raised her head eagerly to savor each of the whistles—she could name them all. When they were silent, she stooped over and patted the little mound, and raised herself wearily and went on her slow journey westward. The mob at last was done with Sugar Pie. And with her burden buried, Sugar Pie at last was done with the mob.

THYRA SAMTER WINSLOW

COOKING IN THE SUBCONSCIOUS

As nearly as I can tell my stories are mosaics. A character trait, a bit of observation, a remark that some one says that fits into a spot that seems to be waiting for that very thing—and before I know it the story is fairly complete. Usually the main character comes to me first and the way that character reacts to specific incidents comes later. Occasionally I start out with the theme, instead. Character and theme are the two important ingredients to me. As you know, my stories don't have much plot. Even when I start out with a fairly decent plot I discard most of it in the writing. I'm interested in the people I try to depict, in what happens to them and how the events affect them, more than in the events themselves. One thing, though—I never start to write a story until every detail is plain in my mind. By the time a story is ready to be written it is finished as far as my construction goes. Not that I don't rewrite, for of course I do. I write very slowly and then rewrite three times or more, but I find that my rewriting consists more of the changing of words and sentence structure than changes in the technique of the story itself.

I find writing terrifically hard work and it seems to get harder instead of getting easier as I grow older. I never have turned out a quantity of work. I have the usual hatred of getting down to work and I can find a hundred things that are more attractive than working—anything distracts me beautifully. When I do get down to work it isn't so bad, though I suffer horribly as I suppose nearly all writers do. I have met only one writer in my whole lifetime who really enjoyed writing.

After my story is down on paper—the first draft—I have a wonderful elation. I feel that I have done a grand piece of work —that at last I have become articulate. Then, when I reread the story, get to work on it again, it seems utterly flat. I can't believe it possible that this is the thing that had seemed so good. I work and work, trying to get back some of that feeling of having expressed myself but it never comes back. Usually, when the story appears in print, I am horribly embarrassed because of my inability to have written the things I wanted to say.

I always have a lot of plots ahead but they are usually vague.

The one that I'm working on is so real that it affects my mood in everything I do, outside of working hours, while I'm on it, and when I have finished it I feel empty and blank, as though I can never write again. Then in the middle of a period of despair, a plot, all done, pops into my mind, a plot that has been "cooking" in my subconscious for a long time. And the first thing I know I'm at work and suffering again.

I do not know where I get my plots. Certainly they are not based entirely on life, though they must be translations of life as it comes to me, colored, of course, with my particular viewpoint. Everything interests me to an unbelievable degree. I almost pop out of my seat in trains and at the theater listening to conversations which are no business of mine. I'm interested in every story I hear, whether or not I know the people. I'm interested in everything I read and my greatest worry is that I haven't time enough to hear the things I want to hear nor read the things that simply must be read right away.

I am usually utterly unable to tell the genesis of any one story of mine. Usually the kernel is based on some personal experience, elaborated and changed. I don't mean necessarily that the thing happened to me but it was something that came to me in such a way that it seemed personal—it could have happened to me in certain circumstances—was comprehensible enough to be part of my own experiences. Haven't we all hated and loved and killed and aspired, had gorgeous adventures, and gone through tragedy and happiness—mentally, anyhow? And aren't those the things, touched with what we feel is our own knowledge of life, that we are trying to put on paper?

CITY FOLKS [1]

I

JOE and Mattie Harper lived in Harlem. They lived in a four-room apartment in the second of a row of brown, unattractive-looking apartment buildings—six of

[1] Reprinted from *Picture Frames* by Thyra Samter Winslow, by and with the permission of and special arrangement with Alfred A. Knopf, Inc., authorized publishers.

them just alike—in One Hundred and Thirty-second
Street.

They lived in Apartment 52, which means the fifth floor,
and there was no elevator. But the rent was reasonable,
fifty dollars, and both Joe and Mattie said they didn't
mind a "walk-up" at all—you get used to it after a while,
and Mattie knew it kept her hips down. Then, too, by
going to the fifth floor, you get a much better view, though
why a view of the building across the street—another
brown barracks of exactly the same age and design—is
desirable, only Joe and Mattie and other similarly situated folks know. The air was cleaner, though, on the fifth
floor—they felt that any one would know that.

One Hundred and Thirty-second Street, Harlem,
lacked all outstanding features. If the street signs had
suddenly disappeared, there would have been nothing to
identify it, to pin it to—a bleak street, without trees, a
fairly clean street, decent and neat looking (after the
garbage man had passed and the tins had disappeared),
wide enough to lack misery, narrow enough to lack
grandeur.

We are about to have two meals with Joe and Mattie—
the most important meals of their day, for Joe's lunch was
usually a sandwich and a glass of milk at the Automat,
or beans or a beef stew in the lunch room across from his
office; Mattie's a glass of soda and a sandwich or a dish of
ice cream, if she were down-town—it is a shame about the
new price of sodas—a scramble of left overs from last
night's dinner, if she spent the day at home.

Breakfast:

The alarm clock had buzzed at six-thirty, as it always
did. It was a good alarm clock and had cost $1.48 at
Liggett's, two years before.

Mattie's little dog, who slept in the front hall, had heard the alarm and scrambled into their bedroom with his usual yip of pleasure—he was rather deaf, but he could make out sounds as definite as the ringing of a bell and he listened for the alarm each morning. He was a nice fellow, a white poodle, overly fat, with red-rimmed eyes. If you didn't molest him nor try to pet him nor step on him, he wouldn't snap or try to bite you. Mattie and Joe were quite fond of him and took him for walks in Central Park on Sundays or around Harlem in the evenings. His name had, in turn, been, stylishly, Snowball, Snoodles and Snookums and had at last reached Ikkle Floppit, all of which he answered to with stolid indifference.

Joe had heard the alarm, had jumped up and turned it off, and had waked Mattie, who slept more soundly. Ikkle Floppit had jumped, wheezily, upon the bed and licked all visible portions of Mattie's face. Mattie, then, had given up trying to doze again and had stroked the dog's uneven coat with a fond hand.

Toilets followed, rapid plunges into the dwarf-sized white tub with its rather insecure shower attachment— Joe talking while he shaved, about the office, the men who worked with him, his boss who didn't appreciate him, the weather that was still too warm for comfort, their friends, the Taylors, who they both agreed were too stuck up for words since Taylor had got his new job.

"His people aren't anything at all," Mattie had said, "awfully ordinary—and the way they do put on airs, you'd think they amounted to something. Why, my cousin Mabel knew his sister in Perryville, where they used to live, and she said they weren't anything at all there. And now, how they do go on with a maid and a car. They've never even taken us for a ride in their old car and they can hold their breath until I'd step into it. It beats all—"

And Joe, his face twisted for the razor's path beyond the possibilities of conversation, had grunted assent.

Now Mattie had completed the simple breakfast, six pieces of toast, buttered unevenly and a bit burned on the edges, as always, a halved orange for each of them, some coffee and some bought preserves with a slight strawberry-like flavor. She and Joe faced each other over the almost clean tablecloth—it had been clean on Sunday and this was just Tuesday morning.

The dining-room was small, lighted vaguely with two court windows. Even now, at seven-thirty, the electric light had been turned on in the red and green glass electrolier.

Mattie knew the electrolier was out of fashion, she would have preferred a more modern "inverted bowl," but this one was included with the apartment, so there seemed nothing to do about it. She would also have preferred mahogany to the fumed oak dining-room set, bought eight years before—she had bought the mahogany tea wagon with her last year's Christmas money from Joe, looking forward to the time when they could buy a whole new mahogany set.

Mattie was not at all a bad-looking breakfast companion, seated there in her half-clean pink gingham bungalow apron—she wore these aprons constantly in the house to save her other clothes. She was a slender, brown-haired woman of about thirty, with clear brown eyes, a nose that turned slightly upward, a mouth inclined to be a little large, rather uneven but white teeth—indefinite features, a pleasant, usual, hard-to-place face.

And Joe, across from her, was equally pleasing, with a straight nose and rather a weak chin, dark hair starting

to recede just a little at thirty-three, sloping shoulders inclined a bit to the roundness of the office man.

"What's in the paper, Joe?" asked Mattie, already
nibbling toast.

Joe, deep in the morning *World*, threw out interesting
items—the progress of a murder trial, news of an airplane flight.

They talked about little things, a friend Joe had passed
on the street the day before, the choice of a show for Friday or Saturday night—they tried to attend the theater
once each week, during the winter.

The door bell rang, three short rings. Ikkle Floppit
gave three asthmatic yips. Mattie threw down her napkin,
sprang to her feet.

"I'll go," she said, as she usually said it, "you go on
eating or you'll be late again. I bet it's nothing but a bill,
anyhow."

She returned in a moment with a thick letter in her
hand.

"From your mother, Joe," she said.

She knew the printed address in the corner of the
envelope, "The Banner Store, General Merchandise, E. J.
Harper, Prop., Burton Center, Missouri," the neat, old-
fashioned handwriting, the post-mark.

Mattie and Joe had come from Burton Center, Mattie
eight years and Joe nine years before. They had grown
up together in Burton Center, one of the jolly crowd who
attended the High School, went to Friday night dances,
later were graduated into the older crowd, which meant
a few more dances, went to the Opera House when a show
came to town, had happy love affairs.

Joe and Mattie became engaged three years after Joe
left High School, which was the year after Mattie gradu-

ated. Joe went to work at the Banner Store, under his father. But youth and ambition knew not Burton Center, so, a little later, Joe had come to New York in search of fortune.

He had not obeyed the usual law of fiction and forgotten Mattie, nor had Mattie changed while she waited. No, though Joe found neither fame nor fortune, he did get an office job that looked as if it might support two in comfort, if Mattie and Joe were the two concerned, took a vacation, went back to Burton Center, found Mattie even more alluring and dimpled and giggling than he had remembered her—how much prettier Burton Center girls looked than those in New York!—and they were married.

Eight years, then, of New York, of subway rides, of the weekly theater, the weekly restaurant dinner, of apartment hunting about every second October, of infrequent clothes buying, of occasional calls on stray acquaintances, of little quarrels and little peace-makings, weekly letters from home—little lives going on—

Joe tore open the letter.

"Gee, it's a thick one," he said.

Then:

"Well, I guess they are all well or ma wouldn't have written so much. Listen, Mattie."

Joe read the letter, a folksy letter—Mrs. Harper, senior, was well and so was "your father," as all mothers speak of their husbands to their children, in letters. She had seen Millie's mother a few days before and she was looking well and hoping to see them soon in Burton Center. The youngest Rosemond girl was engaged to a Mr. Secor from St. Louis, who was in the lumber business.

Then there followed, long and unparagraphed, something that made Joe and Mattie look at each other, hard and seriously, across the table. For Joe's mother had written something that they had always thought might be suggested to them but they had never discussed, even with each other:

"Your father isn't as well as he once was, nor as young, you know, and, though you need not worry about him, he is eating and sleeping fine, even in hot weather, I think it would be better if you and Mattie came here to live. You could step right into the store and take charge of things as soon as you wanted to. It is not a big store as you know, but your father has always made a nice living from it and Burton Center is growing right along. The Millers have put up some new bungalows out on Crescent Hill, you'd be surprised to see how it has grown up out there, all of the young people are moving out there and with the new Thirteenth Street car line it is very convenient. The cottages are all taken but two, both white with green blinds and room back of them for garages and we could get you one of them if you wanted us to. The George Hendricks are living there and Mr. and Mrs. Tucker and the Williams boy, Phillip, I think that's his name, you used to go with. The new country club isn't far from there and you could play tennis after work, which would be good for you. I wish you could make up your mind at once, so you could get here before long or your father will have to get a man to help him, for he really ought to have more time to himself and take a nap after dinner, now that the season's trade is starting. Talk this over with Mattie and let us know as soon as you can. I hope you are keeping well in this changeable weather. Your father sends love to both and so do I.

"Affectionately, your Mother."

Mattie and Joe looked at each other, looked and looked and forgot their toast and coffee. But they saw each other not at all. Nor did they visualize One Hundred and Thirty-second Street, New York, drab and bare, nor even Fifth Avenue nor Broadway.

They saw a little town, with rows of old trees along its quiet streets, little white houses on little squares of green, each house with its hedge or its garden or its hammocked lawn, peace, and the smell of growing things after a rain—

"What say, Mattie?" asked Joe. "Sound pretty good? Of course, you've always said you loved New York and I don't want to persuade you against your will. Perhaps you wouldn't care to move—still, Burton Center, we've got some good friends there—it'd be sort of fun, seeing the old crowd, belong to a country club, tennis, things like that, even managing the business. But, of course, if you wouldn't want to leave the city—"

Mattie, mentally, had far outdistanced him.

She clapped her hands, pleasantly excited.

"Joe, can't you just see that little house—I bet it's awfully cute. Last summer, when we were out in the country, I certainly did envy people living in little houses—I get so tired of New York, sometimes. But I never wanted to say anything, knowing how much you liked it here. But that little house—we could sell all of our furniture except the tea wagon and the table in the living-room and my new dressing-table—it really would be cheaper to buy new things than to pay for shipping. And we could find out how many windows there are and I could get some new cretonne here—sort of set the styles in Burton Center. It sure would be funny, living back there and knowing everybody. Here I never see a soul I know in weeks, or talk to anybody. Honest, sometimes I get just hungry for—for people. The trouble is, we haven't really got anything here."

"I know," Joe nodded. "New York's all right for some people—if you've got money. It's a great city all right, but we don't get anything out of it. I get so sick of being squeezed into subways night and morning—hardly standing room all the way home—and no place to go Sundays or evenings but a movie or a show or to see people who live miles away and don't care anything about you anyhow and who you see about twice a year. Burton Center will look awfully good—folks take an interest in you, there."

"You bet they do."

"And it isn't as if I've failed here. I haven't. I'm due for another raise pretty soon—but we aren't putting anything aside, getting any place. It isn't as if we were terribly poor. You look awfully well in your clothes on the street, but we are always having to skimp and do without things—we never have the best of anything, always cheap seats at shows or cheap meals in second-class restaurants, a cheap street to live on—it gets on a person's nerves."

"Why, I didn't know you felt that way, Joe. I thought you liked New York. Why, it makes me so jealous, going down Fifth Avenue, seeing all those people in limousines, not a bit better nor better looking than I am, all dressed up, lolling back so—so superior, with nasty little dogs not near so nice as Floppit—and with chauffeurs and everything. Why, in Burton Center we'd be somebody, as good as any one. We could fix up that house awfully nice —and have a little garden and all that. But you said you hated the Banner Store so—now don't go and make up your mind—"

"You needn't worry about me. The Banner Store is all right—I think differently about things than I did years ago. I thought the city was just going to fall apart in my hand—but I found some one else got here first. I'm not complaining, you know. It isn't that I've failed—why, in Burton Center they'll look at us as a success, we'll be city folks, don't you see. They know I haven't failed. I didn't come sneaking back the year I left, the way Ray Wulberg did. No, sir, when folks came to New York to visit, we showed them a good time, took 'em to restaurants and shows—they think we got along fine here—that we're all right—"

"You bet they do, Joe. But I just can hardly wait to see that cottage—and everybody. I bet Crescent Hill is awfully pretty. Tonight, you write to your mother—don't make it too sudden, you know, or too anxious—for you know how she is—she means fine, but she'll like to spread the news about us coming back. You just say that, under the circumstances, as long as your father is getting old and needs you, you feel it's your duty to go there and as soon as you can arrange your affairs and resign your position and train one of your assistants so that he can take care of your work—"

"You leave that to me. I can fix that part up all right."

The buzzer of the dumb-waiter zinged into their talk.

"Joe, there's the janitor. It's late. You'd better hurry. You know the call-down you got last week for being late."

Mattie and Joe arose simultaneously, Joe grabbed his paper, folded it conveniently, hurried to the door, Mattie after him.

"Going down-town today?" he asked.

"Thought I would, when I get the house straightened

up. I want to look at a new waist. My good one is starting
to tear at the back."

"All right. I'll be home early, about six-thirty—won't
have to stay over-time. In a few months, I'll be my own
boss, no hurrying off in the morning or rushing home in
subways—we'll fix that letter up tonight."

He brushed off his mouth with his hand and gave Mattie the usual and rather hearty good-by kiss and, closing
the door behind him, Joe and Mattie parted for the day
with visions of little houses nestling in green gardens up-
permost in their minds.

II

Dinner:

Dinner times with the Harpers varied slightly according to the way Mattie had spent the afternoon, the amount
of work at Joe's office and where the Harpers were dining.
They usually dined at home, but, once a week, usually
Saturday, when they followed the feast with a visit to the
theater, they ate at one of the table d'hôte restaurants
some place within ten blocks of Broadway and Forty-
second Street.

They thought themselves quite cosmopolitan because
they had been to Italian, Greek, French, Chinese, Russian
and Armenian restaurants, choosing in each the dish prepared for the curious—and eating it according to American table customs as they practiced them.

This particular Tuesday they were dining at home.

Joe reached the apartment exactly at six-thirty, the
trip home taking nearly an hour. Joe had been watching
the clock for the last twenty minutes of his business day
so as to escape at the first possible opportunity.

Mattie, in the kitchen, heard his key in the lock and hurried to greet him. They kissed quite as fondly as they had in the morning, Floppit gave a little yip of welcome and received a pat on the head in reply.

Dinner was nearly ready, Mattie informed Joe, table set and all.

Joe hurried with his ablutions and reached the dining-room, accompanied by his newspaper, the *Journal* this time, at a quarter of seven. He divided the paper so that Mattie might have the last page, where are shown the strips of comics—he had read them hanging to a strap in the subway. Then he helped Mattie to bring in the hot dishes from the kitchen.

There was a small platter of five chops, fried quite brown, two for each one of them and one—to be cut into bits later—for Ikkle Floppit. Mattie always fried chops or steaks the days she went down-town, and sometimes other days besides.

There were potatoes, in their jackets to save her the trouble of peeling them, a dish of canned corn. There was a neat square of butter, too, and some thinly sliced bread on a silver-plated bread plate—a last year's Christmas present from one of Mattie's aunts—and a small dish of highly-spiced pickles.

Besides this, on the new tea wagon stood two pieces of bakery pastry, of a peculiarly yellow color that had aimed at but far surpassed the result of eggs in the batter.

They sat down. Joe served the chops, Mattie the potatoes and corn. Mattie had put on her bungalow apron as soon as she returned home—so as to save her suit from the spots and wear incidental to dinner-getting. Joe looked just as he had in the morning, plus a small amount of beard and minus his coat and vest.

Yet, as the morning's conversation had been spontaneous and enthusiastic and happy, this evening's meal had a curious cloud of restraint over it.

"Good dinner," said Joe, after his first mouthful.

"Yes, it does taste good," agreed Mattie.

"Go down-town?"

"Uh-huh, I went down about eleven. Just got home an hour ago. I looked at the waists, but didn't get any—they seemed awfully high. I may go down and get one to-morrow or Thursday. Any news in the paper?"

"Not much doing," Joe rustled his own sheets.

He never really read at dinner but he liked to have the paper near him.

"Look at Floppit, Joe. Isn't he cute, standing up that way? I've just got to give him a bite. It won't make him too fat, not what I give him. Come here, Missus' lamb."

Silence, then, save for the sound of knife against plate, a curious silence, a silence of avoidance. Then meaningless sentences, bits about anything, a struggle to appear happy, indifferent.

Joe, then, "See any one down-town you know? Where'd you have lunch? Thought maybe you'd call up and have lunch with me."

"I did think of it, but I didn't come down your way. I stopped at Loft's and had chocolate cake and a cherry sundae. No—I didn't see any one I knew—exactly. . . . Anything happen at the office?"

"Well, nothing much. We got that Detroit order."

"Did you, Joe? I'm sure glad of that."

A silence. Then, Joe, suddenly, enthusiastically, as if some barrier had broken, as if he could no longer stay repressed, upon the path he had set for himself.

"Say, Mattie, guess what happened this afternoon!

You know Ferguson, the fellow who used to be in our office, whose brother is in the show business? Well, he came in and gave me a couple of seats to see 'Squaring the Triangle' for Friday night. They say it's a good show and in for a long run, but they want to keep the house filled while the show is new, till it gets a start."

"Did he, honestly? Say, that's great, isn't it? Where are they, downstairs?"

"Sure. You don't think he'd give away balcony seats, or at least offer them to me, do you? Remember, he gave us some last Spring. That makes three times this year we've been to shows on passes. Pretty good, eh, Mattie?"

"Well, I guess yes. We're some people, knowing relatives of managers. I tell you, I think——"

A pause, then.

Mattie's face lost its sudden smile and resumed its sadness of the earlier part of the meal.

"What's the matter?" asked Joe.

"Nothing the matter with me."

"Something else happened, too," Joe went on, enthusiastically. "At noon, I'd just left Childs'—and guess who I passed on the street?"

"Some one we know?"

"We don't know him exactly."

"Oh, I can't guess. Tell me."

"I know you can't—well, it was—William Gibbs McAdoo! Honest to goodness—McAdoo. It sure seemed funny. There he was, walking down the street, just like I've seen him in the movies half a dozen times. It sure gives you a thrill, seeing people like that."

Why the mention of William G. McAdoo should bring tears to the eyes of a woman who had never met him may be inexplicable to some. But tears came into the eyes of

Mattie Harper. She wiped her eyes on the corner of her bungalow apron, sniffed a little, came over to Joe, put her arms around him.

"I just—just can't stand it," she sobbed. "I've been worrying and worrying. Your seeing McAdoo seems the strangest thing, after what happened to me."

"What was it, Mattie?"

Quite kindly and understandingly, Joe pushed his chair back from the table, gathered his wife on his knee.

"What was it, honey? Come tell Joe."

"It wasn't anything—anything to cry about. I—don't know what's the matter with me. It—it was in Lord & Taylor's, this afternoon. I was looking at gloves—and I looked up—and there, right beside me, not two feet away, stood Billie Burke. Honestly! I know it was her. She looked exactly like her pictures—and I saw her in 'The Runaway' years ago, and not long ago in the movies. Yes, sir, Billie Burke. Joe, she's simply beautiful."

"Well, well, think of seeing Billie Burke!"

"And, Joe, when I saw her, the awfulest feeling came over me. I tried not to tell you about it—after the letter this morning. I'd been thinking about Burton Center—but seeing Billie Burke just knocked it all out. Joe, you know I love you and want to do what you want—but, I—I just can't move to Burton Center—unless you've got your heart set on it. I'd go then, of course—any place. But I don't want to be—buried alive in that little town. Imagine those people—never seeing or doing anything—no new shows or famous people—nor any kind of life. And here I went down-town and saw Billie Burke and you—"

Joe's pats became even fonder. He smoothed her hair with his too-pale hand.

"There, there, don't cry. It's all right. Nobody's asking or expecting you to go to Burton Center. Funny thing, that. I had the same feeling. First, passing McAdoo —and then those theater tickets. I guess there's something about New York that gets you. They've got to forget that stuff about Burton Center, I can tell you that."

Mattie jumped off Joe's lap, took the used dishes from the table, put on the pastry and sat down in her own place, across from Joe.

"This is good," said Joe, taking a bite; "where'd you get it?"

"At that little new French pastry shop we passed the night the black dog tried to bite Floppit."

"Oh, yes, looked nice and clean in there."

They ate their pastry slowly. Mattie dried her eyes. Joe spoke to her:

"Say, Mattie, don't worry for a minute more about that Burton Center stuff. After eight years of living in the city, seeing famous people, living right in the center of things—didn't we see all the warships and airplanes nearly every day? They can't expect us to live in a rube place like Burton Center. We're used to more, that's all there is to it."

"I know," said Mattie, "I'd just die if I couldn't walk down Fifth Avenue and see what people wore. It's just weighed on me, terribly. I just saw us on the train going out there, and living in an awful little house without hot water or steam heat—and seeing Billie Burke just—"

The 'phone burred into the conversation.

Mattie answered it, as usual, assuming a nonchalant, society air.

"Yes, this is the Harpers' apartment. Yes, this is Mrs.

Harper speaking. Who? Oh, Mrs. Taylor. How do you do. I haven't heard your voice in ages. We're fine, thank you. . . . No, I don't know much news. A friend of Mr. Harper's, a brother of Ferguson, the theatrical producer, invited us to see 'Squaring the Triangle' as his guests on Friday. They say it's a wonderful show. We saw 'The Tattle-tale' last Saturday. Yes, we liked it a great deal. . . . Saturday afternoon? Wait and I'll ask Mr. Harper if he has an engagement."

Hand over telephone mouthpiece, then:

"Want to go riding with the Taylors in their new car Saturday afternoon and stop at some road-house for supper?"

Resuming the polite conversational tone of the telephone:

"Yes, thank you, Mr. Harper and I will be delighted to go. Awfully nice of you. At four? Fine. By the way, did I tell you I saw Billie Burke today? I did. She looked simply beautiful, not a day older than she looked last year. Wonderful hair, hasn't she? And Mr. Harper passed William G. McAdoo on the street. Yes, New York is a wonderful city. You did? Isn't that nice! All right, we'll be ready on Saturday—don't bother coming up, just honk for us, that's what all our friends do. Thanks so much, good-by."

Mattie sat down at the table again.

"Well," she said, "it's time they asked us—they'll take us now and be through for a year. Still, we may have a nice time. But—what we were talking about—you sure you are in earnest about Burton Center?"

"You bet I am. The folks at home had the wrong dope, that's all. Why, I've got my position here, too important to give up at any one's beck and call. Didn't the boss congratulate me today on the way I wrote those Detroit letters? I bet I get a raise in another three months."

They folded their napkins into their silver-plated napkin-rings, rose from the table, walked together into the living-room, stood looking out into the drab bleakness of One Hundred and Thirty-second Street, across to the factory-like, monotonous row of apartment houses opposite, where innumerable lights twinkled from other little caves, where other little families lived, humdrum, unmarked, inconsequential, gray. And from the minds of Mattie and Joe faded the visions of little white houses and cool, green lanes.

They remembered, instead, the city, their city—Mattie had seen a moving picture taken, once, from a Fifth Avenue bus—three years ago Joe had been introduced to—actually taken the hand of—William Jennings Bryan—they had both seen James Montgomery Flagg draw a picture for the Liberty Loan on the Public Library steps—a woman in a store had pointed out Lady Duff Gordon to Mattie—they had seen, on the street, a man who looked exactly like Charles M. Schwab—it might easily have been. . . .

"I'll write that letter right away and have it over with," said Joe, "I won't hurt ma's feelings—she and dad mean all right. Living in Burton Center all their lives we can't expect them to understand things. It's ridiculous, of course. I don't know what came over us for a minute this morning. Of course we've got the crowded subways, here, and it costs a lot to live and—and all that. You can't expect a place to be perfect. But—New Yorkers like us couldn't stand that dead Burton Center stuff for five minutes. Why, we're, we're—city folks!"